THE
DYNAMICAL CHARACTER
OF
ADSORPTION

THE
DYNAMICAL CHARACTER
OF
ADSORPTION

BY

J. H. de BOER

SECOND EDITION

OXFORD
AT THE CLARENDON PRESS
1968

Oxford University Press, Ely House, London W.1

GLASGOW NEW YORK TORONTO MELBOURNE WELLINGTON
CAPE TOWN SALISBURY IBADAN NAIROBI LUSAKA ADDIS ABABA
BOMBAY CALCUTTA MADRAS KARACHI LAHORE DACCA
KUALA LUMPUR HONG KONG TOKYO

FIRST EDITION 1953
SECOND EDITION 1968

PHYSICS

PRINTED IN GREAT BRITAIN

PREFACE TO THE SECOND EDITION

In this second edition numerous corrections and changes have been incorporated throughout the text and the concluding section of Chapter X (Capillaries) has been rewritten and extended.

The constant τ_0, introduced in § 25, eqn. (13), which plays such an important role in the fundamental equations of adsorption, has been thoroughly investigated since the first edition. In consequence it has been given a completely new treatment in §§ 29, 83, and 143. The author expresses the hope that the difficulties that some colleagues experienced with the fixed value of 10^{-13} second, which was used in Table 2 (and still is used in Table 2) in order to emphasize the importance of the enthalpy of the adsorption, may disappear by the more exact treatment of the entropy factor τ_0 in the present edition.

Recent investigations have shown that many predictions made in 1953 have since come true, and we may expect an important increase in the knowledge of adsorption phenomena in general and in the dynamical character of these phenomena in particular. The author therefore hopes that this second edition will also serve to stimulate research work in this field.

J. H. DE B.

'S-GRAVENHAGE
August 1967

PREFACE TO THE FIRST EDITION

THE original conception of this book dates from about 1948. I delivered lectures on adsorption at Delft University, the Netherlands, during the preceding years. These lectures were followed up by more specialized courses on the atomic forces leading to adsorption and on the interaction between adsorbed molecules.

At the request of the editors of *Advances in Colloid Science* I wrote a contribution entitled 'Atomic Forces and Adsorption', for vol. iii of the series, which appeared in 1950. In that contribution I have dealt with the questions centred round the subject of adsorption energy.

In the present book I have not, therefore, touched that subject, but have tried to create a picture of adsorption, in other words I have made an attempt to visualize the phenomena. The book deals with the movements of the molecules above and on surfaces and with the way they influence each other in their modes of motion. In the first part of the book especially, great stress has been laid on the picture which we can make ourselves. It is of great importance to bring home to students—and also to graduate research workers—the relative sizes of a molecule and a centimetre. The various pictures have often been illustrated, therefore, with an imaginary 'gas of super bees'.

The movements of the adsorbed molecules, which may have retained a free translation (and rotations) along the surface, can often conveniently be described as those of a two-dimensional gas. The conception of van der Waals, only applied to the two-dimensional field, has been elaborated and many attempts have been made to investigate the possible deductions to which this picture leads. It is especially in the second part of the book that graduate research workers will find much to think about. Much hitherto unpublished work has been incorporated in that part. The chief purpose of the book is to build up a complete picture, as homogeneous as possible, and to study the consequences to which this leads. It is hoped that it may stimulate further research and lead to much new experimental evidence of the real equation of state of adsorbed matter.

In this respect the book does not cover the field of any other known book. There are, of course, many books treating adsorption from one angle or another. The present book, however, is different in so far as it makes an attempt to create a picture, a vision in which we may think.

I wish to thank Mr. F. R. Raevell, now physicist at the Food Research Department of Unilever Ltd. in Sharnbrook (Beds.), England, for the trouble which he took in 1949 in reading the first draft of part of the manuscript, and also Miss Ph. Rosenthal, who was my secretary during the second half of my stay with Unilever Ltd. in Port Sunlight (Cheshire), England.

The manuscript was completed after I returned to the Netherlands, and I thank my present secretary, Miss M. M. H. Pelzer, for her accurate work and for her help in correcting the proofs. Mr. S. Kruyer of the Central Laboratory of Staatsmijnen in Limburg should be mentioned especially and be thanked for his critical corrections and also for his contribution in composing the index.

Many thanks are due to the staff of the Clarendon Press for their skilled help in the production of the book.

Finally, I wish to acknowledge the great help which I had from my wife, Mrs. E. A. de Boer—Malcolm-Swanson, during all stages of the growth of the book.

J. H. DE B.

GELEEN (L.), THE NETHERLANDS
July 1952

CONTENTS

CONTENTS

LIST OF SYMBOLS

(The numbers in parentheses indicate the sections where the symbols are introduced or used extensively)

A Surface area in cm.^{2} occupied by 1 mole (78) or by 1 molecule (89).

    A_s Molar area in the standard state (79) or area available for a molecule in the standard state (80).

    A_c Critical molecular area (96).

B Second virial coefficient of gases (88; 113).

B_0 Constant in the logarithmic form of the equation of vapour pressure (40).

B_a Constant in the logarithmic form of the adsorption isostere (38, equation 15).

C Attraction constant of London forces (100).

D Diffusion constant.

    D_0 Constant in diffusion equation 64 (137).

    D_m Diffusion constant of migration (138).

E Characteristic energy in London forces (100).

E_a Energy of the gas per molecule in the adsorbed state (39).

E_g Energy of the gas per molecule in the gas phase (39).

F Two-dimensional pressure (dynes/cm.) (73).

    F_0 Two-dimensional saturated gas pressure (94).

    F_c Critical two-dimensional pressure (96).

    F_s Spreading force (94).

G Free enthalpy (Gibbs) (80).

    ΔG Difference in free enthalpy (80).

H Enthalpy (heat of adsorption) (80).

    ΔH Difference in enthalpy (80).

K Constant in equation 58 (113).

L Free length of path (5, 13).

    $\bar{L}_m$ Mean free path of migrating molecules (138).

M Molecular weight.

N Number of Avogadro ($6 \cdot 023 \times 10^{23}$ molecules per mole).

N_1 Number of molecules per cm.^{3} (5).

N_a Number of molecules adsorbed on a clean surface of 1 gram of adsorbent (39).

Q Heat of adsorption (25).

    Q_a Heat of adsorption of the first layer in equations for multimolecular adsorption (49).

    Q_{diff} Differential heat of adsorption (39).

    Q_{int} Integral heat of adsorption (39).

    Q_{isoth} Isothermal heat of adsorption (39) = isosteric heat of adsorption (39).

    Q_s Heat of adsorption as caused by interaction with surface only (108).

    Q_t Total heat of adsorption (108).

    ΔQ_a Variations in heat of adsorption caused by the surface (67; 137).

    ΔQ_t Difference in heat of adsorption of perpendicular and of flat molecules (108).

Q_0 Latent heat of evaporation (40).

Q_d Energy of activation in diffusion (137).

R Gas constant, either molar: $R = 8\cdot31_5 \times 10^7$ ergs/°K.,
$\qquad\qquad\qquad\qquad\qquad R = 1\cdot987$ cal./degree,
$\qquad$ or molecular: $R = 1\cdot38 \times 10^{-16}$ ergs/°K.
(It is only in equations 35 and 35 a that k is used for the molecular gas constant (constant of Boltzmann) because R is used as the molar constant in the same equations.)

S Entropy (80).
  ΔS Difference in entropy (80).

T Absolute temperature.
  T_c Critical temperature (96).
  T_{c2} Two-dimensional critical temperature (96).
  T_s Melting temperature (29).

V Volume of a mole.

a Coefficient of accommodation (21).

a Proportionality factor (40).

a Constant in the equation of v. Szyszkowski (84).

a Constant in the van der Waals equation of state (91; 100).
  a_2 Constant of the two-dimensional van der Waals equation (91; 100).
  a_2' Two-dimensional van der Waals constant for dipoles repelling each other (92).
  a_μ Contribution of the Keesom alinement effect (107).

a Hopping distance of molecules migrating over the surface jumping from 'site' to 'site' (138).

b Proportionality factor (40).

b Constant in the equation of v. Szyszkowski (84).

b Constant in the van der Waals equation of state (91; 100).
  b_2 Constant of the two-dimensional van der Waals equation (91; 100).

b_a and b_b Adsorption coefficients in mixed adsorption (61).

b_a' and b_b' Adsorption coefficients in adsorption from solutions (62).

c Concentration in solutions (36).
  c_a and c_b Concentrations of the two components of a solution (62).

d Diameter of a capillary (24).

d Diameter of a molecule (100).

e Base of natural logarithms.

f Partition function: $f = f_{\text{perp}}/f_{\text{flat}}$.
  f_{perp} Partition function for molecules in perpendicular positions (108).
  f_{flat} Partition function for molecules in flat positions (108).

h Planck's constant ($6\cdot62 \times 10^{-27}$ erg.sec.).

i Number of layers in multimolecular adsorption (48).

k Gas constant per molecule in equations 35 and 35 a (82).
(In all other cases R is used for the molecular gas constant as well as for the molar gas constant.)

k Constant in the adsorption equation of Brunauer, Emmett, and Teller (48).

k_0 Constant in equation 14 (35).

k_0 ,,   ,,   ,,   61 (123).

k_1 ,,   ,,   ,,   14 a (35).

k_1 ,,   ,,   reduced form of adsorption isotherm 59 (114).

k_2 ,,   ,,   adsorption isobar 14 b (37).

k_2 ,,   ,,   reduced form of adsorption isotherm 59 (114).

k_3 ,,   ,,   adsorption isostere 15 (38).

k' ,,   ,,   adsorption isotherm for solutions (36).

k_b ,,   ,,   adsorption isotherm 55 c (111).

k'_b ,,   ,,   adsorption isotherm 55 a (111) and 37 (87).

k_u ,,   ,,   Langmuir adsorption isotherm 18 (43).

k'_u ,,   ,,   ,,   ,,   ,,   18 a (84).

k_L ,,   ,,   adsorption isotherm 18 c (113).

k_d Constant in equation 63 (137) proportional to diffusion coefficient D.

l Length of an inequality on a surface (19).

l Length of a capillary (24).

l Length of barrier in a spreading trough (74).

m Mass of a molecule (6).

n Number of molecules striking a unit area of a surface per unit time (4, and Chapter II).

n_1 The same in a liquid (40).

n_v Number of molecules evaporating from a unit area in unit time (34).

n_{perp} and n_{flat} Number of molecules in perpendicular and in flat positions respectively (108).

p Pressure (either in dyne/cm.^{2} or in mm. Hg or in atmospheres).

p_0 Saturated pressure of a liquid or a solid.

p_1 Three-dimensional pressure in equilibrium with two-dimensional standard state (80).

p_a and p_b Partial pressures (61).

p_s Pressure of standard state (80).

q Maximum vapour pressure of an assembly of molecules having the physical structure given by multimolecular adsorption (48; 55).

r Maximum number of layers in a capillary space (59).

r Distance between molecules (100).

t Time (time needed by a molecule to pass a capillary (30, and Chapter X).

u Velocity of molecules (5).

v Rate of evaporation (17).

v Volume of gas which has been adsorbed (48).

v_m Volume of gas which would be present if the surface were just covered by a unimolecular layer (48).

x Relative pressure (p/p_0 or p/q) in equations for multimolecular adsorption (48).

α Fraction of molecules which is reflected from the surface (34).

α Polarizability of molecules (100).

β Proportionality factor in equations for multimolecular adsorption (48).

γ Surface energy (74).

δ Thickness of adsorbed layer (79).

ϵ Potential of attraction between two molecules (100).

θ Fraction of the surface covered with adsorbed molecules (degree of covering; degree of occupation) (43).

  θ_L Apparent θ in equation 18 c (113).

  θ_c Degree of occupation in two-dimensional critical point (118).

ϑ Angle of incidence of a beam (19).

λ Wavelength (of light or of molecular ray) (19).

μ 10^{-4} cm.

μ Dipole moment (107).

ν Frequency of atomic oscillations (34, 82, 83).

π Normal significance.

σ Amount of adsorbed molecules per unit area (4).

  σ_0 Number of adsorbed molecules per cm.^{2} just forming a unimolecular layer (43).

  σ_L Apparent saturation value in equation 18 c (113).

  σ_c Number of adsorbed molecules per cm.^{2} in two-dimensional critical point (118).

  σ_a and σ_b Numbers of adsorbed molecules of different species (61).

  σ_t The value of σ after the time t (137).

τ Time of adsorption (4, and Chapter III); used with various indices.

τ_0 Time of oscillation of adsorbed molecules (25, 29, 83).

τ' Resting time of a hopping molecule (67).

ϕ Fraction of flat molecules in partially erected assembly (108).

ω Index used in Gibbs' equation to denote that the surface area is constant (75).

In accordance with the suggestions of the 'Union Internationale de Physique Pure et Appliquée' the following physical quantities and symbols are used:

internal energy, symbol U,
enthalpy (heat function), symbol H $(U+pV)$,
free enthalpy (Gibbs), symbol G $(H-TS)$.

In the U.S.A. the symbol F is often used where we use G.

I

INTRODUCTION

1. A gas and a surface

A GAS may be pictured as numerous molecules moving along straight paths in all directions. They collide, and both partners of every collision change their velocities and directions of motion. They collide again with other molecules, change their velocities and directions once more, and so on in an unceasing sequence.

Now let us picture one of these molecules. During its wandering through space the molecule may strike a surface, for instance the wall of the vessel in which the gas is enclosed; any surface which is exposed to the gas will serve our purpose. When a molecule hits the surface from an arbitrary direction, one of two things can happen. Either the molecule will bounce back from the surface elastically, more or less like a billiard ball hitting the cushion of a billiard table, with the angle of incidence equal to the angle of reflection, or the molecule will stick to the surface for a certain time, and then fly away, but in a direction unrelated to that from which it came. The latter phenomenon is the more normal one. In the great majority of cases molecules hitting a surface will stay at that surface for a certain length of time. How long that time is depends on various factors, such as the actual place on the surface which the molecule strikes, the nature of the surface and that of the molecule, the temperature of the surface, and the kinetic energy of the molecule. We are speaking here about the kinetic energy of the molecule and not of its temperature, because temperature is not a molecular property. We can only speak about the temperature when we think of a great assembly of numerous molecules, where the average kinetic energy of all these defines the temperature.

2. The fundamental cause of adsorption

The question immediately arises, what will be the result of this? It is clear that when a certain number of molecules strike continually upon a surface and stay there for a certain length of time before re-evaporating, we shall find a higher concentration of the gas at this surface than in the bulk of the gas. This is the phenomenon we call 'adsorption'. We have already stated above, that the normal behaviour of the molecule is to stay at the surface for some time. Therefore we may expect to find adsorption of molecules in every case where a surface is exposed to a gas or to a liquid. We shall find this phenomenon at any contact between a gas and a solid, a gas and a liquid, a liquid and a solid, between two liquids, and even, in certain circumstances, when two solids come into contact.

If the time during which the molecule stays at the surface is very short, we may have difficulty in detecting the adsorbed gas by chemical or physical means. That, however, the phenomenon of adsorption is there, and that it even plays an important role, is proved by the fact that a gas is warmed by a hot surface with which it is in contact, or by the reverse, that a cold surface can be heated by contact with a hot gas. We will come back to this important consequence of adsorption at a later stage, but we should note here that this result of the phenomenon of adsorption is in fact far more important for mankind than all the technical applications of adsorption put together. Without this transmission of heat life on earth would be impossible.

3. Technical applications

If, however, the time during which the molecule stays at the surface is somewhat longer, we have the opportunity of making useful technical applications of the phenomenon of adsorption. It will then be possible to remove undesired impurities from gases or from solutions. Mention may be made here of the clarification of wine, a very old application indeed, and of the bleaching of oils with charcoal or bleaching earth; of the removal of odorous or poisonous gases from air; and the removal of water vapour from air and of water from oily substances. Often adsorption is used for the regeneration of expensive organic solvents, or for the recovering of small amounts of precious metals. One of the most recent applications is the separation of gas mixtures by adsorption instead of by fractional distillation at low temperatures.

In all these cases the only important fact is that the molecule is temporarily withdrawn from the gas or liquid phase. We do not want the molecule to do anything special whilst it is adsorbed. In some other cases, however, we do want something particular from it. When we adsorb dyestuff molecules on cotton we do want the molecules to stay for an indefinitely long time and to absorb special wavelengths of light, preferably without changing themselves. When we are making photoelectric or thermionic cathodes, we adsorb alkali or alkaline earth metal atoms on the surfaces of their oxides. We want these atoms then to emit electrons, and subsequently to recapture electrons from inside. In other cases we use specially selected surfaces which adsorb particular species of molecules and make them react with other species. The time during which the molecules and their reaction products stay at such a catalytic surface should be as short as possible. Phenomena of this kind play an important role not only in technological chemistry, but also in the processes of living nature. We may think here of the action of enzymes, of many processes in protein chemistry, and of the normal assimilation process of the green plant. It is not impossible that our so-called chemical senses, namely, smell and taste, are dependent on the adsorption of specific molecules on the organs in the back of our nose and tongue respectively, where they give a specific impression which we then translate as smell and taste.

4. The fundamental equation

It may be clear from this arbitrary selection of processes that the phenomenon of adsorption is of major importance for life and for technique. The common fundamental cause in all these cases is the temporary stay of the molecules at the surface. This is the basis of adsorption. We have already remarked that the number of molecules which will be concentrated at the surface is dependent on the number which strike the surface and upon the time during which they stay. If n molecules strike a unit area of a surface per unit time and remain there for an average time τ, then we shall find σ molecules per unit area of surface where

$$\sigma = n\tau. \tag{1}$$

We will use cm.^{2} as a unit of area and sec. as a unit of time; hence n is the number of molecules falling on 1 cm.^{2} per sec. (dimensions: cm.$^{-2}$ sec.$^{-1}$), and the dimension of τ is sec. Consequently the dimension of σ is cm.$^{-2}$ It is the number of molecules adsorbed per cm.^{2} of surface. Both the entities n and τ are of great importance for the phenomenon of adsorption and we will therefore consider them separately.

II

THE NUMBER n

5. The kinetic theory of gases†

n IS the number of molecules striking each cm.² of the surface every second. If we are dealing with a gas this number n follows immediately from the kinetic theory of gases. According to this conception every molecule in a gas moves with a constant velocity and in a straight line until it collides with another molecule. Both partners in the collision change their velocities and their directions and move on straightforwardly in their new directions and with their newly attained velocities until they collide again with other molecules, and so on. The length of path, L, which the molecules travel between two successive collisions, is not constant. The values of L vary round an average denoted by $\bar{L}$. This is the average value of the paths between collisions which each individual molecule will travel in the course of time. $\bar{L}$ is also the average of the paths which all the molecules travel at any moment.

The same holds for the average velocity $\bar{u}$, which is dependent on temperature and molecular weight. This average velocity is again the mean of all the velocities of all the molecules of the gas at any moment and also the mean of all the velocities which any molecule will acquire in the course of time, provided the temperature remains constant.

The conception is that of an 'ideal' chaos. From it one may derive a certain number of fundamental equations. The first of these equations is

$$n = \tfrac{1}{4}N_1\bar{u}, \tag{2}$$

where n is the number we are discussing in this chapter. We see that n is dependent on the mean velocity $\bar{u}$ which we have already encountered, and a new entity N_1 by which we mean the number of molecules of the gas per cm.³, hence a number which is directly dependent on the density of the gas or on its concentration. As the dimension of N_1 is number/cm.³ (hence cm.⁻³) and the dimension of $\bar{u}$ is cm./sec. (hence cm. sec.⁻¹), we see that the dimension of n is

---

† Particulars about the kinetic theory of gases may be found in many well known textbooks of physics and of chemistry. Special attention is drawn to a beautiful little booklet by M. Knudsen, *The Kinetic Theory of Gases*, Methuen, London, 1946, in which further particulars about some of the subjects of this chapter may be found.

number of molecules per cm.^{2} and per sec. (cm.$^{-2}$ sec.$^{-1}$) as it should be.

We want, however, to express our number n in terms of the more normal properties of the gas, namely, pressure, temperature, and molecular weight. A few other fundamental equations enable us to do so. The second fundamental equation expresses the fact that the molecules, whilst striking the surface, exercise pressure. This pressure p is given by the equation

$$p = \tfrac{1}{3}N_1 m\overline{u^2} \tag{3}$$

in which N_1 is the same N_1 as in equation (2), whilst m is the mass of a molecule. $\overline{u^2}$ is not the square of $\bar{u}$, but it is the average of all the squares of the velocities. From the dimensions of N_1 (cm.$^{-3}$), m (g.), and $\overline{u^2}$ (cm.^{2} sec.$^{-2}$) we see that the dimension of the pressure p is g. sec.$^{-2}$ cm.$^{-1}$ Hence when we express N_1 in number of molecules/cm.^{3}, m in grams, and u in cm./sec., we get the pressure in dynes (dimension g. cm. sec.$^{-2}$) per cm.^{2}

6. The velocities of the molecules

As we have already remarked, $\overline{u^2}$ is not the same as $(\bar{u})^2$ but there is a direct relation between the two, which follows from Maxwell's law giving the distribution of velocities

$$\tfrac{1}{3}\overline{u^2} = \tfrac{1}{8}\pi(\bar{u})^2. \tag{4}$$

Substituting this equation in equation (3) we get

$$p = \tfrac{1}{8}\pi N_1 m(\bar{u})^2 \,;$$

hence,

$$\bar{u} = \sqrt{\left(\frac{8p}{\pi N_1 m}\right)}.$$

N_1, the number of molecules/cm.^{3}, still figures in this equation. We express this quantity as:

$$N_1 = \frac{N}{V},$$

where N is Avogadro's number giving the number of molecules/mole, whilst V is the volume of a mole expressed in cm.^{3} Substituting in the equation for $\bar{u}$, we obtain

$$\bar{u} = \sqrt{\left(\frac{8pV}{\pi Nm}\right)}.$$

If we use the Boyle–Gay Lussac law, namely,

$$pV = RT$$

where R is the molar gas constant and T is the absolute temperature and if we also realize that

$$Nm = M$$

where M is the molecular weight, we obtain

$$\bar{u} = \sqrt{\left(\frac{8RT}{\pi M}\right)}. \tag{5}$$

Numerically, expressed in metres/sec., we obtain

$$\bar{u} = 145 \cdot 5 \sqrt{\left(\frac{T}{M}\right)} \text{ metres/sec.}$$

For a temperature of 20° C. ($T = 293°$ K.) we get the following figures for a few gases:

$$H_2: \quad \bar{u} = 1{,}760 \text{ metres/sec.}$$
$$N_2: \quad \bar{u} = 470 \text{ metres/sec.}$$
$$O_2: \quad \bar{u} = 440 \text{ metres/sec.}$$
$$H_2O: \quad \bar{u} = 587 \text{ metres/sec.}$$

These are, as we see, rather high figures. The speed of the molecules is more than 1,000 miles per hour. It is faster than the speed of sound (330 metres/sec.).

It is important to realize that the velocities of the molecules are not dependent on the pressure of the gas. The mean free path, however, is inversely proportional to the pressure. The mean number of collisions per second that a molecule makes with other molecules is directly proportional to the pressure (see Table 1 in § 13).

7. The magnitude of n

We have now expressed the mean velocity of the molecules in terms of the more normal quantities of temperature and molecular weight. It is also easy to express N_1 in terms of similar quantities. We have seen already that

$$N_1 = \frac{N}{V}.$$

Using the Boyle–Gay Lussac law again, we find

$$N_1 = \frac{N}{V} = \frac{Np}{RT}.$$

Substituting this value and also equation (5) in equation (2), we get

$$n = \frac{1}{4} \frac{Np}{RT} \sqrt{\left(\frac{8RT}{\pi M}\right)},$$

hence $$n = \frac{Np}{\sqrt{(2\pi MRT)}}. \qquad (6)$$

If we evaluate this expression using the known figures
$$R = 8 \cdot 31^5 \times 10^7 \ \text{erg/}^\circ\text{K}.$$
$$N = 6 \cdot 023 \times 10^{23},$$

we get $$n = 2 \cdot 62^5 \times 10^{19} \times \frac{p}{\sqrt{(MT)}}. \qquad (6\,\text{a})$$

The pressure p in this equation is still expressed in dynes/cm.^{2} (see above). If we want to express the pressure in a more normal way, namely, in millimetres of mercury, then our expression for n becomes

$$n = 3 \cdot 52 \times 10^{22} \times \frac{p}{\sqrt{(MT)}}. \qquad (6\,\text{b})$$

Using this expression we get, at a temperature of 20° C., and a pressure of 760 mm. of mercury:

hydrogen (H_2): $n = 11 \cdot 0 \times 10^{23}$ molecules/cm.^{2} sec.

nitrogen (N_2): $n = 2 \cdot 94 \times 10^{23}$,,   ,,

oxygen   (O_2): $n = 2 \cdot 75 \times 10^{23}$,,   ,,

We see from this result that the numbers n are extremely high. The figure for hydrogen, for instance, teaches us that in hydrogen at room temperature and 1 atmosphere pressure, nearly 2 moles of hydrogen collide with each cm.^{2} of surface every second.

In the following sections we will illustrate the magnitude of n by a few examples.

8. The number n for water molecules in 'dry' atmospheres

It is known that many substances such as inorganic salts or oxides, or organic products such as cellulose, starch, or proteins, readily attract water vapour from moist air. Suppose we expose a surface of one of these substances at 20° C. to an atmosphere with a relative humidity of 10 per cent. This is a relatively dry atmosphere, in which the pressure of the water vapour is 1·75 mm. of mercury. Equation (6 b) then tells us that in equilibrium $8 \cdot 5 \times 10^{20}$ water molecules strike each cm.^{2} per second. As roughly 10^{15} molecules of water are sufficient to cover such a surface with a unimolecular layer of water, we see that in equilibrium this amount strikes the surface roughly every millionth of a second. The enormously high value of n causes adsorption phenomena to take place with great

speed, nearly instantaneously. In order to avoid misunderstanding
it must be remarked that such great speed will be experienced immediately the adsorbent is exposed to the gas, when there are—in
our example—sufficient water molecules in the direct proximity of
the surface to be taken up with the speed suggested by the number n.
The air in the immediate neighbourhood of the surface is, however,
quickly exhausted and a further supply of water molecules has to
come from more remote parts. The speed with which this takes
place is given by the rate of diffusion of water molecules in air.
After the adsorption equilibrium is established, n water molecules
will strike each cm.^{2} per second and n will evaporate, this being the
condition of the dynamic equilibrium.

The water pressure in our example was still rather high. Let us
therefore put our substance in an atmosphere which we have arti-
ficially dried with either concentrated sulphuric acid or rods of pre-
melted potassium hydroxide. The residual water vapour pressure
in such a desiccator is 0·002 mm. of mercury, hence the number n
according to equation (6 b) is

$$10^{18} \text{ molecules per cm.}^2 \text{ and per sec.,}$$

still 1,000 times more per second than are necessary to make a
unimolecular layer of water on the surface. If our substance binds
water very strongly, it will therefore exhaust the water vapour from
its surrounding air very quickly, and the rate of taking up still more
water is determined by the rate with which water can be supplied
from the rest of the air in the desiccator or from the drying agents.
If phosphorus pentoxide (P_2O_5) had been taken as a drying agent, the
residual water vapour pressure would have been smaller than 0·00002
mm. of mercury and our number n would have been smaller than
10^{16} molecules/cm.^{2} sec. A vapour pressure of this magnitude looks
very low to us, but if we realize that a vapour pressure of 0·00001
mm. of mercury corresponds to a concentration of

$$N_1 = 3 \times 10^{11} \text{ molecules/cm.}^3$$

and that we still can smell a substance such as mercaptan in a
concentration which is a hundred times smaller than that, then we may
realize how fortunate it is that water vapour does not give so powerful
a sensation of smell to us as does mercaptan. It may be remarked
that if we take a sniff of air with mercaptan of the above-mentioned

concentration, which we can just smell, there are still 2×10^{13} molecules of mercaptan striking a cm.^{2} of our sense organ per second.

9. The number n in high vacua

Many metal surfaces oxidize immediately when they are exposed to air or to oxygen. In normal air $5 \cdot 5 \times 10^{22}$ molecules of oxygen fall on each cm.^{2} of surface per second. This is roughly 10^8 times more than the amount necessary for a unimolecular layer of oxygen atoms at the surface. Even if we pump the air out of the container in which we store the metal, and we evacuate to a pressure of $0 \cdot 001$ mm. of mercury, the number n is still of the order of magnitude of 10^{17} molecules/cm.^{2} sec. An electron emitting oxide cathode such as used in radio valves, transmitting tubes, and in modern fluorescent light tubes, would immediately be poisoned if exposed to oxygen of that pressure. The same would happen to a hydrogenation catalyst. Even a tungsten wire in an incandescent lamp, will, when heated in such an atmosphere, take up oxygen nearly instantaneously. Suppose we have a filament of tungsten weighing roughly 70 mg. and having a total surface of 1 cm.^{2} in a bulb of 200 cm.^{3} and that we have evacuated the bulb to a pressure of $0 \cdot 001$ mm. of mercury. Suppose that the residual gas consists of oxygen. According to equation (6) $n = 3 \cdot 6 \times 10^{17}$ molecules/cm.^{2} sec. Such a number of molecules however is not present in the bulb. There are only about 66×10^{14} molecules available. These molecules strike the tungsten surface. Oxygen molecules combine there with tungsten atoms and tungsten oxide molecules evaporate from the filament to the wall. The oxygen molecules will ultimately be used up by this process. The pressure decreases whilst this 'cleaning up' is going on. The whole phenomenon takes some time but still goes very quickly and comes to an end when all the oxygen has been taken up. If, however, water vapour is present, every molecule of water vapour hitting the filament will oxidize the tungsten, forming atomic hydrogen at the same time. The tungsten oxide evaporates to the wall and so do the hydrogen atoms. The average free path $\bar{L}$ is roughly 7 cm. at this pressure. At the wall the atomic hydrogen reduces the tungsten oxide and forms water molecules again. These water molecules will strike the filament and the process repeats itself. In a relatively short time a considerable amount of tungsten is transported from the filament to the glass wall, which blackens, and the filament will at last 'burn through'. Despite the very low pressure in the container it is remarkable that the phenomenon goes so quickly. This is caused by the great magnitude of our number n.

In order to prevent things like this happening, the vacua may be improved by chemical means. Usually red phosphorus is used in incandescent vacuum lamps. Inorganic salts such as calcium fluoride, cryolite, and the like, are evaporated from the filament to the wall when the lamp is made in order to reduce the blackness of the tungsten evaporated to the wall of the lamp during its normal life, but they also play a part in this 'cleaning up' procedure.

In radio valves and transmitting tubes metals such as magnesium, barium, or zirconium are used to bind the residual gases. At present barium is by far the most common of these so-called 'getters'.

In chemical industry, where high vacua are wanted, these chemical means are not appropriate. Modern high vacuum pumps, however, may produce vacua up to $10^{-5}\mu$ $(1\mu = 10^{-3}$ mm.). It may be remarked that the expression of such a residual pressure in mm. of mercury has no real physical significance any more, for the height of a mercury column of 10^{-9} cm. would be small even in comparison with the dimensions of 1 mercury atom. High vacua of this magnitude are used in the instruments necessary for producing atomic energy. The path which molecular particles have to travel in cyclotrons, betatrons, or synchrotrons is so enormously long that even at a pressure of $10^{-5}\mu$, where the free path L is of the order of magnitude of many kilometres, a considerable number of these particles are lost by scattering through collision with other particles.

The vacua in electronic tubes are certainly still higher and the residual pressure is in many cases lower than $10^{-6}\mu$. Still, even when the residual pressure is as low as that, the number n according to equation (6) still has a high value. This is caused by the high values of the average velocity $\bar{u}$. We have seen already in § 6 how large these velocities are.

10. A comparison with a 'gas' in astronomy

An interesting comparison may be made from the field of astronomy. The highest vacuum which we can make in our laboratories is of the order of magnitude of $10^{-6}\mu$. The density of the residual gas in such a vacuum is enormously great compared with the density of the gas clouds of the astronomer. There exist, for instance, in our galaxy enormous gas clouds which consist of hydrogen atoms. The temperature of some of these clouds is very high, roughly 10,000° C., which means that the velocity of the hydrogen atoms is about 14,500 metres/sec. The concentration, however, is very low, namely, about 60 atoms/cm.³ Compare this with the concentration of about 30 million molecules/cm.³ in the highest vacuum of $10^{-6}\mu$ which we can produce. If we could expose a surface to the atmosphere of such a galactic gas cloud then the number of atoms falling on every cm.² as calculated from our equation (2) would amount to 2×10^7 atoms/cm.² sec. This is still a great amount. Though 20 million atoms would hit every cm.² of the surface per second, it would nevertheless take us about 3 years to cover the whole surface with a unimolecular layer provided not a single atom escaped in the meantime.

Cosmical bodies, the surfaces of which are exposed to such gas clouds, do travel an astronomically large number of years through them. This is possible because the dimensions of these clouds are so vast that it takes even light about a hundred centuries to travel through them. These bodies, therefore, have ample opportunity to take up hydrogen and other gases during their travel through space. If they pass during the course of their journey into the neighbourhood of the sun, the radiation of the sun will drive the gases out and excite them. It is then that we see the illuminated tail of a comet. This phenomenon, according to this model, is therefore caused by the desorption of gases from the body of the comet.

11. The rate of adsorption

It will be clear from the above considerations that an adsorption equilibrium will establish itself practically instantaneously. If this is not found to be the case in practical examples, we must seek the cause in transport problems. It may be that the transport of the gas to the surface is the cause of the delay, or that the transport of the adsorbed gas from the outer surface of the adsorbent to more interior parts of the porous structure may take time. Diffusion always takes time.

The establishing of an adsorption equilibrium at a free gas/solid interface, or a free gas/liquid interface, will only then take a measurable time if the pressure is so low that even despite the high velocity of the molecules the number n is low. Lately some plasticizers and some lubricants with very low vapour pressures have found technical application. Dibutyl phthalate, for example, has a vapour pressure of 5×10^{-5} mm. at room temperature. Meta-tricresyl-phosphate has a pressure of 4×10^{-8} mm. The so-called Apiezon-L-grease is even alleged to have a vapour pressure of only 10^{-11} mm. of mercury. Let us suppose that this latter grease consists of molecules $C_{30}H_{62}$ only ($M = 422$). The number n then amounts to 10^9 molecules/cm.² sec. If we suppose that every molecule of this grease, when adsorbed at a surface, will cover 150 A² (150×10^{-16} cm.²), we will need $6 \cdot 7 \times 10^{13}$ molecules to cover 1 cm.² of surface with a unimolecular layer. It will then take us $6 \cdot 7 \times 10^4$ sec., that is, nearly a day, to adsorb a unimolecular layer of this grease. Experimentally, it has been found that in a high vacuum apparatus, where this grease was used, it did take several hours before the influence of the vapour of this grease was noticeable on the surface tension of the mercury used in the same apparatus.†

12. A magnified picture

In all our discussions so far we have used figures of such magnitude that we cannot picture them. The number of molecules in a cm.³ of gas at room temperature and atmospheric pressure is so vast that if we decided to count them individually and we could take a number of men to do the counting, reckoning that every man can count up to a hundred in a minute, we should find that there are not enough men on earth to do this counting business. Worse still, there have not been enough men living on earth since the creation to do so.

We may get some impression of these vast numbers when we imagine a magnified picture, using an enormous magnifying factor, for which we choose 32 million. When we magnify all our linear dimensions 32 million times, then the length of 1 cm. becomes 320 kilometres which is roughly 200 miles. To picture 1 cm.² in this magnified conception we may draw a square from Hull to Hastings, from Hastings to Torquay, from Torquay to a point half-way between Holyhead and Dublin, and back to Hull.‡ If we then imagine a cube with a height of 200 miles in the air (or rather beyond it) over this area, then we have the equivalent of 1 cm.³ In the same

† Observed in an experiment, described by C. Kemball, *Trans. Faraday Soc.* **42**, (1946), 536.

‡ For the benefit of readers in the U.S.A., this is roughly the size of the State of Ohio.

magnified scale an oxygen molecule has now attained the size of a
bee. If we now imagine an artificial gas of bees then we have to
enclose 20 trillion bees in this cube in order to get a picture of 1 cm.[3]
of a gas of room temperature and atmospheric pressure. Let us now
take a very small part of this immense cube. For instance, a lecture
room of 1,000 cubic-metre content (35,300 cu. ft.). In this room we
will then have just about 1 million bees. We can now picture what
a vacuum of 0·001 mm. of mercury means in this picture. It would
mean that we had reduced the 1 million bees in our lecture room to
one bee in the same space.

We want to make the speed of the bees the same as the velocity
of the molecules. In order to do this we must also increase our unit
of time, so we must make a slow-motion picture. We have to increase
our unit of time in the same proportion as our unit of length, which
means that instead of 1 sec. we read 1 year. If we do that, then
the speed of our bees is the same as that of our molecules, namely
somewhat more than 1,000 miles per hour. The 1 million bees in
our lecture room now fly with that average speed in straight lines.
Each of them collides 150 times per second with another bee and
the path travelled on an average between two collisions is about
3 yds.

We turn now to our number n. This proves to be so high that even
now ten bees will hit every cm.[2] of the wall of our lecture room every
second, hence, even in this slow-motion picture we can hardly count
the number which strike the surface.

We may now have a good picture of this gas of super bees in our
imagination. Then we must again reduce all linear dimensions by
a factor of 32 million, and we must speed up all that occurs, so that
all the events of a whole year will take place in one second in order
to get a picture of what happens in the molecular world.

13. A comparison of gases of various pressures

We give, in tabular form, all the figures which we have discussed
above for gases of various pressures. This table will make a comparison between various gases easier. We have indicated in the table
the mean free path which is roughly given by the equation

$$\bar{L} \simeq 10^{-5} \times \frac{T}{273} \times \frac{760}{p}\ \text{cm.}$$

When in this equation we express the temperature in absolute degrees C. and the pressure p in mm. mercury, then we get $\bar{L}$ in cm.

TABLE 1

	Gas of atmospheric pressure	Vacuum of 0·001 mm. Hg (1 μ)	High vacuum of $10^{-5}\,\mu$	Gas cloud in galaxy	'Gas of super bees' in magnified picture
Mean free path (L). . .	10^{-5} cm.	7 cm.	7 km.	400×10^{6} km. (3 times distance sun–earth)	3 m.
Average number of collisions per molecule	5×10^{9} per sec.	6,500 per sec.	one per 15 sec.	one per 10 months	5×10^{9} per year (150/sec.)
Number of molecules per cm.³ (N_1)	25×10^{18}	33×10^{12}	33×10^{7}	60	1000/m.³
Number of molecules striking a cm.² of a surface per sec. (n)	$\sim 3 \times 10^{23}$	$\sim 3{\cdot}5 \times 10^{17}$	$\sim 3{\cdot}5 \times 10^{12}$	$\sim 2 \times 10^{7}$	$\sim 3 \times 10^{12}$/m.² year $= 10$/cm.² sec.

14. The dynamic equilibrium between a liquid and its vapour

Let us now picture a molecule hitting the surface of its own liquid. In such a case there is no elastic reflection. Every molecule hitting the surface is caught, condensed as we say in cases like this. If the liquid is in equilibrium with its own vapour, and hence with its saturated vapour, there will be as many molecules hitting every cm.² of the surface per second and consequently being condensed, as there are molecules leaving every cm.² of the surface each second, and hence evaporating. The dynamic equilibrium demands that these two figures be the same. Nevertheless, they have essentially nothing to do with each other. The number of molecules striking each cm.² every second, our number n, is determined by the properties of the gas (vapour) only, and, as we know from equation (6), it depends only on pressure, molecular weight, and temperature. However, the number of molecules evaporating from the surface is determined by, amongst other things, the energy which it takes to tear the molecule away from the binding forces of the other molecules of the liquid. The work which has to be done to overcome these forces is supplied by the thermal movement of the molecules in the liquid. This thermal movement increases with temperature. At each temperature a definite number of molecules leave each cm.² of the surface per second, and when we have the liquid in an enclosed space a vapour is created over the liquid. The vapour pressure increases during this evaporation process until such a value is reached that the number n equals the number of molecules which evaporate from the surface. When this equilibrium point is reached it looks, macroscopically, as if nothing happens any more. In reality, however, the evaporation goes on with the same rate as from the beginning. It is only because just as many molecules return to the liquid as leave it that nothing appears to be happening.

If we perform this experiment with a substance of which we know the molecular weight, and we keep the temperature constant, we can, by means of equation (6) immediately calculate how many molecules will move in either way. We have only to determine the saturation pressure which belongs to the temperature which we choose. Once we know this pressure we know the number n and therefore also the rate of evaporation.

15. The maximum rate of evaporation

If we now maintain the temperature of the liquid at a constant value and we take all the vapour away and keep taking it away, preventing any molecule from returning to the liquid, we can immediately calculate how much liquid will evaporate per cm.² and per second. This is obviously the maximum rate of evaporation which we can ever attain at the chosen temperature. Experiments of this kind can only be done with liquids which have a relatively low rate of evaporation, otherwise it is too difficult, for instance, to keep the temperature constant, and also very difficult to secure that no molecule returns. It is obvious that in such an experiment the surface of the liquid must be thoroughly clean. Experiments of this kind have been done with mercury and it has indeed been proved that the maximum rate of evaporation at a given temperature is exactly determined by equation (6), which was derived from the laws of kinetic theory of gases only.

The determination of the maximum rate of evaporation gives, in many cases where vapour pressures are very low, a handy indirect method for the measurement of vapour pressures. The vapour pressures of alkali metals, alkaline earth metals, and many organic substances of low volatility, have been measured by this method.

A glance at equation (6) reminds us that our number n, and therefore as we now know also the maximum rate of evaporation of a liquid, is dependent on the molecular weight M. The higher the molecular weight of the liquid the lower the rate of evaporation. If we therefore have a liquid consisting of two isotopes, atoms which differ only in their molecular weight, we see that the rate of evaporation for them will be different, the lighter isotope evaporating more easily than the heavier one. Isotopes may be separated by this principle. The conditions must be such that no evaporated atom will return to the liquid, so that it is really the *rate* of evaporation which determines the procedure. Isotopes of potassium and of mercury have been separated to a certain extent, using this principle.

16. The rate of evaporation of water

Lét us turn now to a liquid with a higher vapour pressure, which means a higher rate of evaporation. Let us consider water. If we could evaporate water at room temperature in such a way that the temperature of the liquid was kept constant, and that moreover all the molecules of water leaving the surface were taken away at once, then the rate of evaporation of water would be extremely high. At 20° C. the saturated vapour pressure of water is 17·5 mm. The number n according to equation (6 b) is $8·5 \times 10^{21}$ molecules/cm.^{2} sec. If then we possessed the means of taking all these molecules away at once, 253 mg. of water would evaporate per second and per cm.^{2}, which means a column 9 metres deep in an hour. This would mean that many lakes and seas would be dry in a couple of hours and that the evaporation of the water of the ocean would only be a matter of some days. Needless to say, in reality the evaporation of water does not go at this speed; it goes on roughly 100,000 to 1,000,000 times more slowly. A tropical sea, for instance, evaporates roughly at a rate of 2 metres per year, whilst in more moderate climates this figure will be about 50 cm. per year (0·0017 mg./cm.^{2} sec.).

It is striking that a forest evaporates far more water than a sea does. A lake in moderate climates will evaporate 15,000 litres of water per day per hectare (1,300 gallons per acre per day). A beech wood, however, will evaporate roughly 200,000 litres per day per hectare (17,500 gallons per acre per day). This proportion demonstrates well the climatological importance of forests and woods.

Apart from the fact that the temperature of the water would decrease whilst evaporating, the slow evaporation is mainly due to the fact that there is a thin layer close over the surface where the water vapour pressure is nearly saturated. From there water vapour diffuses into the rest of the air and it is the rate of this diffusion which mainly governs the actual rate of evaporation.

17. Rate of evaporation in some vacuum operations

Apart from the separation of isotopes already mentioned above, there are two procedures both applied in techniques where the maximum rate of evaporation governs the speed of the process.

(1) In the so-called 'unobstructed path distillation', also but less correctly called 'molecular distillation', the condition is fulfilled that every evaporated molecule is taken away immediately. The pressure in the apparatus is kept so low that the mean free path of the molecules is great compared with the distance between evaporator and condenser. At the condenser, steps are taken to prevent re-evaporation, for instance by adequate cooling. The vapour pressure of the substances which are subjected to this sort of distillation is substantially lower than the gas pressure which is maintained in the apparatus by the pumps. The dimensions of the apparatus are determined by this latter gas pressure. The rate of evaporation is given by equation (6). If we prefer to express it in grams per cm.² and per second we may apply the equation

$$v_{\max} = 0 \cdot 0583 p \sqrt{(M/T)} \text{ g./cm.}^2 \text{ sec.}$$

where p is expressed in mm. mercury.

(2) The second example occurs in the procedure of *freeze drying*. The pressure in the apparatus in this case is kept lower than the saturated vapour pressure of the substance which has to be evaporated. In the case of normal liquids such a procedure is impossible because the liquid would boil vigorously. It is only with very viscous liquids or with solids (sublimation) that this principle can be applied. Suppose, for instance, we have ice of $-20°$ C.: the water vapour pressure of ice at this temperature is $0 \cdot 77$ mm. of mercury. According to the equation just mentioned which also applies here,

$$v_{\max} = 0 \cdot 0583 \times 0 \cdot 77 \times \sqrt{(\tfrac{18}{253})} = 0 \cdot 012 \text{ g./cm.}^2 \text{ sec.}$$

If we maintain in the apparatus a pressure substantially lower than $0 \cdot 77$ mm., let us, for instance, say $0 \cdot 1$ mm., we can calculate by means of equation (6) how many molecules of water will recondense on the evaporating ice surface. If we also express this amount in g./cm.² sec. we obtain for the amount of condensed water:

$$v_{\text{cond}} = 0.0583 \times p' \ \sqrt{\left(\frac{M}{T}\right)} = 0.0015 \text{ g./cm.}^2 \text{ sec.}$$

where p' is the pressure which we maintain in the apparatus. The practical evaporation of water from the ice surface therefore is the difference between these two figures:

$$v_{\text{max}} - v_{\text{cond}} = 0.0105 \text{ g./cm.}^2 \text{ sec.,}$$

or, more generally, $\qquad v = v_{\text{max}}\left(1 - \frac{p'}{p}\right).$

The condition for this operation, therefore, is $p' \ll p$; the mean free path of the molecules does not matter in this case.

We have assumed that the rate of evaporation of ice is the maximum rate given by equation (6). This equation, however, holds only when there is no reflection of molecules at the surface. If part of the molecules which strike the surface are reflected, the rate of evaporation is smaller. There are indications that reflection may play an important role in the evaporation and condensation of polar molecules (see § 41). If that is so, the numerical figures which we calculated from the vapour pressure of ice will not be correct. The actual rates of evaporation will then be smaller. The last-mentioned condition, however, still holds (see also § 143).

18. The dependence of n on temperature

In all our considerations so far we have spoken mainly about the dependence of n on the pressure p. We have already indicated a case, however, where the dependence of n on M, the molecular weight, was the dominating factor, namely, in the separation of isotopes. These may be separated by virtue of their different rate of evaporation although they have the same vapour pressure. The conditions necessary to get a successful separation are the same as in the operation of the unobstructed path distillation. A glance at equation (6) reminds us that n is also dependent on the temperature T and we will just mention briefly a case where this dependence governs the phenomena. Suppose we have two rooms, both containing the same gas, hence of the same molecular weight, at the same pressure. The temperature in the two rooms, however, may be different,

$$T_1 > T_2.$$

Suppose now we connect these two rooms by means of a capillary tube with the end in room 1 also having the temperature T_1, the end in room 2 having the temperature T_2. Equation (6) shows that more molecules will enter the capillary each second on the cold side than on the warm side. There will be, therefore, a flow of gas through the capillary from the cold to the warm side. This flow of gas will continue until the pressure on the warm side is raised to such an extent that

$$n_1 = n_2,$$

which means

$$\frac{p_1}{\sqrt{(T_1)}} = \frac{p_2}{\sqrt{(T_2)}},$$

or

$$\frac{p_1}{p_2} = \sqrt{\left(\frac{T_1}{T_2}\right)}.$$

In order to demonstrate this effect the width of the capillary must be such that no mutual collisions between gas molecules will take place in it, hence the width of the capillary must be smaller than the mean free path of the molecules. If this is not the case then the collisions in the centre of the capillary or tube will cause a flow of gas in the opposite direction and will annul the effect. In order to demonstrate the effect in air of atmospheric pressure, we need to use between the two vessels capillaries with a diameter smaller than 10^{-5} cm., or to use a porous wall, the pores of which are of that size. It will be seen later how this principle is made the basis of an absolute determination of extremely low pressure values (§ 22).

THE TIME τ

19. Reflection of molecular rays†

As we have stated already in Chapter I a molecule hitting a surface can do one of two things, it can either be caught by the surface or it can rebound and return immediately to the gas phase. If it is caught it may remain on the surface for a short time and then return to the gas phase, or may stay more or less permanently. When we compare the instantaneous return to the gas phase, when the molecule rebounds, with the return to the gas phase after a short but finite time of lingering on the surface, one very important difference must be pointed out concerning the direction in which the molecule leaves the surface. In the case of a rebounding molecule which returns to the gas phase instantaneously, the direction in which it is reflected is related to the direction of incidence. The relation is the same as in the reflection of light. The angle between the direction of the impinging molecule and the normal to the surface will be equal to the angle between the direction of the reflected molecule and the normal. If, however, the molecule remains on the surface for a short time, before returning to the gas phase, there is no such relation and the direction in which the molecule returns is only governed by the conditions on the surface. The molecules are scattered from the surface.

It looks as if it might be relatively easy to determine experimentally whether an elastic reflection takes place or whether the molecules are scattered in all directions, and to conclude whether or not there is a finite time of lingering on the surface. Experimentally, however, a difficulty arises. If the surface is rough the molecules will be distributed at random in all directions, and even in the case of pure reflection it might appear as if scattering had taken place. Therefore, in order to find experimentally whether reflection takes place or not the surface must be smooth. It is interesting to find out how smooth the surface should be. We may compare the reflection of molecules with the reflection of light. A narrow beam of molecules directed on to a plane smooth surface

† For an excellent account of molecular rays, see the monograph of R. G. J. Fraser, *Molecular Rays*, Cambridge Univ. Press, 1931.

may be compared with a beam of light and, as already stated, the law of reflection of this molecular beam will be the same as in the case of light.

In the case of reflection of light, it is known that the inequalities of a more or less rough surface must be such that their height projected on the incident beam is less than the wavelength of the light used. If ϑ is the angle of incidence and l is the average height of the inequalities of the surface, the condition is

$$2l \cos \vartheta < \lambda, \tag{7}$$

where λ is the wavelength of the light.

This means that when the inequalities of the surface have an average height of 0·01 mm., red light with a wavelength $\lambda = 7 \times 10^{-5}$ cm. will be reflected if the angle of incidence is about 88° or more. Thus the incident beam includes an angle of only 2° or less. For blue light, or for white light, the angle of incidence must be greater still. If the inequalities of the surface are of the order of magnitude of 0·001 mm. ($1\,\mu$), red light will reflect at an angle of about 70° and more. Natural quartz which is not polished, has inequalities of about 2–3 μ. Thoroughly polished surfaces have inequalities of about 0·1 μ and they reflect visible light at all angles.

We may apply the same equation for the condition of reflection of molecules if we insert the wavelength of the material wave corresponding to the moving molecule. Corresponding to a beam of molecules of mass m and velocity u, there is a material wave, the wavelength λ of which is

$$\lambda = \frac{h}{mu} \tag{8}$$

where h is Planck's constant ($h = 6·62 \times 10^{-27}$ erg. sec.). Hydrogen molecules at room temperature have mean velocities

$$\bar{u} = 1,760 \text{ metres/sec.,}$$

a value which we can calculate immediately from equation (5). The mass m of a hydrogen molecule is

$$m = \frac{M}{N} = \frac{2}{6·023 \times 10^{23}} = 3·32 \times 10^{-24} \text{ g.}$$

Inserting these values in equation (8) gives us the mean value of the wavelength of the material wave corresponding to hydrogen molecules at room temperature. This is

$$\bar{\lambda}_{\text{H}_2} = 1 \cdot 13 \times 10^{-8} \text{ cm.}$$

For helium atoms at room temperature with mean velocities of 1,250 metres/sec. (equation 5) and masses of $6 \cdot 64 \times 10^{-24}$ g. the mean value of the wavelength is

$$\bar{\lambda}_{\text{He}} = 0 \cdot 8 \times 10^{-8} \text{ cm.}$$

Thus, with the velocities that hydrogen molecules or helium atoms have at room temperature, the corresponding wavelength is of the order of magnitude of 10^{-8} cm.

The inequalities of the most carefully polished surfaces have, as we mentioned before, heights of the order of magnitude of $0 \cdot 1 \mu = 10^{-5}$ cm. Such a surface gives of course perfect reflection of light, but in order to reflect a beam of hydrogen molecules, $\cos \vartheta$, according to equation (7) must be smaller than 10^{-3}, which means that the angle of incidence must be $> 89° 56'$. Indeed, Knauer and Stern found in 1929 that when a beam of hydrogen made an angle of only a few minutes with a perfectly polished metal surface, there was specular reflection of a few per cent. of the incident beam. This reflection was increased about $1\frac{1}{2}$ times when the temperature of the hydrogen was lowered to $-150°$ C. At this temperature the mean velocity of the hydrogen molecules is only 1,140 metres/sec. and consequently the corresponding wavelength $1 \cdot 75 \times 10^{-8}$ cm., about $1\frac{1}{2}$ times the value corresponding to the velocity at room temperature.

Later reflection experiments were made at the surface of cleaved crystals of lithium fluoride and sodium chloride. These cleaved surfaces are much more perfect than the best polished surfaces. The inequalities arise here from the fact that the constituent ions are in temperature vibration about their positions of equilibria. The inequalities due to this temperature movement are of the order of 10^{-8} cm. Hence, for a beam of helium we may expect reflection when the angle of incidence is greater than about $37°$. It was found experimentally that $0 \cdot 8$ per cent. of the incident beam was reflected when the angle of incidence was $40°$, whilst the reflection amounted to nearly 25 per cent. at an angle of incidence of $80°$. The reflecting power of the crystal surface is increased when the temperature of the crystal is lowered, because the temperature movement of the

ions in the surface is decreased, and it is this movement which causes
the inequalities.

20. Diffraction of molecular waves

The wave nature of the molecular beam not only governs the
conditions for specular reflection of molecules, at crystal surfaces,
but is also responsible for the occurrence of diffraction spectra. We
saw that the wavelength corresponding to the hydrogen or helium
beams is of the order of magnitude of 10^{-8} cm., hence it is of the
same order as the inter-ionic distances in the crystal. The diffraction of X-rays or of electrons by crystals is caused by the three-
dimensional grating formed by the regular arrangement of the ions
in space. This is because X-rays and electron rays penetrate into
the crystal for a distance of several atomic layers. Molecular rays,
however, are reflected at the surface of the crystal and do not
penetrate into it. The two-dimensional grating of the ions of the
surface layer of the crystals, therefore, will be responsible for diffraction phenomena in this case. Diffraction patterns have been successfully obtained with the material waves of hydrogen and helium
and of atomic hydrogen at the cleavage surfaces of lithium fluoride.†
Quantitative results are obtained, especially from the first order
diffraction beams which are formed on both sides of the direct reflected beam $(0, 0$ order$)$ and which result from the joint action of
rows of fluoride ions on the surface. The incident beam in these
experiments strikes the surface (cubic plane) in such a way that the
projection of the molecular ray coincides with the direction of rows
of similar ions (at an angle of 45° with the cleavage edges). The
result of these beautiful experiments is in complete agreement with
the view derived from absorption spectra of adsorbed molecules on
this sort of surface, namely that the negative ions protrude more
than do the positive ions. This is also in complete agreement with
the theoretical views on the constitution of the surfaces of ionic
crystals.

All these experiments prove that cleavage surfaces of alkali halide
crystals are ideal enough to have the smoothness required for the de-
tection of reflection of impinging molecules. Reflection has definitely

---

† The experiments of Stern and Estermann and of Johnson are well described in
Fraser's book mentioned in the previous section.

been found when molecular hydrogen, helium, or atomic hydrogen beams are directed against cleavage planes of NaCl or LiF.

Heavier gases like neon or argon give far less reflection or none. For a beam of oxygen molecules the mean wavelength $\lambda \simeq 0\cdot28 \times 10^{-8}$ cm. If there were specular reflection one could therefore expect this at angles of incidence of 74° or more. No reflection, however, is observed. It looks as if all the molecules linger for some time on the surface before evaporating again. Careful experiments have been made by John B. Taylor, who directed beams of lithium, potassium, and caesium against the above-mentioned cleavage surfaces at different angles of incidence. There was not the slightest trace of reflection. The amount, if any, was certainly less than one-hundredth of 1 per cent. All atoms were scattered in exact agreement with the Knudsen law, which states that the number of molecules emerging from the surface in a certain direction is proportional to the cosine of the angle which that direction makes with the normal to the surface. Apparently all these atoms after striking the surface remain there for some time, after which they re-evaporate in directions which have no longer any relation to the original direction of impact.

21. Exchange of heat: coefficient of accommodation[†]

It is clear from the preceding section that an answer to the question whether or not a finite time of lingering exists can only be given by reflection experiments, if they can be done with really smooth surfaces. There may be far more cases where reflection takes place especially with the very light molecules, but they cannot be found by reflection experiments.

Another source of information is found in the exchange of energy of the molecule with the surface. When molecules of a gas, with a temperature T_1, strike a solid surface at a temperature T_2, there will be exchange of heat provided the time of contact is long enough. In the case of specular reflection there is hardly any degree of exchange of energy. Complete exchange of heat will be found when the impinging molecules stay at the surface for a length of time which is great compared with the time of vibration of the surface molecules. The time of lingering should be at least a hundred times greater than this time of vibration. If the time of contact is smaller

[†] A survey of exchange of energy at surfaces may be found in J. H. de Boer, *Z. Elektrochem.* **44** (1938), 488.

than that, there is only a partial exchange of heat. Knudsen has defined a coefficient of accommodation (a):

$$a = \frac{T'_2 - T_1}{T_2 - T_1}, \tag{9}$$

where T_1 is the temperature of the gas, T_2 the temperature of the surface, and T'_2 the temperature of the gas molecules evaporating from the surface. If there is no exchange of energy the gas molecules do not alter their temperature, hence $T'_2 = T_1$ and $a = 0$. If there is complete exchange of energy the molecules leave the surface with the same temperature as the surface itself, hence $T'_2 = T_2$ and $a = 1$. In intermediate cases the time during which the molecules stay at the surface may be such that exchange of heat only takes place partially. T'_2 will have values in between T_2 and T_1 and a coefficient of accommodation will have figures between 0 and 1.

From the experience of the reflection experiments we may expect gases such as helium and hydrogen to give coefficients of accommodation smaller than 1 when in collision with many surfaces. This is indeed what is found experimentally. But in addition other molecules such as those of neon, oxygen, carbon dioxide, etc., may have values smaller than 1 on certain surfaces at certain temperatures. With neon, for instance, J. K. Roberts found $a = 0 \cdot 07$ on a clean tungsten surface at room temperature. However, when the tungsten surface was covered with oxygen $a = 0 \cdot 6$. For helium on a clean tungsten surface he found $a = 0 \cdot 057$ at room temperature. At lower temperatures the value of a decreases in this case and he found $a = 0 \cdot 025$ at a temperature of $79°$ K. It is in accordance with theoretical expectations that the coefficient of accommodation decreases with temperature in the case of reflecting molecules.

Apparently at the low temperature of $79°$ K. the time which helium atoms stay on the tungsten surface is not longer than that corresponding to the time of vibration of the tungsten molecules. On oxygen-covered metal surfaces, however, a value of $a \simeq 0 \cdot 3$ is found for helium at room temperature, and this figure increases substantially with decreasing temperature. At $12 \cdot 1°$ K. a value of $a = 0 \cdot 67$ is found for helium on a glass surface which was probably covered with a layer of water molecules. Neon and hydrogen give a value $a = 1$, at about $17°$ K. on the same surface, and nitrogen gives $a = 1$ at about $86°$ K.

The values for a given gas and the surface of a certain sort of material are appreciably increased when the surface is roughened. The principal cause of this is purely mechanical, namely, that the number of collisions may be more than 1 when molecules strike a surface which is provided with cracks, cavities, and holes, an effect which may be compared with the black body effect in light absorption. Secondly, as we shall see later, the time of adsorption will be somewhat higher at such surfaces. Hydrogen, for instance, when striking a bright platinum ribbon shows a value for $a = 0 \cdot 323$. When the platinum ribbon is covered with platinum black its value is $0 \cdot 586$.

The exchange of heat plays an important part not only in technical applications but also in daily life. A great part of the energy of the sun which comes to us as radiant heat is absorbed by the ground. The molecules of the air striking the surface of the earth stay there for a sufficiently long time to take up that heat and to leave again with a higher speed than that at which they came, heating the air in this way. Daily we feel the effect of this exchange of heat by lingering molecules. We feel quite comfortable when we are bombarded incessantly by the molecules of the air, heating us, at an average speed of 465 metres/sec. When, however, the average speed of these molecules gets lower than 450 metres/sec., we think it is pretty cold and we start to shiver. When the average speed of the molecules heating us gets higher than 480 metres/sec., we think it is hot. When the average speed gets as low as 410 metres/sec. or as high as 500 metres/sec., the conditions would become unbearable.

22. Exchange of heat and its result on pressure

The exchange of heat discussed in the previous section has an influence on the pressure which is exercised by a gas on a surface. From equations (2), (3), and (4) we can easily derive the equation

$$p = \tfrac{1}{2}\pi\, nm\bar{u}. \tag{10}$$

The pressure p in this equation is expressed in terms of the number n and the product $m\bar{u}$ (the momentum). In the case of molecules which rebound elastically from the surface, the momentum of impact is of exactly the same magnitude as the momentum with which they leave the surface but is of opposite sign. It is this change of momentum which causes the pressure. When the molecules do not rebound elastically but linger for some time at the surface before re-evaporating, half of the pressure is due to the momentum of impact which they lose to the surface and the other half to the momentum which they receive from the surface in an opposite direction when they evaporate. These two momenta, however, are only exactly equal when the temperature of the gas is exactly the same as the temperature of the surface. If the temperature of the gas is T_1 and the temperature of the surface T_2, the contribution to the pressure resulting from the impact will be

$$\tfrac{1}{4}\pi\, nm\bar{u}_1,$$

the velocity $\bar{u}_1$ corresponding to the temperature T_1. If the exchange of heat is complete, when the coefficient of accommodation $a = 1$ (equation (9)), the molecules will leave the surface with a mean velocity $\bar{u}_2$ and the contribution to the pressure derived from the re-evaporation is

$$\tfrac{1}{4}\pi\, nm\bar{u}_2.$$

The pressure which is exerted by the gas in this case is

$$\tfrac{1}{4}\pi\, nm(\bar{u}_1 + \bar{u}_2).$$

If we call p the pressure which would be exerted by the gas on a surface which is of the same temperature as the gas itself (T_1) and if we call p' the pressure which is exerted in reality, we have the equation

$$p' = \tfrac{1}{2}p \times \left(1 + \frac{\bar{u}_2}{\bar{u}_1}\right). \tag{11}$$

If T_2 is higher than T_1 this pressure is higher than p and if T_2 is smaller than T_1 the pressure will be lower than p. This equation is of course only true when the mean free path of the molecules is greater than the dimensions of the apparatus.

The relationship of equation (11) is applied by Knudsen to the design of a new type of manometer. In principle it is the following:

A light rectangular vane carrying a mirror is suspended from a torsion filament. The temperature of the vane is the same as the temperature of the gas whose pressure we are measuring. On opposite sides of the vane two strips are located which can be heated. One strip is placed in front of one-half of the vane, the other strip at the back of the other half. When the gas and the vane are at the temperature T_1 and the strips are heated to the temperature T_2, the molecules re-evaporating from the heated strips will exert, on the portions of the vane which are opposite the strips, a pressure given by equation (11). On those portions of the vane which are not exposed to molecules coming from the heated strips, a pressure p will be exercised. The vane is therefore repelled from the heated strips by a force arising from the pressure difference

$$\Delta p = \tfrac{1}{2}p\left(\frac{\bar{u}_2}{\bar{u}_1}-1\right).$$

Applying equation (5) we can also write

$$\Delta p = \tfrac{1}{2}p\left\{\sqrt{\left(\frac{T_2}{T_1}\right)}-1\right\}.$$

This force is balanced by the torsion of the suspension. Provided the mean free path of the molecules is greater than the distance between the hot and cold surfaces and provided also that the coefficient of accommodation $a = 1$, the force of repulsion is directly proportional to the pressure and independent of the nature of the gas. Under such conditions the instrument functions as an absolute manometer. Various types of manometers have been constructed on this principle. With the best designs pressures as low as $10^{-5}\mu$ of mercury may be measured, that is pressures which could not be measured by the height of a real column of mercury because the height of a tenth of an A unit is far smaller than the size of a mercury atom.

If the coefficient of accommodation is smaller than unity we may still use equation (11) provided instead of $\bar{u}_2$ we write the velocity $\bar{u}_2'$ corresponding to the temperature T_2' which is in between T_1 and T_2. Applying equation (5) again we may also write

$$p' = \tfrac{1}{2}p\left\{1+\sqrt{\left(\frac{T_2'}{T_1}\right)}\right\}.$$

From equation (9), $T_2' = T_1+a(T_2-T_1).$

Inserting this in the above equation, we get

$$p' = \tfrac{1}{2}p\left\{1+\sqrt{\left(1+a\frac{T_2-T_1}{T_1}\right)}\right\}.$$

Knudsen applied this phenomenon to strips of platinum which were bright on one side and black on the other. As the coefficient of accommodation is not the same on both sides there is a pressure difference when the platinum strip has a temperature different from that of the surrounding gas. The differences in coefficient of accommodation measured in this way are in excellent agreement with those measured by heat conduction.

23. An attempt to measure τ directly

Attempts to measure the time of lingering τ in a direct way were made in 1926 by Holst and Clausing.[†] A stream of molecules was directed against a quickly rotating plate. If the molecules stay for some time τ at this plate, before re-evaporating, they will have travelled a short distance with the rotating plate before they escape again. The re-evaporated molecules go in all directions and there is no preferential direction. If the evaporating molecules are then condensed on a stationary plate which is strongly cooled, the centre of the spot of condensed molecules will not coincide with the opening through which the original beam of molecules emerged, but it will be displaced by a certain length in the direction of rotation of the rotating plate. The length of this displacement will be dependent on the magnitude of τ and will depend of course on the speed of the rotating plate. A correction term must be applied because the re-evaporating molecules possess an extra component of velocity equal to the velocity of the rotating plate. This correction, however, can be calculated exactly.

Measurements were worked out for cadmium molecules impinging on glass at 200° K. The experimental difficulties, however, were too great to enable exact measurements to be made. It could be shown, however, that a finite time τ did exist, the value of which was between 10^{-12} sec. and 10^{-6} sec. in this case.

24. A stream of molecules through a capillary

In later years Clausing worked out a far more reliable indirect method of measuring τ. This method[‡] is based on the estimation of the velocity with which molecules of a gas pass through narrow capillaries when the pressure is so low that no mutual collisions of the gas molecules take place. Streaming through the capillary the molecules collide with the wall and will be kept there for an average time τ. They re-evaporate without preference of direction. As we have already stated above, the number of molecules evaporating from the surface in a certain direction is proportional to the cosine of the angle which that direction makes with the normal of the surface. According to this law, which is often called the cosine law or Knudsen's law, the molecules have just the same chance of

† *Physica*, **6** (1926), 48; **8** (1928), 289.
‡ P. Clausing, Thesis, Leiden, 1930, *Ann. d. Physik*, **7** (1930), 489, 521.

re-evaporating in the direction which we want as in the opposite direction. This phenomenon, itself completely independent of the existence of a finite time of lingering, τ, causes an appreciable delay in the flow of gas through the capillary. In addition to this there is also the delay caused by the actual time of lingering. Clausing calculated that the average time $\bar{t}$ which a molecule needs in order to proceed through a capillary of a length l and a diameter d will be

$$\bar{t} = \frac{l^2}{2d\bar{u}} + \frac{l^2\tau}{2d^2} \tag{12}$$

where $\bar{u}$ is the mean velocity of the molecules. (For a correction due to surface migration, see Chap. X, § 138.) The first term of this expression arises from the delay caused by the cosine law of re-evaporation, the second term from the existence of a time τ. When $\bar{t}$ is measured τ can be evaluated by means of equation (12). We get the following expression

$$\tau = \frac{2d^2}{l^2}\left(\bar{t} - \frac{l^2}{2d\bar{u}}\right) = \frac{2d^2}{l^2}\bar{t} - \frac{d}{\bar{u}}.$$

Experimenting with argon in glass capillaries, Clausing obtained the following results

at 90° K.: $\tau = 3\cdot1 \times 10^{-5}$ sec.

at 78° K.: $\tau = 75 \times 10^{-5}$ sec.

He found the same order of magnitude for nitrogen on glass whilst, however, for neon on glass at about 90° K. a figure of $\tau < 2 \times 10^{-7}$ sec. was found.

25. The dependence of τ on temperature

From the two figures which we mentioned as values for τ for argon on glass at two different temperatures, one may conclude that the magnitude of τ is greatly dependent on temperature. This is what might be expected theoretically from an equation already given in 1924 by Frenkel, namely,

$$\tau = \tau_0 e^{Q/RT}, \tag{13}$$

where τ_0 is the time of oscillation of the molecules in the adsorbed state, referring especially to vibrations perpendicular to the surface. Q in this equation is the heat of adsorption, that is the amount of heat which is liberated when the molecule is brought from the gaseous state to the adsorbed state, and hence also the energy involved in the process of re-evaporating the adsorbed molecule from the surface. T in equation (13) is of course again the absolute temperature and R the molar gas constant. τ_0 has no relation to the time of vibration of the constituent molecules or atoms of the adsorbing surface, but is often of the same order of magnitude, namely, 10^{-12}–10^{-14} sec. These times of vibration are proportional to the square root of the molecular weight, while they also depend on the distance to neighbouring atoms or molecules, which means that they are related to the molecular volume (see § 29). The two figures for τ, which Clausing found for argon on a glass surface, when represented by equation (13) give

$$\tau = 1 \cdot 7 \times 10^{-14} \times e^{3800/RT},$$

and we may conclude that τ_0 is indeed of the order of magnitude of 10^{-14} sec. in this case and the heat of adsorption is roughly 4 k.cal./mole, which is of the right order of magnitude. As an illustration we will give another example where measurements have been made at very high temperatures and where Q, the adsorption energy, has very high values. Johnson and Vick in 1935 measured the time τ for oxygen atoms at a tungsten surface in the neighbourhood of 2,200° C. They found the following figures:

at 2,548° K.: $\tau = 0 \cdot 36$ sec.

at 2,362° K.: $\tau = 3 \cdot 49$ sec.

which can be represented by

$$\tau = 8 \times 10^{-14} \times e^{147000/RT}.$$

We see that τ_0 is again of the same order of magnitude; the adsorption energy Q amounts to 147 k.cal./mole in this case. In § 143 we shall see that τ_0 can be estimated by means of statistical mechanics.

26. τ, the time of adsorption

It will be clear that the adsorption energy Q is the all-determining factor for the magnitude of τ. Indeed the heat of adsorption is mainly responsible for the length of time during which the adsorbed molecules will stay at the surface before re-evaporating. We may therefore call τ in future the *time of adsorption*.

27. Adsorption forces, physical or chemical adsorption

It is not within the scope of this book to discuss the energy of adsorption or the forces which cause adsorption, their origin, and their magnitude.† We will, therefore, make only a few general observations. First, it must be stated that there are no special adsorption forces. The forces which cause the cohesion in solids and in liquids, and which are responsible for the deviation of the behaviour of real gases from the law of ideal gases also cause adsorption. In general one can say that any pair of atoms or molecules attract each other mutually. This attraction may lead to a temporary or more or less permanent binding of the two. If one of the molecules or atoms of this pair happens to be a constituent atom of a surface and the other is a free gaseous molecule or a molecule dissolved in a liquid, the result of their interaction is that the latter molecule will be bound at the surface for some length of time, hence adsorption has taken place. If in this act of binding the individuality of the adsorbed molecule and of the constituent parts of the surface is preserved, we may speak of physical adsorption. If, on the other hand, in the act of adsorption a molecule loses an electron to the surface, or receives an electron from it, or if it splits up into atoms or radicals which are bound separately, or if it shares electrons with one or more of the constituent particles of the surface, then we may speak of chemical adsorption or chemisorption.

28. The magnitude of the heat of adsorption, Q, for helium and hydrogen

The adsorption energy in the case of physical adsorption is, generally speaking, lower than the energy involved in the process of chemisorption. In physical adsorption the binding is caused by van der Waals' forces. They may be of the type of non-polar van der Waals' forces, they may be of the type of dipole interaction, or they may be caused by a more or less static polarization. The adsorption energy caused by them is of the order of magnitude of some k.cal./mole, let us say up to 20 k.cal./mole. In chemisorption processes the energies may be far higher, as, for instance, in the case mentioned above, for the adsorption of oxygen atoms at a tungsten surface where the energy is 147 k.cal./mole.

As the liquefaction of gases is also caused by van der Waals' forces, it is not surprising that the adsorbability of gas molecules, and hence their capacity for being adsorbed at various surfaces, runs more or

† For a full discussion see J. H. de Boer in *Advances in Colloid Science*, iii. 1–67, Interscience Publ. New York, 1950.

less parallel to the ease with which they are condensed to liquids. The comparability of these two properties, which was already known at the commencement of the study of adsorption, teaches us that a gas like helium which is so very difficult to liquefy, will also show a very poor capacity for being adsorbed. The heats of adsorption which helium molecules show at various surfaces, will be very low indeed. Next will come hydrogen and neon, and other gases such as argon, oxygen, nitrogen, etc., will follow.

Equation (13) shows that it must be the very low value of Q, the adsorption energy, which accounts for the fact that the gases helium and hydrogen are not adsorbed by the cleavage surfaces of lithium fluoride, so that specular reflection and diffraction phenomena can be observed. It is remarkable that from one of the very careful experiments on the reflection of helium, mentioned in § 20, a rough estimation may be derived for the heat of adsorption. The helium beam was homogenized by rotating disks at a velocity of 1,635 metres/sec. Equation (8) gives then the value of $0 \cdot 610 \times 10^{-8}$ cm. for the wavelength. From the known inter-ionic distance of the fluoride ions of the surface, and the diffraction angles which were found, the effective wavelength of the helium beam may be calculated as $0 \cdot 599 \times 10^{-8}$ cm. It is very unlikely that this deviation is caused by a deviation of the inter-ionic distance of the fluoride ions. If there were any effect of this kind one would expect an effect in the opposite direction. It is more likely, however, that the attraction between the ions of the surface and the impinging helium atom by their mutual van der Waals forces, small as the interaction may be, causes an increase of the velocity of the helium atoms. An increase of the velocity from 1,635 metres/sec. to 1,665 metres/sec., which implies an increase of kinetic energy of about 45 cal./mole would give the wavelength which is actually observed. We may conclude that the interaction in this case only leads to an adsorption energy much smaller than 100 cal./mole, which does not in effect lead to any noticeable effect of adsorption, but, on the contrary, causes the molecules to rebound elastically.

We have seen that the temperature dependence of the accommodation coefficient of helium on a pure tungsten surface does not give any indication of adsorption (§ 21). We have also learned that at a temperature of 12° K. the accommodation coefficient of helium on a glass surface is still smaller than unity. As one might expect the exchange of energy to be more or less complete when the time of adsorption τ is roughly a hundred times the time of oscillation τ_0, or longer, we may conclude that the index of e in equation (13) is less than 4·6 in this case. As RT has only the value of 24 cal./mole this means that the energy of adsorption of helium on a glass surface is less than 110 cal./mole.

We have just seen that the energy of adsorption must be roughly 4–5 times the value of RT in order to cause the coefficient of accommodation a to be unity. We have seen that the accommodation coefficient for neon on tungsten is smaller than unity at room temperature, hence the adsorption energy of neon on a tungsten surface will be less than 3,000 cal./mole. The accommodation coefficient, however, is unity for neon on a glass surface at 18° K., hence the adsorption energy for neon on glass will be greater than 150 cal./mole. Similar conclusions may be drawn for hydrogen. We also saw that the experimental value for τ which Clausing found for neon on a glass surface was less than 2×10^{-7} sec. at 80° K. Assuming τ_0 to be 10^{-13}, this means that the adsorption energy for neon on glass is less than 2,300 cal./mole. It is indeed a fact that the heat of adsorption for hydrogen and for neon is of this order of magnitude.

29. Magnitude of τ and Q

In order to get a rough idea about the magnitude of τ, the time of adsorption, we will calculate this quantity for a few energies of adsorption, assuming room temperature and assuming τ_0 to be 10^{-13} sec.

The exact magnitude of the constant τ_0, however, is related to the loss of entropy upon adsorption from the gaseous phase. The character of this relationship will be treated in more detail in Chapter VI, § 83. For the moment, it is sufficient to state, that whenever a molecule upon adsorption has lost exactly one degree of freedom of translation, whilst retaining at the same time all its degrees of freedom of rotation and of internal vibration, τ_0 may be shown to be equal to h/kT, which amounts to $1·6 \times 10^{-13}$ sec. at room temperature. If the entropy loss upon adsorption is partially converted into vibrational entropy, giving rise to an excited vibration in the direction perpendicular to the surface, τ_0 may be shown to be somewhat larger than 10^{-13} sec. On the other hand, if the translations of the molecules along the surface of the solid are hindered, or if the molecules, upon adsorption, lose rotational or vibrational freedom, τ_0 may be substantially lower than 10^{-13} sec. In the extreme case of localized adsorption, τ_0 is reduced to the order of magnitude of 10^{-16} sec. There are, however, indications that localized adsorption is the exception rather than the rule. From a critical analysis of literature data, by the author and Kruyer, it is apparent that at room temperature only water and hydrogen are locally adsorbed, the latter in the form of separate atoms. Most other gases are mobile adsorbed at room temperature, although occasionally some restriction of two-dimensional translations may occur, as indicated by the loss of entropy upon adsorption.

In calculating the data for Table 2 we have used the rough value $\tau_0 = 10^{-13}$ sec. throughout. In doing this we assume the entropy of the adsorbed molecules to be the same in all cases.

TABLE 2

Q	τ
100 cal./mole	$1 \cdot 2 \times 10^{-13}$ sec.
1,500 cal./mole	$1 \cdot 3 \times 10^{-12}$ sec.
3·5 k.cal./mole	4×10^{-11} sec.
4 k.cal./mole	1×10^{-10} sec.
10 k.cal./mole	$3 \cdot 2 \times 10^{-6}$ sec.
15 k.cal./mole	$1 \cdot 8 \times 10^{-2}$ sec.
20 k.cal./mole	1×10^{2} sec.
25 k.cal./mole	6×10^{5} sec. = about one week
30 k.cal./mole	4×10^{9} sec. = more than one century
40 k.cal./mole	1×10^{17} sec.
147 k.cal./mole	About 10^{95} sec. = about 10^{85} centuries

The values in Table 2 are calculated for room temperature. We see that for 100 cal./mole τ is of the same order of magnitude as τ_0, but that for 1,500 cal./mole the calculated value for τ is already ten times as great. 1,500 cal./mole is the order of magnitude of the heat of adsorption of hydrogen at various surfaces. This value of τ already leads to a noticeable adsorption. At lower temperatures the value of τ will of course be greater leading to stronger adsorption. Values of about $3\frac{1}{2}$–4 k.cal./mole give the order of magnitude of the heat of adsorption for gases like argon, oxygen, nitrogen, carbon monoxide, etc., at various surfaces. τ at room temperature has a value of the order of magnitude of 10^{-10} sec. and is thus roughly a thousand times

τ_0. Heats of adsorption between 10 and 15 k.cal./mole represent figures found for many gases consisting of heavier molecules, including the molecules of many organic substances, at various technical adsorbents. The order of magnitude of τ at room temperature is about the same as that for the light gases at liquid air temperatures.

We may remark here that the figures of heats of adsorption for physical adsorption, mentioned in this section and also in many of the previous sections, only hold for the most active parts of the surface. Somewhat lower figures, e.g. one-half or two-thirds of those mentioned may be found for the less active major part of the surfaces (see §§ 45 and 52).

We have also included in Table 2 a few values which might be found in cases of chemisorption, and we see that when the heat of adsorption amounts to 20 k.cal./mole, τ at room temperature will already be 100 sec., which is more than $1\frac{1}{2}$ minutes. We also see that the value of τ increases very rapidly with an increase of the figure for the heat of adsorption. This increase is so great that at 25 k.cal./mole τ already has a value of about 1 week, and at 30 k.cal./mole the value of τ is already more than a century. At 40 k.cal./mole we calculate a value of 10^{17} sec. which is a length of time just about the same as the age of our earth. For 147 k.cal./mole, the value which as we have seen above was found for the adsorption of oxygen atoms at a tungsten surface, we see from the table that it does not matter whether we express τ in seconds or in centuries.

Once more, we emphasize the point that all the values for τ in Table 2 are calculated for room temperature, assuming τ_0 to be 10^{-13} sec. As we have already seen above, the value for a gas like argon which, according to Table 2, is of the order of magnitude of 10^{-10} sec. at room temperature, increases to the order of magnitude of 10^{-4} sec. at liquid air temperature, and we have also seen that the fantastic value for τ for oxygen atoms at a tungsten surface at room temperature reduces to the order of magnitude of roughly 1 sec. at a temperature of about 2,200° C.

30. The resistance of capillaries in adsorption

Now that we have an idea of the order of magnitude of the time of adsorption, it may be worth while seeing to what value of $\bar{t}$ equation (12) leads us for various gases streaming through capillaries, such as may be encountered in practical cases of adsorption.

Technical adsorbents consist mainly of porous substances and they contain a great number of capillaries of various sizes. An estimation of the time $\bar{t}$, namely, the average time which it will take for a molecule to pass through a capillary of a certain length and certain width, may therefore give us an idea of the time which it may take in practical cases to let the adsorbed molecule penetrate into the deepest cavities and pores of an adsorbent. We have assembled a few of these calculations in Table 3. We have chosen three kinds of molecules, giving at the surface of certain adsorbents, times of adsorption, τ, of 10^{-12} sec., 10^{-10} sec., and 10^{-4} sec. respectively. Table 2 shows that cases of this nature may be represented by the molecules of hydrogen, nitrogen, and an organic substance, respectively, at a surface at room temperature. We know from equation (5) that the mean velocity which also enters into equation (12) depends on the molecular weight and we have accordingly chosen the values for $\bar{u}$ to be 15×10^4 cm./sec., 5×10^4 cm./sec., and 1×10^4 cm./sec. respectively.

The values for $\bar{t}$ have been calculated by means of equation (12) and the results for the two terms of this equation are shown separately in Table 3. The calculations have been made first for a capillary of length 10 cm. and width 1 mm. We see from the result that in cases 1 and 2 (the numbers refer to the numbers indicated in Table 3) the average time of passing is governed by the first term of equation (12), that is by the influence of the cosine law.

TABLE 3

	$\tau = 10^{-12}$ sec. $\bar{u} = 15 \times 10^4$ cm./sec.	$\tau = 10^{-10}$ sec. $\bar{u} = 5 \times 10^4$ cm./sec.	$\tau = 10^{-4}$ sec. $\bar{u} = 10^4$ cm./sec.
$l = 10$ cm. $d = 10^{-1}$ cm.	(1) $3 \times 10^{-3} + 5 \times 10^{-9}$	(2) $10^{-2} + 5 \times 10^{-7}$	(3) $5 \times 10^{-2} + 5 \times 10^{-1}$
$l = 10^{-1}$ cm. $d = 10^{-4}$ cm.	(4) $3 \times 10^{-4} + 5 \times 10^{-7}$	(5) $10^{-3} + 5 \times 10^{-5}$	(6) $5 \times 10^{-3} + 50$
$l = 10^{-2}$ cm. $d = 10^{-6}$ cm.	(7) $3 \times 10^{-4} + 5 \times 10^{-5}$	(8) $10^{-3} + 5 \times 10^{-3}$	(9) $5 \times 10^{-3} + 5000$
$l = 10^{-3}$ cm. $d = 10^{-7}$ cm.	(10) $3 \times 10^{-5} + 5 \times 10^{-5}$	(11) $10^{-4} + 5 \times 10^{-3}$	(12) $5 \times 10^{-4} + 5000$

In case 3, however, it is already the second term, and hence the influence of the time of adsorption, which governs the speed of passing.

Cases 4, 5, and 6 are calculated for what we may take as a representation of a macro-capillary in an adsorbent, the length of which is 1 mm. and the width of which is $1\,\mu$. Again, in cases 4 and 5, that is for the molecules which are not adsorbed strongly, it is the cosine law which governs the phenomena. In the case of a strongly adsorbed molecule (case 6) the time of adsorption alone governs the rate of passing and it already takes 50 sec. or nearly a minute for a molecule of this kind to pass through this capillary.

Cases 7, 8, and 9 give the calculations for a capillary which may be termed a micro-capillary in adsorbents with a length of 0·1 mm. and a width of 100 A. Micro-capillaries, however, may be narrower still and therefore cases 10, 11, and 12 have also been included, representing another micro-capillary of a length of 0·01 mm. and a width of 10 A. We see from the results 7, 8, 10, and 11 that in the cases of the lighter molecules the time of passing through the capillary is governed by both influences, the cosine law as well as the time of adsorption. In the case of a more strongly adsorbed molecule, case 9 and case 12, it is of course the time of adsorption again which causes the very long time of 5,000 sec., roughly $1\frac{1}{2}$ hours, in our example.

The molecules have an alternative means of passing through a capillary, namely, by sliding along the wall. They may also make such sliding movements during the time τ which they spend on the wall. We will discuss later (§ 138) what corrections such a surface migration introduces.

The length of the capillaries may be greater than we have assumed in our examples and in many practical cases times up to several hours, or even days, would be found. We will return to this problem later (§ 137).

31. Visualizing the passage of a molecule through a capillary

Because of the importance of this problem, however, we will try to visualize the phenomena by referring to our 'gas of super bees', which we introduced in § 12. If we apply a linear magnification, 32 million, to our units of length and time, in case 6 of Table 3, we will have to imagine a tube of length 20 miles and of width of about

100 ft. The speed of our super bees is the same as that of the molecules in case 6, namely, 10^4 cm./sec., which means that our bee could
fly the length of the tube in 5 minutes. Entering the tube, however,
in an arbitrary direction, the bee will collide with the wall. It then
takes 3,200 sec., which is somewhat less than one hour to rest,
whereupon it flies away in an arbitrary direction; all the bees doing
this obey the cosine law. After each collision with the wall the
average time of resting for the bees is again somewhat less than one
hour and every time after resting they fly away in an arbitrary
direction as given by the cosine law. We then come to the conclusion
that it takes an average time of 50 years for a bee to pass through
this tube, a distance which could be flown in 5 minutes.

It is worse still, if we apply the magnification, not to a macro-
capillary but to a micro-capillary. For instance in case 9 of Table 3,
we have to visualize a tube 2 miles long and 1 foot wide, the average
resting time of our bees again is somewhat less than 1 hour and their
speed 10^4 cm./sec. = 100 metres/sec. It takes an average time of
5,000 years for the bees to pass the tube, while they could fly the
distance in $\frac{1}{2}$ minute.

THE QUANTITY σ: THE DYNAMIC EQUILIBRIUM IN ADSORPTION AND CONDENSATION PHENOMENA

32. The magnitude of adsorption for helium and hydrogen

WHEN we see the very small values for τ in Table 2 we may wonder whether such low values of the time of adsorption will in reality cause the adsorption of gases to be of such a magnitude that it can be measured. Equation (1),

$$\sigma = n \times \tau,$$

however, shows us that the number of molecules adsorbed per unit of surface is given by the product of n, the number of molecules which impinge upon the surface, and τ. Now this number n is sufficiently great, in most cases, to over-compensate the small value of τ. It is only when τ has an extremely low value comparable with the time of oscillation τ_0 of the molecules at the surface that no adsorption will take place.

Let us first take helium. In most cases the heat of adsorption of helium at various surfaces is, as we saw in § 28, less than 100 cal./mole, which means that the value of τ does not, in practice, exceed the value of τ_0. If τ_0, therefore, is of the order of magnitude of 10^{-13} sec., τ will have the same value. At room temperature the velocity of helium atoms is 1,250 metres/sec. (equation (5)). In 10^{-13} sec., therefore, they cover a distance of $1 \cdot 2$ A. Travelling with their normal speed, the molecules cover during their 'time of adsorption' a distance of atomic dimensions only. The condition that they are to be in the direct vicinity of the surface for 10^{-13} sec. can be fulfilled by moving with their normal speed. The molecules are apparently not held up by the mutual attracting forces between the surface and the atoms. On the contrary, they are speeded up, as we have already seen in § 28. The 'adsorption energy', if we still call the energy associated with these forces by this name, does not lengthen the time during which the molecule is 'at the surface', but shortens it in this case.

Even at temperatures as low as 90° K. the value of τ hardly exceeds the value of τ_0. At liquid air temperatures and at pressures even up to 100 atmospheres, helium will, on most surfaces, not adsorb to more than a few per cent. of a unimolecular layer at the utmost. Helium, therefore, is the most suitable gas for density measurements by the method of gas displacement. It is only at extremely low temperatures which can be reached, as it happens, with helium, that the adsorption will assume appreciable values.

Stout and Giauque[†] measured the adsorption of helium at nickel sulphate, $NiSO_4.7H_2O$ at $4\cdot23°$ K. They found an adsorption energy of 140 cal./mole. With $\tau_0 = 10^{-13}$, equation (13) gives us the value of $\tau = 10^{-6}$ sec. under these circumstances. Such a time of adsorption indeed gives rise to adsorption phenomena of the same order of magnitude as that of many organic gases in contact with charcoal at room temperature.

At still lower temperatures, namely, in the range from $1\cdot0°$ K. to $2\cdot5°$ K., helium is strongly adsorbed and even shows, according to extensive investigations by Frederikse,[‡] the phenomena of multi-molecular adsorption.

The adsorption of hydrogen on many surfaces will hardly be noticeable at room temperature. Since τ is of the order of magnitude of 10^{-12} sec., and n is 11×10^{23} molecules/cm.^{2} sec. at room temperature and atmospheric pressure, σ is calculated to be of the order of magnitude of 10^{12} molecules/cm.^{2} This is a very low surface density and we see clearly how low it is when we compare the figure with the number of molecules which we would find to be there already because of the normal concentration of the hydrogen molecules in hydrogen gas at room temperature and atmospheric pressure. As $N_1 = 25 \times 10^{18}$ molecules/cm.^{3} (see § 13, Table 1) we may take the $\frac{2}{3}$rd power of this figure, viz. $8\cdot55 \times 10^{12}$ to get an idea of how many molecules are found in the gas at a cross-section of 1 cm.^{2}

When, however, we lower the temperature, adsorption becomes appreciable. Lowering the temperature means that both n and τ increase. For hydrogen at $190°$ K. and 1 atmosphere pressure, n increases to about 2×10^{24} whilst τ increases to 10^{-10} sec.; σ, therefore, is calculated to be about 2×10^{14} molecules/cm.^{2}, hence about 20 per cent. of the surface will be covered by hydrogen at liquid air

† J. W. Stout and W. F. Giauque, *Jour. Am. Chem. Soc.* **60** (1938), 393.
‡ H. P. R. Frederikse, *Physica*, **15** (1949), 860, and Thesis, Leiden University, 1950.

temperature and 1 atmosphere pressure. At some surfaces the adsorption energy of hydrogen may be greater than 1,500 cal./mole and the adsorption will be higher and may even be of some importance at room temperature.

33. The magnitude of adsorption for other gases

Let us turn to those gases which at room temperature show a figure for τ of about 10^{-10} sec. The molecular weight of those gases which include argon, carbon monoxide, oxygen and nitrogen, is such that at room temperature and atmospheric pressure the number $n = 3 \times 10^{23}$. σ, therefore, assumes the value of 3×10^{13}, which means that a few per cent. of a surface of an adsorbent may be covered in these circumstances. At a lower temperature, for instance at liquid air temperature, both n and τ increase again, n to the figure of $5-6 \times 10^{23}$, τ to a value of the order of magnitude of 10^{-5} sec. Under these circumstances we may expect the surface to be covered completely with adsorbed molecules. Even at a pressure of 1 mm. of mercury, where $n \simeq 7 \times 10^{21}$, σ is calculated to be 7×10^{16}, which is still far more than necessary for building up a completely covered surface layer. These gases, therefore, will be adsorbed to full capacity at these temperatures.

If we now consider the group of gases including ammonia, carbon dioxide, ethylene, etc., which have a heat of adsorption of roughly 8 k.cal./mole on various surfaces, we find a value for τ of about 10^{-7} sec. Consequently with gases of this group, at room temperature, and a pressure of about 10 mm. of mercury, over 10 per cent. of an adsorbent surface will be covered. A similar value for τ holds also for neon at liquid air temperatures.

It is customary in analytical practice to estimate the (superficial) water content of many substances by drying the sample at 110° C. The heat of adsorption of water molecules adsorbed at various surfaces may be 10 k.cal./mole or higher. At 110° C. the time τ will then be 5×10^{-8} sec. or longer. If, during the heating to 110° C., the air is not carefully dried the number n may be such that together with this value for τ the quantity σ may still be intolerably high. If the room temperature is 20° C. and the relative humidity is 60 per cent., there will be a water vapour pressure of about 10 mm. of mercury leading to a value of n of about $0 \cdot 4 \times 10^{22}$ molecules per cm.^{2} and per sec. The quantity σ will then be 2×10^{14} or more, hence 20 per cent. or more of the surface is still covered with water molecules. If the substance is highly porous, having a specific surface area of 150 m.^{2}/g. or more, such a residual adsorbed water layer represents more than 1 per cent. of the weight of the sample. If one dries the air with a drying agent (e.g. with $CaCl_2$) the water vapour pressure is reduced to about $\frac{1}{3}$ mm. of mercury and less than 1 per cent. of the surface will be covered by water molecules at 110° C. unless the heat of adsorption of water molecules is considerably higher than 10 k.cal./mole, which it often is.

Still more appreciable is the adsorption for the big group of molecules, mostly organic gases, which show a value for τ of 10^{-5} sec. or longer at room temperature. At a pressure as low as 0·1 mm. of mercury, the value of n, calculated with equation (6), is a few times 10^{19} molecules/cm.^{2} sec. Combined with $\tau = 10^{-5}$ sec., σ becomes a few times 10^{14} molecules/cm.^{2} Even at this rather low pressure, therefore, a substantial part of the surface is already covered and when τ is of the order of magnitude of 10^{-4} sec. or higher, an adsorbed layer is fully established at those low pressures.

Despite the low values for the time of adsorption, therefore, the number of adsorbed molecules may be appreciable because the value of n is high. Even at relatively low pressures, this value may still be appreciable because of the high speed of the molecules. We may illustrate this with the aid of our 'gas of super bees', applied to the last example.

A pressure of 0·1 mm. of mercury translated into the language of our 'gas of super bees', means that we shall have an average concentration of one bee per 10 cubic metres. If we expose a surface of 1 square metre to this gas of super bees, we may find that, on an average, ten bees will hit this square metre every second. Corresponding with $\tau = 10^{-5}$ sec. we assume that the bees have a resting time of about 5 minutes. We then find that there will be an average of 3,000 bees adsorbed on a square metre, at any moment. These bees are in dynamic equilibrium with the gas of super bees with which they are in contact, and where the concentration, as we already mentioned, is one bee per 10 cubic metres. Every second an average of ten bees depart from each square-metre surface and ten other bees land. In 5 minutes' time, therefore, all the super bees have been exchanged for new ones. Translating this back to our last-mentioned example we have to decrease all linear dimensions by a factor 32 million, and also speed up the time by this same factor. Doing this we see then that every second 3×10^{19} molecules leave each cm.^{2} of the surface and that 3×10^{19} molecules will arrive on each cm.^{2}, staying there an average length of time of 10^{-5} sec. and leaving an average of 3×10^{14} molecules/cm.^{2} At an average, therefore, every 10^{-5} sec., the adsorbed layer is completely exchanged for a new one.

34. The dynamic equilibrium at the surface

In any adsorption equilibrium the number of molecules falling in on the surface and being adsorbed must be equal to the number of molecules which are set free from the surface and re-evaporate. We will call this latter number n_v, hence:

$$n = n_v.$$

As we have seen in § 21 the adsorbed molecules exchange energy with the constituent atoms of the surface and, provided the time of adsorption is long enough, they will be in thermal equilibrium with them. In order to re-evaporate, the adsorbed molecule has to take up sufficient from the fluctuations of thermal energy of the surface, so that the energy corresponding to the vertical component of its kinetic vibrations surpasses a certain limit (vertical is meant to be normal to the surface). This just means that in the act of re-evaporation the kinetic energy of the adsorbed molecule must be great enough to free itself from the attracting forces, hence it must conquer the adsorption energy.

According to statistical considerations the number of molecules which have taken up an amount Q from the fluctuations of thermal energy will at any moment be proportional to

$$e^{-Q/RT}.$$

The number of molecules leaving the surface by re-evaporation, n_v, therefore, must be proportional to this power of e. n_v must also be proportional to the number of molecules which are adsorbed, σ. We can therefore write

$$n_v = \nu \sigma e^{-Q/RT}.$$

ν is the factor of proportionality. As n_v has the dimension of a number of molecules/cm.^{2} sec., and as σ has the proportion of a number of molecules/cm.^{2}, the factor ν must have the dimensions of sec.$^{-1}$, hence it must be of the dimension of a frequency. We can see immediately that this is the case if we compare the result of these considerations with our former equation (1), in which we substitute the value for τ given by equation (13). We then get

$$\sigma = n\tau_0 e^{Q/RT},$$

and as $n = n_v$, we see that

$$\nu = \frac{1}{\tau_0},$$

hence it is a frequency.

If not all the molecules which strike the surface are adsorbed but if a certain fraction α is reflected, then the number of molecules which will be adsorbed per cm.² and per sec. will be $n(1-\alpha)$. Applying this in equation (1) we get

$$\sigma = n(1-\alpha)\tau.$$

Hence the number n_v will also be multiplied by the factor $(1-\alpha)$ and a dynamic equilibrium is established again, with the result, however, that fewer molecules will be adsorbed on the surface than corresponds with equation (1) and with a number n as given by the kinetic theory of gases.

When such a phenomenon of partial reflection and partial adsorption occurs in a practical case, the result will be that the average time of adsorption, τ, appears to be smaller by a factor $(1-\alpha)$. Whether assigned to the number n or to the time τ, a factor $(1-\alpha)$ only alters the numerical values of the various figures, and it does not alter the form of the equations.

35. The simplest form of the adsorption isotherm

Inserting in equation (1) the values for n from equation (6) and for τ from equation (13), we get

$$\sigma = \frac{Np}{\sqrt{(2\pi MRT)}} \times \tau_0 e^{Q/RT}.$$

If we study the adsorption of a particular gas on the surface of a particular adsorbent, M and τ_0 are constant, so that we can write

$$\sigma = \frac{k_0 p}{\sqrt{(T)}} e^{Q/RT}, \tag{14}$$

in which

$$k_0 = \frac{N\tau_0}{\sqrt{(2\pi MR)}}.$$

We will study equation (14), keeping each one of the variables constant in turn. If we start our considerations with the assumption that we keep the temperature constant, we derive the very simple equation

$$\sigma = k_1 p, \qquad (14\,a)$$

which shows that the amount of gas which will be adsorbed is directly proportional to the pressure. Keeping the temperature constant we work under isothermal conditions. (14 a) is an equation for the adsorption isotherm. It is in fact the simplest equation for the adsorption isotherm and it is only valid when the condition is fulfilled that the adsorbed molecules are not mutually influencing each other in any way. In addition to that it is also assumed that the adsorption energy Q is the same for all the molecules.

In practice, these conditions will be only more or less fulfilled when the number of molecules adsorbed on the surface is very small. If the degree of occupation of the surface by the adsorbed molecules is only small, let us say of the order of 1 per cent., the condition that the molecules do not influence each other will be very well fulfilled. If the surface, however, is rather heterogeneous in character, the condition that Q is constant need not be fulfilled and it is possible that even with such a small number of adsorbed molecules equation (14 a) does not hold. When the adsorption is studied at the surface of a liquid the probability that Q is constant is far greater, and it is in this case that equation (14 a) will hold over a longer range of adsorption values than in cases of adsorption on the surfaces of technical adsorbents in powder form. It may be remarked that a degree of occupation of 1 per cent. is not so very small, however, if we visualize it with the aid of our 'gas of super bees'. In that language it just means that we will find an average of 100 bees per square metre, which indeed is not so very small.

As long as equation (14 a) holds, a graph showing the number of adsorbed molecules σ as a function of the pressure p gives a straight line, the slope of which gives k_1. The line is steeper for greater k_1, hence also for greater τ and greater Q. When the number of adsorbed molecules gets so great that their mutual influence will be noticeable, then the adsorption isotherm will rise less or more steeply, as we shall see later.

36. Adsorption from solutions

A similar equation to (14 a) will hold in the case of adsorption from solutions. The number of molecules which will be adsorbed at the surface of a solid or a liquid from solutions will be proportional to the concentration c:

$$\sigma = k'c. \tag{14a'}$$

The kinetic picture is very similar to that of the adsorption of gases. Solute molecules move in all directions. So do the molecules of the solvent. Each molecule is, however, constantly in contact with a few other molecules of solvent and/or solute. Their movements, therefore, in any direction, are far more restricted, though not in vigour. The restriction is in the free path. They can hardly move over any length without being influenced by other molecules. This is the reason that diffusion in liquids proceeds so much more slowly than in gases. Still, a very great number of solute molecules reach the surface every second and may stay there for a certain length of time, after which they redissolve into the solution. The time of adsorption depends again, amongst other things, on the energy of adsorption. Numerically the picture may be different, essentially it is the same and it is therefore not surprising that we find a similar sort of relationship between the number of molecules which are adsorbed and the concentration which may take the place of the pressure (or rather take the place of the number N_1 as used in our equations (2) and (3)). In being adsorbed, however, the solute molecules have to compete with the molecules of the solvent, a problem to which we will return later (see § 62).

37. The adsorption isobar

If we keep the pressure constant in equation (14) we get a direct relation between the number of adsorbed molecules and the temperature

$$\sigma = k_2 \frac{e^{Q/RT}}{\sqrt{(T)}}, \tag{14b}$$

which is the equation of the adsorption isobar. The influence of $\sqrt{(T)}$ is small with respect to the power of e. Consequently the number of adsorbed molecules, at constant pressure, falls exponentially with increasing temperature. In a graph representing σ as a function of T, the isobar at a high pressure lies above the isobar at a lower pressure.

In some cases the exponential decrease of σ, with increasing T, is disrupted and at a certain temperature a sudden substantial increase of σ may be noticed. This means that a substantial change takes place in the nature of the adsorption and it very often is a sign that the molecules pass from a state in which they are physically adsorbed, into a closer relation with the surface, that is to say, they become chemisorbed. In this state again the isobar, starting from a new higher value for σ, will decrease exponentially with increasing temperature. In some cases a second discontinuity may be found at higher temperatures, again leading to a sudden increase of σ. This may mean that the molecules pass into another form of chemisorption or it may mean that they enter into a still closer relationship with the solid, namely, that they penetrate into the interior of the solid; hence that they become absorbed instead of adsorbed.

38. The adsorption isostere

If we consider equation (14) and keep σ, the number of adsorbed molecules constant, we get a relation between the pressure and the temperature corresponding to the same degree of occupation of the surface:

$$p = k_3 \sqrt(T) . e^{-Q/RT}, \qquad (14\,c)$$

the equation of the adsorption isostere. Again to a first approximation we may neglect the influence of $\sqrt(T)$ with respect to the power of e. Then, after taking logarithms we get the equation

$$\ln p = -\frac{Q}{RT} + B_a \qquad (15)$$

in which B_a is a constant.

A plot of $\log p$ against $1/T$ for a constant value of σ, therefore, will as a first approximation, give a straight line, the slope of which gives us the heat of adsorption, Q (see also § 40).

39. The various heats of adsorption

We now discuss the various heats of adsorption which can be found in the literature.

If N_a molecules of a gas are adsorbed on to the clean surface of 1 gram of adsorbent, a certain amount of heat will be liberated in the process. This amount of heat is called the *integral heat of adsorption* and we will denote it by Q_{int}. If E_g is the energy of the gas per molecule in the gas phase and E_a is the energy of the gas per molecule in the adsorbed state, the loss of heat from the system by the process of adsorption, assuming that no external work is done, is

$$Q_{\text{int}} = N_a(E_g - E_a).$$

Q_{int} therefore, expressed in k.cal./g. of adsorbent, is proportional to the amount of gas which is adsorbed. If we increase this amount by dN_a an additional amount of heat dQ will be liberated. Keeping the temperature constant, the differential coefficient

$$\left(\frac{dQ_{\text{int}}}{dN_a}\right)_T$$

is called the *differential heat of adsorption* which we will denote by Q_{diff}.

If we differentiate the above-mentioned equation for Q_{int} with respect to N_a, we obtain

$$Q_{\text{diff}} = \left(\frac{dQ_{\text{int}}}{dN_a}\right)_T = E_g - E_a + N_a\left(\frac{d(E_g - E_a)}{dN_a}\right)_T.$$

E_g, for an ideal gas, is a function of the temperature only, hence

$$Q_{\text{diff}} = E_g - E_a - N_a\left(\frac{dE_a}{dN_a}\right)_T.$$

If the adsorption is performed under isothermal conditions and without change in the total number of molecules, then work is done in the process. A volume dv of gas at a pressure p, corresponding to dN_a the number of molecules which are adsorbed, has disappeared. The work, therefore, will be (ideal gas)

$$p\,dv = dN_a\,RT.$$

The work done per molecule, therefore, is RT. Because of the isothermal conditions of the process, Hückel[†] defines the quantity

$$Q_{\text{isoth}} = Q_{\text{diff}} + RT$$

as the *isothermal heat of adsorption*.

The heat of adsorption may be measured experimentally by calorimetric determinations. The *calorimetric heat of adsorption* will have a value somewhere between Q_{diff} and Q_{isoth}, depending on the conditions of the experiment. Fortunately, in most cases RT is small with respect to both Q_{diff} and Q_{isoth}.

It can be proved thermodynamically that the heat of adsorption derived from the equation of the adsorption isostere equals Q_{isoth}. We may, therefore, follow Brunauer's[‡] custom and call this heat of adsorption the *isosteric heat of adsorption*.

† E. Hückel, *Adsorption und Kapillarkondensation*, Leipzig, Ak. Verl. Ges., 1928.
‡ In his well-known book, *The Adsorption of Gases and Vapours*, Oxford Univ. Press, London, 1943.

E

40. Vapour pressure and latent heat of evaporation

Equation (15) closely resembles the well-known relation between the saturated pressure of a liquid and its temperature, the equation being

$$\ln p_0 = -\frac{Q_0}{RT} + B_0, \tag{16}$$

where p_0 is the saturated vapour pressure of the liquid at a temperature T, Q_0 the latent heat of evaporation, and B_0 a constant. The close resemblance is not surprising because the mechanism of the dynamic equilibrium of a liquid and its saturated vapour is essentially the same as the mechanism of the adsorption equilibrium. The number of molecules which hit the surface of the liquid from the saturated vapour phase, is given exactly by equation (6) when we substitute p_0 for p. Assuming that all the molecules which hit the surface are condensed (see §§ 14 and 17), the number of molecules which evaporate per cm.^{2} of surface and per second, must be equal to this number n. Let us assume that n_1 molecules reach every cm.^{2} of the surface each second from inside. Only those molecules which have a kinetic energy greater than Q_0 will escape, that is, will evaporate. This number is proportional to n_1 and to

$$e^{-Q_0/RT}.$$

We may therefore write

$$a n_1 e^{-Q_0/RT} = n = \frac{N p_0}{\sqrt{(2\pi M R T)}},$$

where a is a proportionality factor. Rearranging this equation and collecting constant factors into one constant b, we get

$$p_0 = b e^{-Q_0/RT}.$$

Taking logarithms we arrive at

$$\ln p_0 = -\frac{Q_0}{RT} + \ln b = -\frac{Q_0}{RT} + B_0,$$

which is equation (16).

The molecular picture of the surface of a liquid in equilibrium with its saturated vapour is therefore just as vivid as the molecular picture of a layer of adsorbed molecules in equilibrium with a gas. Enormously large numbers of molecules leave the surface at any moment and equal numbers fall in from the vapour phase and condense. The average lifetime of a molecule in the surface of a liquid is therefore a very short one comparable with the small time of adsorption which we have encountered above. At the surface of water at room temperature about 10^{22} water molecules fall in on every cm.^{2} every second, and the same amount leave the surface. As roughly only 10^{15} molecules can be at a cm.^{2} of the surface at any time, we see that the average lifetime in this case is of the order of magnitude of 10^{-7} sec.

Both equations (15) and (16) may also be obtained from a well-known principle of thermodynamics, the equation of Clapeyron

$$Q = RT^2 \frac{d \ln p}{dT},$$

which gives

$$\ln p = \int \frac{Q}{RT^2} dT.$$

Assuming Q to be independent of temperature, we obtain

$$\ln p = -\frac{Q}{RT} + \text{constant}.$$

As in reality Q in these equilibria is not independent of temperature (in adsorption phenomena, since it is the isothermal heat of adsorption (see previous section) it contains, for example, RT) the 'constant' derived in this way, and hence B_0 and B_a of equations (16) and (15) may not be identified directly with data obtained from kinetic arguments (see also § 83).

41. Rate of evaporation of a liquid in case of reflection of molecules

The picture that the number of molecules which evaporate equals the number n as given by equation (6), is only true if and when no reflection of molecules takes place (see § 34). Again, if a fraction α of the molecules reflect at the surface, instead of being condensed, only $n(1-\alpha)$ will condense, and consequently the state of dynamic equilibrium is that where the rate of evaporation equals $n(1-\alpha)$. If reflection occurs it just means that the maximum rate of evaporation at any temperature is not a direct measure for the saturated vapour pressure at that temperature. We need to know the reflection coefficient α in this case to calculate that vapour pressure from the rate of evaporation. If again there is reflection at the surface and we know the saturated vapour pressure by direct measurement, we cannot calculate the maximum rate of evaporation with the aid of equation (6); the maximum rate of evaporation is smaller than that given by equation (6) and we need to know how great α is in order to estimate the rate of evaporation.

It is known experimentally that there is no reflection of molecules in the dynamic equilibrium between mercury vapour and liquid mercury. There are, however, indications that when we are dealing with unsymmetrical molecules not every impact of a molecule at the surface of its liquid will lead to condensation; there are even indications that in the case of polar molecules like water and glycerol, reflection of molecules plays an important part at the surface. Consequently, the rate of evaporation of these liquids may be far smaller than what we might expect from kinetic considerations with the aid of equation (6). Alty and collaborators[†] found that, whilst carbon tetrachloride did not show any reflection phenomena ($\alpha = 0$), nearly 96 per cent. of water molecules hitting a water surface reflect ($\alpha \simeq 0{\cdot}96$). The rate of evaporation of water would, consequently, be only 4 per cent. of the rate calculated with equation (6). Other polar molecules also show α-values of some significance, for instance benzoic acid was found to have a reflection coefficient $\alpha = 0{\cdot}7$ (see also § 143).

If the surface of the liquid is contaminated with a layer of dust or grease or, for instance, with a unimolecular layer of a fatty acid, again a great number of molecules impinging from the vapour phase will reflect when they hit the contaminated portion of the surface. The rate of condensation, therefore, is reduced; the rate of evaporation is reduced to the same extent.

42. Heat of adsorption and entropy of adsorption

If we compare equation (15) and equation (16) and we realize that p, the pressure, which is in equilibrium with a certain amount of molecules adsorbed at a surface, must always be lower than p_0, the saturated vapour pressure of the same molecules at the same temperature, then we see that we can derive an equation for p/p_0 by subtracting equation (16) from equation (15). We get

$$\ln \frac{p}{p_0} = -\frac{Q-Q_0}{RT} + B_a - B_0.$$

If we rule out the phenomenon of supersaturation, p/p_0 must be

† T. Alty, *Proc. Roy. Soc.* A **131** (1931), 554; T. Alty and C. A. Mackay, ibid. A **149** (1935), 104 (water); T. Alty, ibid. A **161** (1937), 68 (benzoic acid), and more articles in *Proc. Roy. Soc.* See also Max Volmer, *Kinetik der Phasenbildung*, Theodor Steinkopff, 1939.

smaller than unity, hence $\ln p/p_0$ will be negative. This is possible either when $Q > Q_0$ and is not compensated for by the influence of $B_a - B_0$ or when $B_a < B_0$, and is not compensated for by the influence of Q and Q_0, or when both conditions are fulfilled. Generally speaking both conditions are fulfilled in the adsorption of gases on the surfaces of most adsorbents. This means that generally speaking the heat of adsorption will be greater than the latent heat of evaporation or condensation of the substance, the adsorption of which we are studying, and it also means that the entropy of the molecules, when adsorbed at a certain surface, will be greater than the entropy of the same molecules in their liquid or solid states. The term $B_a - B_0$ contains, amongst other things, this difference in entropy.

In general we study the adsorption of rather volatile gases on the surfaces of solid substances. As the van der Waals forces between different molecules are approximately the geometrical mean between the values for each of the two molecules, when combined with a molecule of its own kind, we see that the van der Waals forces of a molecule of a volatile substance on the surface of a solid, will in general be greater than the van der Waals forces exercised in binding it in its own liquid. In most practical cases which have been studied the heat of adsorption is indeed substantially greater than the heat of liquefaction. There are, however, some exceptions. Water molecules, when adsorbed at a charcoal surface, are only weakly bound; their polar character does not help them in this case. The heat of adsorption is smaller than the heat of liquefaction. Adsorption, nevertheless, takes place because the influence of the difference of entropy is dominating (see also § 82).† We find a similar case in the adsorption of iodine molecules at charcoal or of iodine at the surfaces of inorganic salts. The fact that the entropy in the adsorbed state is higher than in a solid or liquid state points to a fact that the adsorbed molecules have a far greater degree of freedom than the molecules in the liquid or the solid. We will discuss this greater degree of freedom and its kinetic consequences later (see Chapter VI) (see also § 143).

---

† See for a fuller discussion, J. H. de Boer in *Advances in Colloid Science*, iii. 1–60, Interscience Publ. New York, 1950.

THE QUANTITY σ: UNIMOLECULAR AND MULTIMOLECULAR ADSORPTION

43. The Langmuir adsorption isotherm

WE saw in § 35 that equation (14 a) only holds as long as there is no mutual influence between the adsorbed molecules. One way in which they may influence each other is that adsorbed molecules may bar the way for other molecules coming from the gas phase. Let us consider a surface on which a certain number of molecules is already adsorbed. There is then a chance that impinging molecules will not strike the surface at an empty space but will strike immediately on top of an adsorbed molecule which is already there. The chance that this will happen increases of course with the number of molecules which is adsorbed. It may be assumed that in many cases molecules hitting on a molecule which is already there will either reflect or will be bound for such a short time only that they do not materially contribute to the adsorption.

In 1916 Langmuir developed this picture of adsorption, leading to a unimolecular layer of adsorbed molecules. He made two assumptions. He first assumed that the heat of adsorption will be the same for every molecule which strikes the bare surface and that this heat of adsorption is independent of the other molecules which are held there. Secondly, he assumed that every molecule which strikes a molecule already adsorbed, returns immediately to the gas phase.

This last assumption leads immediately to the conception of a unimolecular layer as the upper limit of adsorption. The maximum amount of adsorption will be that where the surface is just covered with an adsorbed layer of molecules closely packed two-dimensionally, and no adsorption can take place upon this unimolecular adsorbed layer. If we denote the number of adsorbed molecules/cm.^{2} surface which would form a completely filled unimolecular layer by σ_0, and if we denote by σ the number of molecules which is actually adsorbed, we see that the number of places available for adsorption will be $\sigma_0 - \sigma$. If n molecules strike every cm.^{2} of the surface each second, a fraction σ/σ_0 will strike on molecules which are already there, and will, according to the simplified picture, return to the gas phase immediately. It is therefore the fraction $1-\sigma/\sigma_0$ which is available for adsorption. It is assumed that there is no reflection from the bare surface, hence the reflection coefficient α is zero (§ 34).

Equation (1) now modifies to

$$\sigma = n\left(1 - \frac{\sigma}{\sigma_0}\right)\tau.$$

This may be remodelled to

$$\sigma = \frac{\sigma_0 n\tau}{\sigma_0 + n\tau}. \tag{17}$$

If, therefore, the product $n\tau$ is small in comparison with σ_0, equation (17) reduces to equation (1), and we get our original result. If, however, $n\tau$ is large in comparison with σ_0, which means that the product $n\tau$ is many times greater than the amount of molecules which can be accommodated at the surface, equation (17) reduces to $\sigma = \sigma_0$, and a completely filled unimolecular layer will be formed. Instead of expressing the adsorption in terms of σ, the amount of adsorbed molecules/cm.^{2}, we may express it in terms of σ/σ_0, which is the fraction of the surface that is covered with adsorbed molecules, the degree of covering. We will call this fraction $\theta = \sigma/\sigma_0$. Dividing both sides of equation (17) by σ_0, we get

$$\theta = \frac{n\tau}{\sigma_0 + n\tau} = \frac{\dfrac{n\tau}{\sigma_0}}{\left(1 + \dfrac{n\tau}{\sigma_0}\right)}.$$

Introducing equation (6) and denoting

$$\frac{N}{\sqrt{(2\pi MRT)}} \times \frac{\tau}{\sigma_0} = k_u$$

we get

$$\theta = \frac{k_u p}{1 + k_u p}. \tag{18}$$

An equation of the form of equation (18) can be derived in various other ways. One may arrive at the same form of the Langmuir adsorption isotherm by thermodynamical reasoning or by means of statistical considerations. Because we are, however, interested in the kinetic background of these phenomena, we will only make use of the picture of the kinetic movement of molecules.

We must, however, remark here that all these derivations of the Langmuir adsorption isotherm are based on the conception of molecules adsorbed on definite sites of the surface of the adsorbent

prescribed by the structure of the surface. The surface of a crystalline substance may be considered as having a two-dimensional regular
atomic pattern, causing a two-dimensional regular potential pattern.
In the conception leading to the Langmuir adsorption isotherm the
adsorbed molecules are supposed to be adsorbed at definite points
of this regular pattern. The quantity σ_0, therefore, is governed by
the atomic distances in the surface of the adsorbent and not by the
size of the adsorbed molecules themselves. In this model these
adsorbed molecules stay at their adsorption sites during their whole
time of adsorption, τ. There is a dynamic equilibrium between the
gas and the surface with its empty and occupied sites; there is, however, in this model no moving of molecules along the surface.

As we shall discover later (Chapter VI) this model is not correct.
Always, whenever a dynamic equilibrium exists between the gas and
the adsorbed layer, the molecules will also move over the surface.
This surface migration leads to a different form of adsorption isotherm; and as this surface migration is always present under those
circumstances when one can speak of an adsorption isotherm (equilibrium), one can also say that strictly speaking a Langmuir adsorption isotherm does not exist. We shall see later (§ 113) under what
conditions the adsorption isotherm will apparently take the form of
a Langmuir adsorption isotherm.

44. The form of the Langmuir adsorption isotherm

The form of the adsorption isotherm depends, according to equation (18), on the magnitude of k_u. If k_u is small, so that $k_u p \ll 1$,
the fraction of the surface covered by adsorption will be proportional
to the pressure, we get equation (14 a). If k_u is large, so that $k_u p \gg 1$,
the fraction $\theta = 1$, and the unimolecular layer will be completed.
With intermediate values of k_u, so that $k_u p$ is of the order of magnitude of unity, the form of the isotherm giving θ as a function of p
is concave to the pressure axis. We give a few examples in Fig. 1.
Curves A, B, C, and D are drawn for values of k_u of 10^{-3}, 10^{-2}, $0\cdot1$,
and $1\cdot0$ respectively.

The value of k_u depends largely on the magnitude of τ. With the
aid of equation (6 b) and assuming σ_0 to be of the order of magnitude
of 10^{14}–10^{15} molecules/cm.^{2}, we see that at room temperature and
with gases of molecular weights between about 20 and 300, the value
of k_u will be somewhere between $4 \times 10^5 \tau$ and $10 \times 10^5 \tau$.

If, therefore, $\tau = 10^{-10}$ sec. or smaller, one gets a value for k_u of roughly 5×10^{-5} and the adsorption isotherm will be a linear one for all practical purposes up to a few hundred mm. of pressure. This is the case with argon on charcoal or silica gel, or even with krypton on charcoal. At a pressure of 1 atmosphere the surface will only be covered up to a few per cent. of a unimolecular layer.

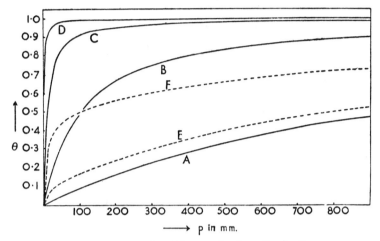

FIG. 1. A few examples of Langmuir adsorption isotherms.

With τ in the neighbourhood of 10^{-8} sec., the isotherm will be linear for pressures up to a few mm. of mercury. At a pressure of 1 atmosphere, however, about 85 per cent. of a unimolecular adsorption layer will be formed, whilst $\theta = \frac{1}{2}$ will approximately be reached at a pressure between 100–150 mm. of mercury. The adsorption of ammonia on charcoal might serve as an example which falls not far away from this region.

With τ in the neighbourhood of 10^{-6} sec., θ will assume the value $\frac{1}{2}$ at pressures just a little higher than 1 mm. of mercury. At 100 mm. of mercury nearly 99 per cent. of a unimolecular layer will be formed and for higher pressures the layer will be fully occupied for all practical purposes.

The above-mentioned examples hold for room temperature. At lower temperatures we know that the value of τ increases greatly, the value of k_u will increase to the same extent. As an example we may mention that the adsorption of nitrogen on charcoal shows no saturation at room temperature up to 100 atmospheres of pressure, whilst at $-77°$ C. saturation is reached at a pressure of 35 atmospheres. At $90°$ K. half of the saturation value for nitrogen on mica is reached at a pressure of about 0·004 mm. of mercury.

Approximately, therefore, adsorption isotherms of a pronounced concave character, for pressures between 1 and 760 mm. of mercury with a saturation at the highest pressures may be obtained at room temperature in cases where the heat of adsorption is about 9–10 k.cal./mole; at $190°$ K. (about $-80°$ C.) in cases where the heat of adsorption is about 6 k.cal./mole and at $90°$ K. (liquid air temperature), in cases where the heat of adsorption is approximately between $2\frac{1}{2}$ and 3 k.cal./mole.

45. The assumption of a constant heat of adsorption

All this holds only when the behaviour of the adsorbed molecules does not deviate too strongly from the assumptions made in the derivation of the Langmuir adsorption isotherm. The adsorption energy is certainly not constant over the surfaces of most of our adsorbents. In practice the molecules will be adsorbed in the first place at those spots of the surface where the attraction is greatest and where the heat of adsorption assumes the greatest value; we may call these places the most active places of the surface. At those spots the heat of adsorption is greatest, hence τ has the greatest value and so has the constant k_u. The isotherm starts with a steeper slope. When the active spots are occupied, the value of k_u will fall gradually or maybe, in some cases, rather suddenly. The slope of the isotherm decreases considerably. A variation in the heat of adsorption due to a heterogeneous surface, therefore, also has the tendency to give a strong concave character to the adsorption isotherm. Curves E and F in Fig. 1 may serve as examples. Curve E has been drawn assuming that a substance is adsorbed at a heterogeneous surface and that the value of k_u of equation (18) assumes the figure 0·1 on 10 per cent. of the surface, whilst its value is 10^{-3} on the remainder of the surface. In constructing curve F the assumption was made that on 50 per cent. of the surface k_u took the value 0·1 and on the other 50 per cent. of the surface $k_u = 10^{-3}$.

For testing purposes the equation is usually put into another form. When we write (18) in the form

$$\theta = \frac{\sigma}{\sigma_0} = \frac{k_u p}{1 + k_u p}$$

and we rearrange terms, we can obtain

$$\frac{p}{\sigma} = \frac{1}{k_u \sigma_0} + \frac{p}{\sigma_0}.$$

A plot of p/σ against p should give a straight line. The slope of the line gives σ_0, hence it is a measure for the magnitude of the surface (see, however, § 113). The intersection with the p/σ axis then gives

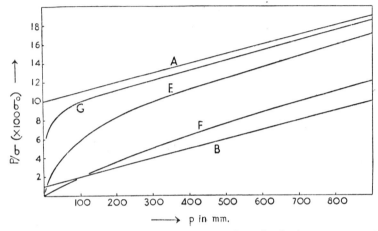

FIG. 2. Plot to test the Langmuir adsorption isotherm.

k_u. The lines corresponding to curves A and B in Fig. 1 are shown in Fig. 2 as curves A and B. Deviations due to a heterogeneous character of the surface show themselves as deviations from the straight character of the line; the values for p/σ for small p-values may fall far below the straight part of the curve. Curves E and F in Fig. 2 correspond to E and F in Fig. 1. Curve G in Fig. 2 corresponds to a surface with 1 per cent. active spots where $k_u = 0.1$ whilst the remainder of the surface is homogeneous with $k_u = 10^{-3}$.

After the active places have been filled one may in many practical cases expect the heat of adsorption caused by the mutual attraction of molecule and surface to be practically constant over a long range. Its value is lower than that which is found at active spots, it may be $\frac{2}{3}$ or $\frac{1}{2}$ of it† (see §§ 29 and 52). When, however, the degree of occupation becomes greater, the adsorbed molecules will influence each other not only because of the space they occupy, but also

† See the article on 'Atomic forces and adsorption' by J. H. de Boer in *Advances in Colloid Science*, iii. 1–60, Interscience Publ., New York, 1950.

because of the mutual van der Waals' forces between them. If these forces are very small, with respect to the forces between surface and molecule, the practical conditions may not deviate too dramatically from the assumptions made. The Langmuir adsorption isotherm, therefore, may hold relatively well in cases of chemisorption, where the forces between surface and molecule are strong, cases, it may be said, for which Langmuir originally derived his equation. The equation may also hold relatively well for asymmetrical molecules having a dipole at one end with which they are relatively strongly bound to a polar surface, whilst at the same time other molecules cannot be adsorbed on their non-polar ends. In both those cases actual saturation phenomena may easily be observed.

46. The assumption of unimolecular adsorption

The assumption that molecules which strike on those places where molecules are already adsorbed will either be reflected or else be held only for a very short time, is the most important of the assumptions for the occurrence of a Langmuir adsorption isotherm. It is this assumption which provides for a saturation value which limits the number of molecules which can be adsorbed. It need not be that the molecules would not be bound altogether on top of the first layer of adsorbed molecules. As we shall see later, for such a saturation phenomenon to occur it is only necessary for the time of adsorption for molecules in a second layer to be very short with respect to the time of adsorption in the first layer (§§ 51 and 54) and also short with respect to the time which they spend in the surface of their own liquid (§§ 56 and 57). This condition is certainly also fulfilled in cases of chemisorption. It is also fulfilled when long polar molecules with a dipole on one end are adsorbed on polar surfaces. The adsorption of fatty acids or fatty alcohols on surfaces of inorganic salts, or oxides, or on a water surface, therefore, tends to obey the Langmuir adsorption isotherm. The conditions for adsorption from solutions are very often such that they resemble the conditions for a Langmuir adsorption isotherm better than when gases are adsorbed. We have, however, then a competition for the adsorption of the solvent and the solute molecules, a problem which resembles the adsorption of a mixture of gases, with which we shall deal later (§ 61).

The conception of a saturation value for the adsorption, a level which is reached more or less asymptotically with increasing pressure (or with increasing concentration in the case of adsorption from solutions), is the most important result of Langmuir's treatment of the problem. One may often find adsorption isotherms in practice which show a tendency to lead towards a saturation value, assumed to be a unimolecular layer. Whether or not the shape of the isotherm actually obeys equations (17) or (18), isotherms which have a concave character and which strive towards a saturation value may be referred to as to be of the 'Langmuir type'.

47. The possibility of multimolecular adsorption

If molecules, when striking on a layer of molecules which are already adsorbed are attracted by sufficiently great forces, their time of adsorption may not be negligible. If this occurs conditions are fulfilled for adsorption in more than one layer, that is for multimolecular adsorption. Langmuir, and others after him, tried to derive an equation for the adsorption isotherm in the case of multimolecular adsorption. The most successful attempt, however, was made in 1938 by Brunauer, Emmett, and Teller. In their simplified assumptions we still find the condition that the molecules of one layer do not mutually influence each other, whilst this layer is being built up. We also still find the condition that the adsorption energy of the molecules of the first layer is constant, whilst similarly, of course, the heat of adsorption for the molecules in each following layer is also thought to be constant.

48. A derivation of the equation for the isotherm

We will not follow exactly the arguments of Brunauer, Emmett, and Teller in the derivation of their equation. These may be found in their original publications† or in books.‡ Because of the great importance which the equations of Brunauer, Emmett, and Teller have obtained in practical work during the last years, and also because of the numerous criticisms which have been published, we will in the following pages give a derivation which, though following the line of thought of the originators, is in more direct line with the arguments which we have followed up till now.

† S. Brunauer, P. H. Emmett, and E. Teller, *Jour. Am. Chem. Soc.* **60** (1938), 309.

‡ S. Brunauer, *The Adsorption of Gases and Vapours*, Oxford Univ. Press, London, 1943; P. H. Emmett in *Advances in Colloid Science*, vol. i, Interscience Publ., New York, 1942.

We will call θ_1 that fraction of the surface which is covered with molecules in a layer of unimolecular thickness, a fraction θ_2 of the surface will be covered with molecules on top of which other molecules have been adsorbed to form a layer of a thickness of *two* molecules. Similarly, we will call that fraction of the surface which is covered by a layer of *three* molecules thick, θ_3, etc., hence a fraction θ_i is covered by molecules which form part of a layer of a thickness of i molecules.

The total number of molecules which is adsorbed per cm.², therefore, is

$$\sigma = \sigma_0\,\theta_1 + 2\sigma_0\,\theta_2 + 3\sigma_0\,\theta_3 + \ldots + i\sigma_0\,\theta_i + \ldots,$$

where σ_0 is the number of molecules which would cover one cm.² of the surface with a complete unimolecular layer, i.e.

$$\sigma = \sigma_0 \sum_{i=1}^{i=\infty} i\theta_i.$$

At equilibrium all these fractions θ_i are constant. This means that the bare part of the surface is also constant. We will call this fraction θ_0,

$$\theta_0 = 1 - \theta_1 - \theta_2 - \theta_3 \ldots - \theta_i - \ldots = 1 - \sum_{i=1}^{i=\infty} \theta_i.$$

The number of molecules striking the bare part (θ_0) and adsorbed there ($n\theta_0$) must therefore be equal to the number of molecules evaporating from fraction θ_1, which is $v\sigma_0\,\theta_1$, hence

$$n\theta_0 = v\sigma_0\,\theta_1$$

where n is the number of molecules (equation (6)) striking 1 cm.² of the surface per second and where v as in § 34 is a proportionality factor (of dimension sec.⁻¹, i.e. frequency). Similarly the fraction θ_1 is maintained by molecules adsorbed on the bare part ($n\theta_0$) and by molecules evaporating from the top (second) layer of the fraction θ_2 (this amount is $v_1\,\sigma_0\,\theta_2$) on the one side and by molecules evaporating from θ_1 (the number being $v\sigma_0\,\theta_1$) and by adsorbing on θ_1 (the quantity being $n\theta_1$) on the other side, hence

$$n\theta_0 + v_1\,\sigma_0\,\theta_2 = v\sigma_0\,\theta_1 + n\theta_1.$$

As we know already that the first terms of both sides of this equation equal each other, we obtain

$$n\theta_1 = v_1\,\sigma_0\,\theta_2.$$

Continuing the argument in the same way, we get

$$n\theta_{i-1} = v_{i-1}\,\sigma_0\,\theta_i.$$

Instead of the constants ν_i we may use $\tau_i = 1/\nu_i$, in order to get our familiar 'times of adsorption'. Consequently we obtain the following set of equations:

$$\sigma_0\,\theta_1 = n\theta_0\,\tau$$
$$\sigma_0\,\theta_2 = n\theta_1\tau_1$$
$$. \quad . \quad . \quad . \quad .$$
$$\sigma_0\,\theta_i = n\theta_{i-1}\tau_{i-1}$$

where τ is the time of adsorption of molecules which are directly bound to the surface, τ_1 is the adsorption time of molecules adsorbed on top of the first layer, etc.

We will now assume

$$\tau_1 = \tau_2 = \dots = \tau_{i-1} = \tau_1,$$

which means that we assume the time of adsorption for a molecule bound on top of another adsorbed molecule of its own kind will be the same irrespective of the number of layers. This assumption is a very reasonable one because the mutual attracting forces will be roughly the same.

The above set of equations can then be simplified to

$$\theta_2 = x\theta_1, \quad \text{where } x = \frac{n\tau_1}{\sigma_0},$$
$$\theta_3 = x\theta_2 = x^2\theta_1$$
$$. \quad . \quad . \quad . \quad .$$
$$\theta_i = x^{i-1}\theta_1.$$

Moreover $\qquad \theta_1 = \dfrac{n\tau}{\sigma_0}\theta_0 = \dfrac{x\tau}{\tau_1}\theta_0, \qquad \theta_i = x^i\dfrac{\tau}{\tau_1}\theta_0.$

We can, therefore, write for the total number of molecules which is adsorbed

$$\sigma = \sigma_0 \sum_{i=1}^{i=\infty} i\theta_i = \sigma_0\frac{\tau}{\tau_1}\theta_0 \sum_{i=1}^{i=\infty} ix^i.$$

θ_0 in this expression may be derived from the following equation which we have already mentioned above

$$\theta_0 = 1 - \sum_{i=1}^{i=\infty} \theta_i = 1 - \frac{\tau}{\tau_1}\theta_0 \sum_{i=1}^{i=\infty} x^i,$$

hence $\qquad \theta_0 = \dfrac{1}{1 + \dfrac{\tau}{\tau_1} \displaystyle\sum_{i=1}^{i=\infty} x^i}.$

Introducing this into the equation for σ and writing

$$\frac{\tau}{\tau_1} = k$$

we obtain

$$\sigma = \frac{\sigma_0 k \sum\limits_{i=1}^{i=\infty} i x^i}{1 + k \sum\limits_{i=1}^{i=\infty} x^i}.$$

The summation in the numerator can be written as follows:

$$\sum_{i=1}^{i=\infty} i x^i = \frac{x}{(1-x)^2}$$

and for the summation in the denominator we obtain

$$\sum_{i=1}^{i=\infty} x^i = \frac{x}{1-x}.$$

Substituting this in the equation for σ we get

$$\sigma = \frac{k\sigma_0 x}{(1-x)(1-x+kx)}. \tag{19}$$

Returning to our expression for x,

$$x = \frac{n\tau_1}{\sigma_0}$$

we may note that x is dimensionless.

As n is proportional to the pressure p (equation (6))

$$n = \frac{Np}{\sqrt{(2\pi MRT)}} = \beta p,$$

we may write

$$x = \frac{\beta\tau_1}{\sigma_0} p.$$

$\sigma_0/\beta\tau_1$ has the dimensions of a pressure and we will denote it by q, hence

$$q = \frac{\sigma_0}{\beta\tau_1}, \tag{20}$$

where

$$\beta = \frac{N}{\sqrt{(2\pi MRT)}}.$$

Hence

$$x = \frac{p}{q}.$$

If with increasing pressure, p, the point $p = q$ is reached, the value of x becomes unity. This would mean that n_q, the value of n corresponding to the pressure q, is such that

$$n_q \tau_1 = \sigma_0.$$

If the adsorption takes place on a free surface (and is not limited by boundaries of capillaries or the like) this means that the second, third, etc., layers are all filled to capacity, accommodating σ_0 molecules/cm.[2] σ, therefore, becomes infinite, as we may also see directly by substituting $x = 1$ in our expression for σ.

Inserting $x = p/q$ in equation (19), we obtain, after rearranging terms

$$\sigma = \frac{kp\sigma_0}{(q-p)[1+(k-1)p/q]}. \tag{21}$$

This equation for the adsorption isotherm has three constants, viz. k, q, and σ_0.

One might remark that σ_0 might be evaluated from the dimensions of the molecules or from the dimensions of the adsorption 'sites' (§ 44) of the surface in cases of 'localized' adsorption (see § 82). Unfortunately, however, the surface area of adsorbents is, in general, not known, so we cannot evaluate σ from the adsorption data. The total number of adsorbed molecules, which is measured experimentally, is proportional to the total surface area S of the adsorbent; the quantity which is measured is $S\sigma$. If the practical figures are not expressed in numbers of molecules but in the volume of gas which has been adsorbed, we may follow the notation used by Brunauer in his book and denote this volume by v, which is directly proportional to $S\sigma$. Equation (20) then assumes the form

$$v = \frac{kpv_m}{(q-p)[1+(k-1)p/q]}, \tag{21a}$$

v_m being the volume of gas adsorbed when the entire adsorbent surface is covered with a complete unimolecular layer. If the three constants k, q, and v_m are evaluated from practical plots the value for v_m gives a direct measure for the surface area S of the adsorbent (see § 132).

49. A further simplification

In order to simplify the equation and to reduce it to one with two constants only, we may follow the example of Brunauer, Emmett, and Teller, who in their derivation implicitly identify q with p_0, the saturation value of the pressure of the adsorbate at the temperature of the experiment. This assumption means that in a plot of v as a function of p/p_0 the value of v is expected to approach infinity as p/p_0 approaches unity. The equation of the isotherm

$$v = \frac{kpv_m}{(p_0-p)[1+(k-1)p/p_0]} \qquad (21\,\mathrm{b})$$

shows that v reaches infinity when p approaches p_0. The graph approaches asymptotically a vertical erected at the point $p/p_0 = 1$. If this assumption is made we can put the equation in the form

$$\frac{p}{v(p_0-p)} = \frac{1}{v_m k} + \frac{k-1}{v_m k} \frac{p}{p_0},$$

and the function
$$\frac{p}{v(p_0-p)}$$

should give a straight line if plotted against p/p_0.

In harmony with this simplification we have also to assume with Brunauer, Emmett, and Teller that the heat of adsorption and the probability of evaporation of molecules adsorbed on top of other adsorbed molecules equals the heat of evaporation and the probability of evaporation of the molecules from their own liquid.

In our derivation this means that in

$$k = \frac{\tau}{\tau_1}$$

$$= \frac{\tau_0\, e^{Q_a/RT}}{(\tau_0)_1\, e^{Q_1/RT}}$$

we put $\tau_0 = (\tau_0)_1$ and $Q_1 = Q_0$, the latent heat of evaporation of the adsorbate in liquid form. Q_a stands for the heat of adsorption of the first layer when the molecules are adsorbed to the surface directly. We then obtain $k = e^{(Q_a-Q_0)/RT}$, and the intercept of the above-mentioned straight line, $1/v_m k$, and its slope, $(k-1)/v_m k$, give the constants v_m and k and, therefore, the surface area S and the heat of adsorption of the first layer Q_a, the latent heat of evaporation Q_0 being known.

50. The form at low values of p/p_0

We will now discuss a few peculiarities of the equations that we have derived above. Because of the way that we derived them and defined our constants, it is easiest to start our discussions from equation (19), which we will write in the form

$$\frac{\sigma}{\sigma_0} = \theta = \frac{kx}{(1-x)(1-x+kx)}. \tag{22}$$

We have again expressed σ/σ_0 as θ, the degree of covering of the surface. Whilst, however, in our discussions of the Langmuir equation, θ is essentially less than 1, we must remember here that σ may assume values far greater than σ_0 now we are discussing multimolecular adsorption. θ, therefore, may have, theoretically, all values from zero to infinity. If $x \ll 1$, equation (22) reduces to

$$\theta = \frac{kx}{1+kx} \tag{22 a}$$

provided k is sufficiently great for kx to be not small with respect to one. This is the equation of the Langmuir adsorption isotherm. We can see this immediately when we remember that $k = \tau/\tau_1$, and

$$x = \frac{p}{q} = \frac{p\beta\tau_1}{\sigma_0}.$$

The product kx is, therefore,

$$kx = \frac{\tau}{\tau_1} \times p\frac{\beta\tau_1}{\sigma_0} = \frac{\tau}{\sigma_0}\beta p.$$

As (§ 48)

$$\beta = \frac{N}{\sqrt{(2\pi MRT)}},$$

we obtain

$$kx = \frac{\tau}{\sigma_0}\frac{N}{\sqrt{(2\pi MRT)}}p = k_u p.$$

k_u is, as we see, essentially the same as the k_u of equation (18) (§ 43). For small values of p/q equation (22) therefore reduces to the Langmuir adsorption isotherm. If q has a value approximately equal to p_0, which is generally assumed to be the case, this means that equation (22) reduces to the Langmuir adsorption isotherm for small values of p/p_0.

In § 56, however, we will discuss cases in which q assumes values which are far higher than p_0. In those circumstances the Langmuir adsorption isotherm results from equation (22) even for high values of p/p_0.

51. The total shape

If x assumes values between 0·5 and 1·0 and k is so great that

$$kx \gg 1-x$$

equation (22) reduces to $\theta = \dfrac{1}{1-x}.$ (22 b)

We will illustrate this behaviour and the results of the preceding section by constructing an isotherm. As a great deal of the applications of the multimolecular adsorption theory of Brunauer, Emmett, and Teller have been made with nitrogen, argon, and the like at liquid air temperatures, we shall assume a gas of a molecular weight of 30, a boiling-point of 80° K. and a heat of evaporation of 1,500 cal./mole. We shall calculate the adsorption isotherm for this hypothetical gas at 90° K. We assume that $p_0 = q$, and, in accordance with this, that the heat of adsorption for the second and higher layers equals the heat of evaporation. With the aid of equation (13) we can then immediately calculate the time of adsorption τ_1 for the second and higher layers,

$$\tau_1 = \tau_0 e^{Q_0/RT},$$

by assuming τ_0 to be 10^{-13} sec., a rough approximation which has been made throughout our considerations. When $Q_0 = 1,500$ cal./mole we get $\tau_1 = 4 \cdot 6 \times 10^{-10}$ sec.

We assume the adsorption time τ for the first layer of molecules directly adsorbed at the surface of our adsorbent to be

$$\tau = 10^{-5} \text{ sec.,}$$

as we have seen in § 33 that this is the order of magnitude for the time of adsorption of argon, nitrogen, etc., at 90° K. The constant k in our equation (22) is therefore

$$k = \frac{\tau}{\tau_1} = 2 \cdot 18 \times 10^4.$$

Fig. 3 gives the adsorption isotherm calculated with equation (22). The first part (a) shows the values of θ at very small values of $p/p_0 = x$, values up to $p/p_0 = 4 \times 10^{-4}$. The isotherm in this range of pressures is one exactly equivalent to the Langmuir adsorption isotherm (equations (18) and (22 a)). θ does not reach the value 1 yet. In part (b) the pressure scale has been reduced a hundredfold and the scale for θ twofold. In this part up to $p/p_0 = 0 \cdot 02$, the adsorption isotherm is still practically of the Langmuir type. In part (c) we have reduced the pressure scale again by a factor 20 and the θ scale also by a factor 20. This part of the isotherm is governed completely by the simplified form (22 b).

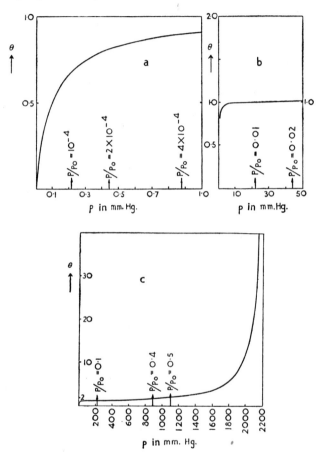

FIG. 3. The total form of an adsorption isotherm according to equation (22).

Although it is not necessary for the calculation, it may be pointed out that we can estimate the value for q (which equals p_0 in this case). It can be evaluated from equation (20) provided we make a reasonably good assumption for the number of molecules/cm.² contained in a complete unimolecular layer σ_0.

We assume $$\sigma_0 = 6 \cdot 75 \times 10^{14},$$

which means that each molecule occupies a surface space of about 15 A^2. The value of β, calculated with $M = 30$ and $T = 90°$ K., amounts to $6 \cdot 75 \times 10^{20}$ whilst for τ_1 we take the figure $\tau_1 = 4 \cdot 6 \times 10^{-10}$ sec. as mentioned above. $q \ (= p_0)$ then is 2,180 mm. of mercury, which is a reasonable figure for the saturated vapour pressure of our hypothetical gas at 90° K. With the aid of this value for $q = p_0$, we have calculated the values for the pressure which are indicated on the pressure axis of Fig. 3.

It may be emphasized, however, that neither of the actual values for p, q, τ, or τ_1 are essential for the form of the adsorption isotherm when plotted as θ as a function of p/p_0. Nor is the temperature essential. The same form of isotherm calculated with equation (22) will be obtained with any example if we choose $k = 2 \cdot 18 \times 10^4$.

52. Ruling out the influence of active spots

Isotherms of this shape, with such a long linear part in the middle region of the relative pressures, meanwhile, are hardly found in practice. In reality the actual values for the constant k in equation (22) seem to be smaller (see also the next section); values in the neighbourhood of 100 do occur frequently but not values as high as over 10,000. It looks as if the values for τ and therefore the values for Q_a, the heat of adsorption, are smaller with respect to τ_1 and Q_0, the heat of evaporation, than we assumed. It seems as if the values for the heat of adsorption which we have encountered up till now (see e.g. §§ 28, 29, and 33) are only the values experienced at the most active places (§ 45) of the surface. After a small percentage of the surface has been covered, at small pressures, the heat of adsorption may fall considerably, for instance to half of the original value. This behaviour is also found experimentally when heats of adsorption are measured as a function of the amount of gas which is adsorbed.

The heat of adsorption on the less active part of the surface may be a half or two-thirds of that which governs the adsorption on the active spots. The differential heat of adsorption for the first molecules of argon on graphite is $3 \cdot 9$ k.cal./mole; with increasing amount of adsorption this value falls to $2 \cdot 2$ k.cal./mole which may be considered to be the heat of adsorption on a flat graphite surface.[†]

† R. M. Barrer, *Proc. Roy. Soc.* A **161** (1937), 476. See also J. H. de Boer, 'Atomic forces and adsorption', in *Advances in Colloid Science*, iii. 1–60, Interscience Publ., New York, 1950.

For nitrogen the corresponding figures are 4·4 k.cal./mole and 2·3
k.cal./mole; for hydrogen 1·8 k.cal./mole and 0·9 k.cal./mole.

Just as in the case of the Langmuir equation (§ 45) the plot of
$p/\{v(p_0-p)\}$ against p/p_0 does not give a straight line for values of
p/p_0 smaller than say 0·05. It is, as Brunauer says in his book, the
active part of the surface which is covered at these low relative
pressures. The application of the multimolecular theory of Brunauer,
Emmett, and Teller starts from $p/p_0 = 0\cdot05$. The adsorption energy,
Q_a, and the corresponding time of adsorption τ which figure in the
constant k of equations (19), (21), and (22) (see § 50) are thus for the
less active part of the surface.

We had, consequently, chosen a too high value for τ in our example
of the previous section. The time of adsorption, τ, which plays a role
in the middle and higher ranges of p/p_0 values, though generally
still greater than τ_1 $(Q_a > Q_0)$, is less than the time of adsorption
which is observed at the more active spots of the surface. The latter
τ dominates the first part of the adsorption isotherm at low values
of p/p_0.

53. The form when $k = 1$ or less

Still assuming the simplification $q = p_0$, it is worth while pointing
out that equation (22) reduces to the form

$$\theta = \frac{x}{1-x} \qquad (22\,\text{c})$$

when $k = 1$.

If the adsorption, therefore, takes place on a surface, the attraction of which would give rise to a heat of adsorption exactly equal
to the heat of evaporation, the adsorption isotherm should have the
simplified form (22 c). A case resembling this behaviour may be
found when a gas is very strongly adsorbed in the first unimolecular
layer. If we then take the surface together with this unimolecular
layer as a fresh surface, on which we study the (additional) adsorption, that is, if we only count the amount of gas which is adsorbed
from the second layer onwards, we get equation (22 c). If, of course,
we include the first layer into our counting we get

$$\theta = 1 + \frac{x}{1-x} = \frac{1}{1-x}$$

which is equation (22 b). As a matter of fact, Fig. 3 can serve
excellently for illustrating this case.

If $k < 1$, the adsorption isotherm will always be convex to the pressure axis (see § 58).

54. Two examples

A very accurate investigation of the adsorption of argon and of nitrogen on crystals of potassium chloride, carried out by Orr,† may provide us with a few examples illustrating the points of the three previous sections. Orr measured the heat of adsorption as a function of the quantity of molecules which were adsorbed. The heat of adsorption for the first molecules of nitrogen is well over 3 k.cal./mole, the figure decreases when more nitrogen is adsorbed, passes through a minimum at about 2·4 k.cal./mole, rises again to pass a maximum at 3 k.cal./mole and decreases then rather sharply to a figure which is not much higher than the heat of evaporation of liquid nitrogen. Orr identifies the point at which the above-mentioned maximum is reached with the completion of the first unimolecular layer. This enables us to express his figures for the number of molecules which are adsorbed in terms of θ, the degree of occupation. In Fig. 4 the isotherm of nitrogen on KCl at 73·57° K. is given, calculated from the data published by Orr. There is some resemblance with the shape of the curves of Fig. 3; parts a and b of Fig. 4, however, are not Langmuir adsorption isotherms, there is an increasing slope in part b instead of a saturation value. There is obviously a less strict separation between the left-hand and right-hand parts of the figure than in Fig. 3, the reason being that the value of k is smaller than that of § 51. As stated in § 52 the heat of adsorption of the first molecules will be too high as they are adsorbed at active spots. This is exactly what Orr found; the heat of adsorption does not fall, however, to a constant value, but passes a minimum and increases again. This increase is caused by the mutual attraction of the adsorbed nitrogen molecules, eventually leading to a two-dimensional condensation phenomenon (Chapter VII). This behaviour is even essential for the occurrence of multimolecular adsorption, as we shall discuss in Chapter IX. Taking 2·5 k.cal./mole as a mean value of the heat of adsorption of nitrogen in the region of $\theta = 0\cdot2$ to $\theta = 0\cdot7$, we obtain the value of $2\cdot5 \times 10^{-6}$ sec. for τ, the time of adsorption on the bare KCl surface at 73·57° K. Since the heat of evaporation is 1·4 k.cal./mole, the time of adsorption in

† W. J. C. Orr, *Proc. Roy. Soc.* A **173** (1939), 349.

the second and following layers at 73·57° K. may be taken as $\tau_1 = 1·6 \times 10^{-9}$ sec. The constant k of equation (22) is therefore

$$k = \frac{\tau}{\tau_1} = \text{about } 1{,}500.$$

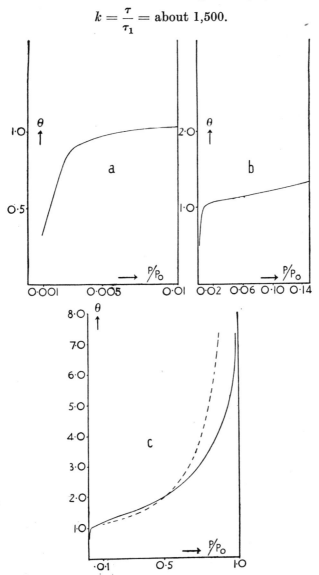

FIG. 4. Adsorption isotherm of N_2 on KCl at 73·57° K., from measurements of Orr.

This is considerably smaller than the figure we used for the construction of Fig. 3 in § 51.

The difference between τ and τ_1 (and so between the heat of adsorption Q_a of the first layer and Q_0 of the following layers) is far smaller still for many other gases. This results in a much less prominent flat part in the adsorption isotherm. In Fig. 5 we give as an example the adsorption isotherm of argon on KCl at $86 \cdot 9°$ K.

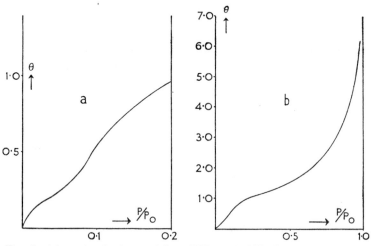

FIG. 5. Adsorption isotherm of A on KCl at $86 \cdot 9°$ K., from measurements of Orr.

(the boiling-point of argon), also derived from data published by Orr. Here again the heat of adsorption falls from a figure well over 2 k.cal./mole to a minimum of about $1 \cdot 8$ k.cal./mole, it then passes through a maximum at about $2 \cdot 1^5$ k.cal/.mole and falls to a figure comparable with the heat of evaporation of the liquid. Fig. 5 (for values of $p/p_0 > 0, 1$) corresponds roughly to an isotherm derived from equation (22) with a value of $k =$ about 10. Taking the mean value of $Q_a = 1 \cdot 9$ k.cal./mole, the time τ at $86 \cdot 9°$ K. is $5 \cdot 6 \times 10^{-9}$ sec.; the heat of evaporation $Q_0 = 1 \cdot 5$ k.cal./mole gives $\tau_1 = 5 \cdot 6 \times 10^{-10}$ sec. The shape of the isotherm of Fig. 4 is more convenient than that of Fig. 5, if it is to be used for finding the point where the first unimolecular layer is completed, for the purpose of estimating surface areas. It is for this reason that nitrogen (having practically always a greater difference between Q_a and Q_0 than other, comparable, gases) is preferred for such estimations.

The form of the isotherms at higher values of p/p_0 is only qualitatively in harmony with the shape expected from equation (22). The dotted curve in Fig. 4c is the theoretical isotherm according to equation (22 b). The deviation of the argon isotherm at low values of p/p_0 (< 0.1) is caused by the influence of the active spots of the surface.

55. The form of the isotherm when $q \neq p_0$

Our assumption $q = p_0$, however, is a simplification which does not always hold. In many cases q will be greater than p_0 and may even be very great compared with p_0; on rare occasions q may be less than p_0. If the heat of adsorption of the second and higher layers is smaller than the heat of evaporation of the liquid, the time of adsorption τ_1 will be smaller than the value which would correspond to the heat of evaporation. We will call this latter value $(\tau_1)_0$.

Because of this the value of the constant k will increase. We will illustrate this point with an example. We choose again our hypothetical gas of § 51, having a molecular weight 30, boiling-point about 80° K., and heat of evaporation $Q_0 = 1,500$ cal./mole. In accordance with the observation which we made in § 52, namely, that only the heat of adsorption on the less active part of the surface will influence the conduct of multimolecular adsorption, we choose a smaller value for τ than in § 51. We assume $\tau = 4.6 \times 10^{-8}$ sec. If q is still equal to p_0, the value for τ_1 ($= (\tau_1)_0$), calculated from Q_0, is 4.6×10^{-10} sec. and the value for k is 100, an order of magnitude which, as we saw, is often found. A value $\tau = 4.6 \times 10^{-8}$ sec. corresponds to a heat of adsorption of 2,320 cal./mole, which is 0.71 times the value which we had assumed in § 51. There we had chosen $\tau = 10^{-5}$ sec. which corresponds to $Q_a = 3,280$ cal./mole. Curve A in Fig. 6 corresponds to the case just mentioned.

We now assume the adsorption energy of the second and higher layers to be smaller than 1,500 cal./mole. For curve B we made the assumption $\tau_1 = 4 \times 10^{-10}$ sec., corresponding to a heat of adsorption of 1,475 cal./mole. The curve would approach the vertical B asymptotically. At $p/p_0 = 1$ the value of θ is a restricted one, namely, 8.4. Adsorption isotherms of this shape cutting the axis $p/p_0 = 1$ at a definite angle are very often found in practice. At saturation pressure the adsorption is limited as indicated by this sharp intersection point. We see from this example that the heat of adsorption for the second and higher layers need only be less than 2 per cent. smaller than the heat of evaporation in order to get this effect.

If the heat of evaporation Q_1 for the second and higher layers is considerably smaller than the heat of evaporation of the liquids, we do not even observe the sharp rise of the adsorption isotherm.

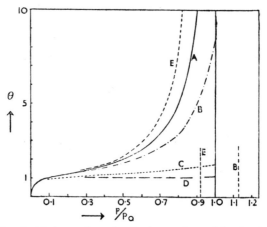

FIG. 6. Various adsorption isotherms for multimolecular adsorption, varying q.

Curves C and D in Fig. 6 are constructed for the values $\tau_1 = 2 \times 10^{-10}$ sec. and 5×10^{-11} sec., respectively, corresponding to a heat of adsorption Q_1 of 1,350 cal./mole and 1,100 cal./mole respectively. The positions of the vertical lines to which these curves would approach asymptotically, are not indicated in the figure, they would lie too far away. These positions, however, can easily be calculated by the relation

$$q = \frac{(\tau_1)_0}{\tau_1} p_0. \tag{23}$$

In the case of curve C, therefore, q would be situated at a value

$$\frac{p}{p_0} = 2 \cdot 3,$$

and in the case of curve D, at a value

$$\frac{p}{p_0} = 9 \cdot 2.$$

If the heat of adsorption for the second and higher layers, Q_1, is greater than the heat of evaporation, examples of which may also be found in practice, a curve of the shape of curve E may be found. Curve E is calculated for a value of $\tau_1 = 5 \times 10^{-10}$ sec., hence for a value for $Q_1 = 1{,}520$ cal./mole, $1\frac{1}{2}$ per cent. higher than the heat of evaporation. Curve E approaches a vertical E asymptotically. The position of the vertical E is at a value of p/p_0 given by the relation between $(\tau_1)_0$ and τ_1 (equation (23)), which in this case is

$$q = \frac{4 \cdot 6 \times 10^{-10}}{5 \times 10^{-10}} p_0 = 0 \cdot 92 p_0.$$

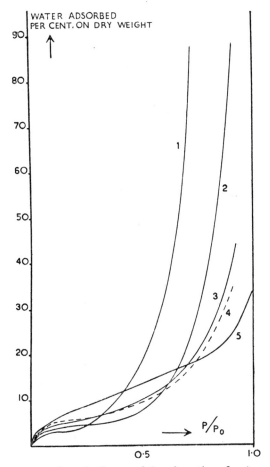

FIG. 7. Some isotherms of the adsorption of water at various foodstuffs.

As already indicated, curves of the behaviour of curve B are often found in practice, whilst also a few examples of curve E are known. Curves of the shape of C and especially D are also found frequently.

In Fig. 7 we give some isotherms of the adsorption of water at various foodstuffs at 10° C.† Curves 1 and 2 are for apple pectin and plums respectively; both curves show the character of curve E, approaching asymptotically to a vertical at a p/p_0 value smaller than unity. Curves 3 and 4 are obtained with fodder yeast and blanched

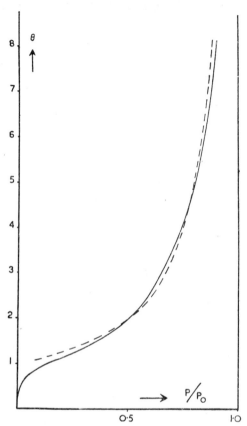

FIG. 8. Comparing one of the lines of Fig. 7 with a 'theoretical' line.

potatoes respectively; they resemble the theoretical curve A rather well. This latter fact is more clearly shown in Fig. 8 where the full line is the same as curve 3 of Fig. 7, but plotted in such a way that at $p/p_0 = 0.5$ we obtain the degree of occupation $\theta = 2$. The theoretical curve of equation (22 b)

$$\theta = \frac{1}{1-x}$$

† Examples taken from an investigation of R. Gave in *Progress Report of the Department of Scientific and Industrial Research* (1943).

gives $\theta = 2$ for $x = p/p_0 = 0.5$. This curve is shown as a dotted line in Fig. 8. Curve 5 of Fig. 7 is for maize, a definite intersection with the vertical at $p/p_0 = 1$ is shown.

In Fig. 9 curve 1 gives the water sorption of Australian wool (it may be taken as representative for any wool) and curve 2 of

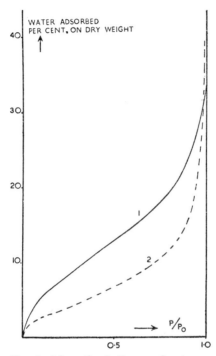

FIG. 9. Adsorption isotherms of water on
textile materials.

American cotton. The first curve again gives a definite intersection point with the vertical at $p/p_0 = 1$, but curve 2 also does not approach asymptotically to this vertical but rather to a vertical line somewhere between $p/p_0 = 1.15$ and 1.20.

56. A Langmuir isotherm when $q \gg p_0$

Curve D of Fig. 6 is for all practical purposes a normal Langmuir adsorption isotherm. We shall always find this isotherm when the value of q is very large with respect to p_0. q in such a case takes the role of the saturated vapour pressure of a hypothetical multimolecular adsorption layer which would be adsorbed if we could get to sufficiently high pressures. Long before q is reached we reach p_0 and condensation sets in on or next to the adsorbed layer. The adsorption layer, therefore, is restricted and condensation is *not* a continuation of this adsorption.

It can easily be shown that our equation reduces to the Langmuir equation for $q \gg p$, when we start from equation (21),

$$\theta = \frac{\sigma}{\sigma_0} = \frac{kp}{(q-p)[1+(k-1)p/q]}.$$

Rearranging it slightly we obtain

$$\theta = \frac{kpq}{(q-p)(q-p+kp)}.$$

If p may be neglected with respect to q, this becomes

$$\theta = \frac{kpq}{q(q+kp)} = \frac{kp}{q+kp} = \frac{kp/q}{1+kp/q}.$$

Inserting $k = \tau/\tau_1$ (§ 48) and $q = \sigma_0/\beta\tau_1$ (equation (20)), we obtain

$$\frac{k}{q} = \frac{\beta\tau}{\sigma_0}.$$

As
$$\beta = \frac{N}{\sqrt{(2\pi MRT)}} \quad (\text{§ 48}),$$

$$\frac{k}{q} = \frac{N}{\sqrt{(2\pi MRT)}} \frac{\tau}{\sigma_0} = k_u \quad (\text{§§ 43 and 50}).$$

Hence
$$\theta = \frac{k_u p}{1+k_u p}$$

which is the Langmuir equation with the same k_u as in § 43.

It is instructive to see to what hypothetical value q would approach if the heat of adsorption for molecules on top of the first layer were really zero. In that case τ_1 would assume the lowest value possible, namely, τ_0 (equation (13)), hence it would be of the order of magnitude of 10^{-13} sec. As σ_0/β is a few times 10^{-6}, such a value of q would be about 10^7 mm. or roughly 10,000 atmospheres. Even far lower values of q are still high enough to ensure the Langmuir form of the isotherm holding. The heat of adsorption of molecules on top of the first layer may, therefore, even assume appreciably high figures and we may still find a Langmuir adsorption isotherm even up to the saturated pressure p_0 (see curve D of Fig. 6, where the assumed value for Q_1 is as high as about $\frac{3}{4}$ that of Q_0).

The condition $q \gg p_0$ may, with the aid of equation (23), also be formulated as $(\tau_1)_0 \gg \tau_1$. Hence, the time $(\tau_1)_0$ corresponding to the normal heat of evaporation of the liquid (see § 55) must be large with respect to the time of adsorption of molecules on top of the first unimolecular layer.

If the condition (see § 51) $\tau \gg \tau_1$ is fulfilled, the saturation value of the unimolecular adsorption will be already reached at low values of p/p_0.

The condition $(\tau_1)_0 \gg \tau_1$ results in maintaining the unimolecular adsorption up to high values of p/p_0 and preventing multimolecular adsorption from taking place.

57. Conditions for multimolecular adsorption

When we consider a single molecule of the first adsorbed layer we can hardly imagine that a molecule of a second layer situated on top of that isolated adsorbed molecule would be bound strongly enough to show a heat of adsorption of the order of magnitude of the heat of evaporation. Its heat of adsorption will be far smaller than that. As long as in the first adsorbed layer we are dealing with isolated molecules, adsorbed at random, we cannot expect the adsorption energy of the second layer to be anything like the heat of evaporation. In all such cases the value of q will be very large, because τ_1 is very small. The adsorption isotherm will be of the Langmuir type showing a tendency to saturation. We can only expect the heat of evaporation (heat of adsorption) for the second and higher layers to come in the neighbourhood of the heat of evaporation for the liquid, if the molecules of the first layer are more or less closely packed two-dimensionally, or form at least closely packed two-dimensional patches on the surface or on parts of the surface. We come then to the conclusion that two-dimensional condensation will precede the formation of second or higher layers, hence that the condition for multimolecular adsorption is the formation of a condensed layer or at least of a relatively closely packed layer or of condensed patches in the first adsorbed layer. We will deal with this phenomenon of two-dimensional condensation in the next chapters, and then we will continue the argument of this section in Chapter IX.

58. The shape when $Q_a < Q_0$

We saw in § 53 that the adsorption isotherm, according to the multimolecular theory of adsorption, will always be convex to the vertical axis if $k < 1$. The conclusion has been derived from this in the literature that a convex nature will always be found when the heat of adsorption of the first layer Q_a is smaller than the heat of

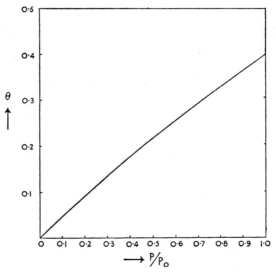

FIG. 10. Adsorption isotherm for a case where $Q_a < Q_0$ whilst there is still a concave character of the curve.

evaporation Q_0. We have learned, however, in the previous section, that very often the heat of adsorption of the second and higher layers may be smaller than the heat of evaporation. In Fig. 10 we have calculated an adsorption isotherm for 20° C. for a substance showing a value for $\tau = 5 \times 10^{-3}$ ($Q_a = 14 \cdot 35$ k.cal./mole) whilst the time of adsorption for the second and higher layers $\tau_1 = 10^{-3}$ sec. ($Q_1 = 13 \cdot 4$ k.cal./mole), the substance, however, having a heat of evaporation of $14 \cdot 7$ k.cal./mole, and hence a $(\tau_1)_0$ value of 10^{-2} sec. The adsorption at saturated vapour pressure is of course restricted and amounts to a layer which is not even half filled. This is because the value for q in this example is high, namely $10 \times p_0$. This example serves to show that a concave character of the isotherm may still be found when $Q_a < Q_0$.

59. Restricted adsorption at $p = p_0$

As we have seen in previous sections a value of q greater than p_0 restricts the number of layers which can be adsorbed at saturated pressure. There may be other causes for such a restriction. If the adsorption does not take place on free surfaces but in capillaries, the number of layers cannot reach infinitely high figures. Brunauer, Emmett, and Teller consider the case when adsorption takes place in a capillary space restricted by two plane parallel walls. If then the maximum number of layers which can be adsorbed on each wall of this capillary space is r, they arrive at the equation

$$v = \frac{v_m kx}{1-x} \frac{1-(r+1)x^r+rx^{r+1}}{1+(k-1)x-kx^{r+1}}, \tag{24}$$

and they show then that, for $r = 1$, this equation reduces to

$$v = \frac{v_m kx}{1+kx}$$

which is our equation (22 a), i.e. the Langmuir equation.

As we have remarked already in § 55, the adsorption isotherms very often intersect the pressure axis at saturated pressure at a sharp angle. From relative pressures p/p_0 of 0·5 onward the amount of substance which is adsorbed increases more slowly than it would if governed by equation (21 b). It is very difficult to say which cause will in effect have restricted the number of layers which can be adsorbed. It is premature to reach conclusions about the size of capillaries or pores or even the distribution of these sizes, from the portion of the isotherm at higher values of p/p_0. We can only do this when we are completely sure that the heat of adsorption of these layers is exactly the same as the heat of evaporation of the liquid.

It would be very interesting if data were available for multi-molecular adsorption on surfaces of liquids, where no capillaries are present to play a role. Cassel,[†] measuring carbon tetrachloride on liquid mercury, found a restricted multimolecular adsorption; unfortunately, however, as Kemball and Rideal[‡] pointed out, these data are not reliable because of a mistake made in the calculations. There are, however, indications of multimolecular adsorption of acetone on mercury in Kemball's excellent work.[§] The data in his

[†] H. Cassel, *Trans. Faraday Soc.* **28** (1932), 177.
[‡] C. Kemball and E. K. Rideal, *Proc. Roy. Soc.* A **187** (1946), 53 (especially p. 72).
[§] C. Kemball, ibid. A **190** (1947), 117.

work are not given in the form of adsorption isotherms in the sense
that we use them here, but such an isotherm may be derived from
them. Fig. 11 is constructed by taking data from Kemball's figures
and plotting them as the amount of adsorbed acetone molecules/
cm.² of mercury surface, σ, as a function of p/p_0 of acetone at 25° C.

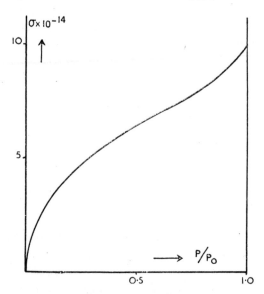

FIG. 11. Adsorption isotherm of acetone on mercury,
calculated from data taken from Kemball's work.

The curve is drawn through the points as smoothly as possible.
There is a sharp intersection with the vertical at $p/p_0 = 1$; according
to Kemball there are certain indications that a fourth layer of acetone
molecules has begun to be adsorbed at that moment (see also § 126).

60. Criticisms

The theory of multimolecular adsorption as developed by Brunauer,
Emmett, and Teller, has been criticized from various sides and with
various arguments. Brunauer himself gives a very fair set of criticisms in his own book. On the other hand, the theory has been
successfully applied by many investigators for the purpose of estimation of the surface area of adsorbents based on the principle which
we discussed at the end of § 48. The simplified form of equation (21 b)
(§ 49) as derived by Brunauer, Emmett, and Teller, is used in such
determinations. In most cases quite reasonable values for the surface

area are obtained. The same equation may be derived by statistical arguments provided the same simplified picture is used. Terrell L. Hill[†] has investigated this problem thoroughly in an excellent series of articles.

The various simplifications, however, in the derivation of the equation may give a warning against a tendency to assume too great an accuracy for the values obtained by the method. The greatest attraction of the theory is its simplicity. More refined conceptions can be tried and have been suggested in the literature, leading in general to very complicated equations, far more complicated than, for instance, equation (24). Brunauer, Emmett, and Teller suggest the use of the simplified equation only for the region of p/p_0 values between 0·05 and 0·35. It is in that region that the influence of the active places of the surface is no longer felt (§ 52), whilst the influences which restrict the number of layers at higher relative pressures (§ 59), have generally not yet become strong enough to make themselves noticeable.

Though the equation may, for practical purposes, be used in that region, the physical picture on which the theory is built is inadequate. We shall return to this problem later (Chapter IX, especially § 132).

61. Adsorption of a mixture of gases

We now briefly consider the case when a mixture of two gases is in contact with the surface of an adsorbent. Let the partial pressures of the two gases be p_a and p_b, the numbers n (equation (6)) being n_a and n_b respectively. We assume that σ_a molecules of the first sort and σ_b molecules of the second sort are adsorbed per cm.² We will restrict ourselves to the case of unimolecular adsorption for both gases. This means, as we have seen before, that a time of adsorption for any of the two molecules in a second layer will be small with respect to its time of adsorption on the bare surface of the adsorbent. We define now

$$\theta_a = \frac{\sigma_a}{\sigma_0} \quad \text{and} \quad \theta_b = \frac{\sigma_b}{\sigma_0}$$

where σ_0 represents the number of molecules of the gases a or b or both which would be present if the surface were covered with a

† Terrell L. Hill, *Jour. Chem. Physics*, **14** (1946), 263, 441; **15** (1947), 767; **16** (1948), 181.

complete unimolecular layer of molecules. It is, therefore, assumed that the surface offers a definite number of sites, σ_0 for adsorption. An argument similar to that used in § 43 leads to the following two equations

$$\sigma_a = n_a(1-\theta_a-\theta_b)\tau_a,$$
$$\sigma_b = n_b(1-\theta_a-\theta_b)\tau_b,$$

where τ_a and τ_b are the times of adsorption of gases a and b respectively. According to equation (6) the numbers n are proportional to the pressure p. A simultaneous solution of the two equations leads us to the following pair:

$$\left.\begin{aligned}\theta_a &= \frac{b_a p_a}{1+b_a p_a+b_p p_b}\\[2mm]\theta_b &= \frac{b_b p_b}{1+b_a p_a+b_b p_b}\end{aligned}\right\} \tag{25}$$

where

$$b_a = \frac{N}{\sqrt{(2\pi M_a RT)}}\frac{\tau_a}{(\sigma_0)_a}$$

and

$$b_b = \frac{N}{\sqrt{(2\pi M_b RT)}}\frac{\tau_b}{(\sigma_0)_b}$$

where M_a and M_b are the molecular weights of the gases a and b respectively. The expressions for b_a and b_b are, as we see, comparable with the expression for k_u in equation (18).

At very low pressures of both gases these equations of course reduce to

$$\theta_a = b_a p_a, \qquad \theta_b = b_b p_b,$$

and both gases are adsorbed as though the other were not present. If $b_a p_a$ is not small, but $b_b p_b$ is still negligible with respect to it, the equations reduce to

$$\theta_a = \frac{b_a p_a}{1+b_a p_a}, \qquad \theta_b = \frac{b_b p_b}{1+b_a p_a}.$$

In such a case the adsorption of gas a takes place as if no gas b were present. The adsorption of gas b, however, decreases with increasing pressure of gas a. We find this sort of relationship when strongly adsorbable organic gases are adsorbed from air. With increasing concentration of the organic vapour in air, more and more molecules of this vapour will be adsorbed and fewer molecules of oxygen and nitrogen from the air will be found at the surface of the adsorbent, even though the pressure of the air has not decreased.

It is customary to say that the organic vapour displaces air from the surface of the adsorbent. The mechanism of this displacement is that every second an enormously great number of molecules will leave the surface anyhow, whilst another great number impinges upon it. When molecules arrive, those having a longer time of adsorption (molecules a) stay longer and a greater part of the surface will be covered by them.

When we say that the adsorption of gas a is not influenced by that of gas b, we do not refer to the rate at which the adsorption takes place. In all practical cases the rate is determined, not by the rate of the process of adsorption itself, but by the rate of diffusion. The speed with which the adsorption equilibrium is reached is decreased by the presence of the other gas b.

62. Adsorption from solutions

If p_a is small and p_b is large, so that $p_b \gg p_a$, but if, at the same time $b_a \gg b_b$ and is even so much larger that $p_a \times b_a > p_b \times b_b$, whilst at the same time both $p_a b_a$ and $p_b b_b$ are large with respect to unity, the equations (25) reduce to

$$\left.\begin{aligned}
\theta_a &= \frac{b_a p_a}{b_a p_a + b_b p_b} = 1 - \frac{b_b p_b}{b_a p_a} \\
\theta_b &= \frac{b_b p_b}{b_a p_a + b_b p_b} = \frac{b_b p_b}{b_a p_a}
\end{aligned}\right\} \qquad (26)$$

A relationship like this may apply to relatively dilute solutions of a substance a in a liquid b. Instead of the pressures we have then to use the term concentrations and, of course, the numerical values of the constants b will be different. Hence we can write

$$\theta_a = 1 - \frac{b_b' c_b}{b_a' c_a}, \qquad \theta_b = \frac{b_b' c_b}{b_a' c_a}.$$

At any moment $\theta_a + \theta_b = 1$. Only θ_a or a corresponding entity is, however, estimated in practice. If b_b' is sufficiently smaller than b_a', θ_b will become negligible at relatively low concentrations c_a. In such a case a completely filled unimolecular layer of substance a will already be formed from dilute solutions. This can only happen if not only the heat of adsorption of substance a is very great and hence its adsorption time long, but also the condition must be fulfilled that the heat of adsorption of the solvent molecules b is small and hence their time of adsorption short. We may therefore find

numerous examples of this behaviour when we adsorb strongly adsorbable substances from aqueous solutions at non-polar adsorbents
such as charcoal or from solutions in aliphatic hydrocarbons (pentane, ligroin) at the surfaces of polar adsorbents like aluminium
oxide and silica gel. Also the adsorption of, for instance, fatty acids

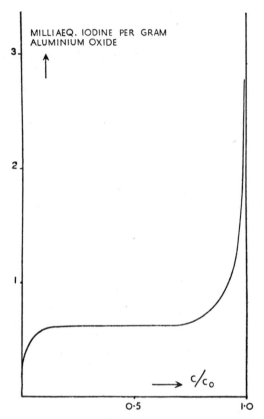

Fig. 12. Multimolecular adsorption from solutions;
iodine on aluminium oxide.

from dilute solutions in hydrocarbons, on metal powders, falls into
this category.

Under most circumstances a second layer of substance a on top
of the first unimolecular one will not easily be formed. The attraction between the molecules of the solvent and the molecules of
the first adsorbed layer of substance a, will be greater than the
attraction between a solute molecule and a similar molecule of the

unimolecular layer. This after all, apart from the influence of entropy, is one of the reasons why the substance is in solution. We may, moreover, expect that the adsorption of a second layer of substance a on top of the first, will be accompanied by a change in entropy which is about the same as with the adsorption of solvent molecules on top of the unimolecular layer of substance a.

We may therefore expect that in reality multimolecular adsorption takes place but it is a layer of solvent molecules rather than of solute molecules which will be found on top of the first unimolecular layer. When speaking of the adsorption of substance a only, therefore, we can say that the phenomenon is restricted to a unimolecular layer.

There are, however, some cases where multimolecular adsorption of the solute molecules may take place from solution. Aluminium oxide adsorbs iodine from its solution in pentane, forming layers of several molecules thickness. The adsorption isotherm has a shape which is comparable to an adsorption isotherm of multimolecular adsorption from the gaseous phase,† as is shown in Fig. 12. The straight part shown with relative concentrations between 0·1 and 0·7 is horizontal; in the case of adsorption from the gaseous phase this part has a more or less steep slope.

† See doctor's thesis of G. M. M. Houben, Delft, 1951.

VI

IDEAL TWO-DIMENSIONAL GASES

63. Movements of the molecules during the time τ

THE dynamic model which we have developed in the previous chapters is largely dominated by the time of adsorption τ. Up till now we have only been concerned with the length of this time and we have shown how many features of the dynamic equilibrium depend on the magnitude of this time of adsorption. We were not concerned with the fate of the molecule during the time which it spent at the surface. Apart from the fact that we have seen that there is complete exchange of thermal energy between the adsorbed molecules at the surface provided the time of adsorption is long enough, we do not know how the molecule behaves during its time of adsorption. We will now look into this matter more closely.

The period of time which an individual molecule spends at the surface comes to an end by the re-evaporation of the molecule. This happens when it picks up so much energy from the fluctuations of the thermal movement that it can overcome the forces which try to keep it at the surface. In the restless movements of the atoms of the surface and of the adsorbed molecule there is a continuous exchange of energy by means of collisions. If, in this continuous game of mutual pushing about, the adsorbed molecule picks up such a momentum that the component of this momentum, perpendicular to the surface, is so great that the corresponding energy is greater than the adsorption energy, the molecule will escape. What, we may now ask, will happen when the molecule receives a momentum in a lateral direction, in a direction along the surface, such that the component perpendicular to the surface is not great enough to warrant an escape. The molecules may then move sideways, maintaining contact with the surface. Instead of evaporating and contributing to the dynamic character of the equilibrium the molecules may therefore be expected also to move over the surface.

64. Spreading and wetting

Moving of the molecules along the surface can be shown experimentally in various ways. There are many phenomena which are caused directly and wholly by this lateral migration or which are indirectly a result of this surface wandering. We shall, in this section, mention a number of well-known phenomena which are caused by this surface movement.

When a drop of a liquid A is placed on the surface of a liquid B, with which it does not mix, we may in many cases observe that A spreads over B; a drop of oil for instance spreads quickly over water. This spreading is caused by the movement of the water molecules along the surface of the water and along the interface between the two liquids. They take with them molecules of the oil adhering to them and even a great number of other oil molecules adhering by cohesion forces to the ones which are in direct contact with the water. As a result a film of considerable thickness, which can be seen by the naked eye, spreads over the free surface. Because so many more molecules are carried along with those which move in the surface, the problem becomes one of a hydrodynamic nature or of the nature of streaming of a liquid. In some instances the layer which is formed in this way, and which is of macroscopical thickness, is a stable one such as in the cases of benzene or hexane on water. In other cases, however, the initial spreading of a macroscopic thick layer is followed by a retraction of the surface of the spread liquid, leaving behind a unimolecular layer of molecules over the water surface. The rest then forms lenses of oil on top of this unimolecular layer. This behaviour is shown by oil molecules which have polar groups at the end of a long hydrocarbon chain as for instance oleic acid.

Whilst the spreading of liquids on a liquid surface proceeds very quickly, the spreading of molecules from solids over a liquid surface goes much more slowly. The rate of spreading of solid fatty acids, for instance, is 100 to 1,000 times as small as the rate of spreading of liquid oils. No thick layers of molecules are carried away in this case. A layer of unimolecular thickness only is formed from the beginning. In order to give an idea of the rate we may mention that at 25° C. myristic acid spreads from a glass rod of 1 mm. diameter over a water surface forming a surface area of 27 cm.² in a minute. This surface is then covered with a complete unimolecular layer of myristic acid molecules. The rate of spreading depends very much on temperature. At 20° C., for instance, it takes three times as long to cover the same area.

The spreading of liquids over solid surfaces causes the so-called wetting of substances by liquids. Here again, we have an example where a macroscopically thick layer of liquid is carried along with the molecules moving along the surface. This wetting is a condition for the rise of water in capillary tubes, and for the so-called suction of liquids into porous substances, such as the taking up of ink by blotting paper, the suction of tea in a lump of sugar, the wetting of a cloth by water. The penetration of liquid water, for instance rain, through a textile fabric, is in the first place caused by the adsorption of water molecules at the surface of the textile fibres and, secondly, by the two-dimensional movement of these adsorbed water molecules which carry with them a film of water, causing the wetting. This film is an essential condition for the penetration of the liquid water into the capillaries between the textile fibres. In order to make such a fabric waterproof it is therefore not necessary to fill all the capillaries up with a substance making the whole impregnable for gas molecules. It is sufficient to prevent the primary cause of these phenomena, the adsorption of the water molecules. If the surface of the textile fibres is covered with molecules which prevent the adsorption of water molecules, or which cause a very poor adsorption of them, the surface migration of the water molecules cannot follow, the fibres are not wetted, the capillaries do not 'suck up' the water, the fabric is not penetrated. Gas molecules, for instance air, will penetrate freely, sometimes even more freely than before the waterproofing. Single water molecules of course will still penetrate, hence water vapour, but not liquid water.

When solutions of a substance A in a liquid B spread over a surface in the above-mentioned way, and the solvent molecules evaporate from the film of liquid which is caused by the spreading, the substance A may stay behind. This phenomenon can be observed when we have a glass half-filled with wine. A mixed film of water and alcohol spreads over the glass surface above the liquid. The alcohol evaporates more quickly from this film, droplets more rich in water contract and stream back into the wine. Another example is the creeping of crystals up the walls of the vessels in which the solution crystallizes. The walls are wetted by the solution, the solvent, for instance water, evaporates and the crystals stay behind. In some instances the crystals can in this way creep over the wall of the vessel and even reach the table on which the vessel stands. In order to prevent this happening, it is again sufficient to prevent the primary adsorption of water molecules on the wall of the vessel. Covering it for instance with a very thin layer of grease prevents this, and so prevents the wetting and hence the creeping.

Because of the dynamic nature of all these phenomena, the higher the temperature, the more quickly they proceed.

65. Surface migration

The two-dimensional migration of molecules along a surface has also been investigated directly by more microscopic methods.† Some 25 years ago Volmer and collaborators developed an admirable experimental technique for studying the phenomenon of the surface migration of molecules. They could, for instance, show that when a crystal of benzophenone was placed on a glass surface single molecules of benzophenone leave the crystal and move over the glass surface. Distances up to nearly 0·1 mm. have been observed.

It could also be shown in a very elegant way that molecules move along the surface of their own crystals. This happens often when crystals are formed in the molten substance. Needle-like crystals, for instance, often protrude for a length of the order of magnitude of 0·1 mm. above the surface. It could also be shown that mercury atoms can move for distances of more than 0·3 mm. over the surface of solid mercury at −63° C. It may look as if these figures are not very great, but when expressed in the mutual distance of atoms in solids as a unit we discover that the above-mentioned moves are of the order of magnitude of 500,000 atomic distances. Translating it into the dimensions of the 'gas of super bees' which we discussed in §§ 12 and 31, it means that the bees moving along the surface, cover a distance of 10 kilometres or roughly 6 miles.

The surface migration can also be shown for those atoms which are bound very firmly to surfaces by chemisorption provided the temperature is high enough. Some 20 years ago Becker showed the surface migration of various atoms on tungsten surfaces by studying electron emission phenomena. Barium atoms, for instance, which do not evaporate noticeably at temperatures below 1,150° K. from a tungsten surface at which they are adsorbed, move over long distances over this surface already at 900° K. Thorium atoms start their surface migration on tungsten surfaces at about 1,655° K.,

† For a good description, see E. K. Rideal, *An Introduction to Surface Chemistry*, Cambridge Univ. Press, 1930.

whilst their evaporation is only noticeable at temperatures higher than 2,300° K. The migration of oxygen atoms, chemisorbed on a platinum surface, could also be demonstrated in a similar way.†

66. The picture of a two-dimensional gas

We will now study the phenomenon of this surface migration more closely. Let us suppose the surface of the adsorbent to have such a nature that the heat of adsorption is exactly the same at any arbitrary point of the surface. It would not matter then where the molecules were bound and it would not require any energy to move them freely from one place to another. In such a case, however, we might expect the surface to be unable to give a lateral push to the adsorbed molecules. We would nevertheless expect surface migration. Every molecule striking the surface in a direction which makes a certain angle with the normal, that is any molecule having a component of its velocity in a direction parallel to the surface, would move over that surface. The surface would not hinder this movement at all and the molecule would migrate in a straight line until it collided with a similar adsorbed molecule. As even at low pressures the number of molecules, σ, which are adsorbed already has an appreciable value if the time of adsorption τ is not too small (§ 33), there would be a great number of such molecules taking part, hence there would be a great number of collisions of these gliding and sliding molecules. Consequently a completely chaotic movement would be created over the surface: a chaotic movement in two dimensions. The picture, therefore, would be that of a two-dimensional gas, molecules moving along the surface in all directions and in straight lines with constant velocity until they collide with similar molecules, then changing their direction and their velocity until they collide again, and so on. There would be an average free path in that two-dimensional movement. Because the two-dimensional density would be rather great, and far greater than the corresponding density of the three-dimensional gas with which the adsorbed layer is in equilibrium, this average free path along the surface would be far smaller than the average free path in the three-dimensional gas.

† See for further details e.g. J. H. de Boer, *Electron Emission and Adsorption Phenomena*, Cambridge Univ. Press, 1935; German translation, Leipzig, Joh. Amb. Barth, 1937.

However, a surface of this kind does not exist. Even if there were no structural influences of the surface, the temperature movement of the atoms of the surface would give fluctuations. There are fluctuations in the location of the atoms in directions along the surface as well as perpendicular to it. These vibrations cause fluctuations of the binding energy. This is the very reason that there is exchange of energy with the adsorbed molecules. Even if an adsorbed molecule were temporarily at rest it would be pushed aside the next moment and it would move along the surface until it either collided with another similar molecule or until it received another push from the surface atoms changing its direction and speed. This picture again is that of a two-dimensional gas. The mean kinetic energy of the chaotically moving molecules is the same as in the case of an energetically ideal smooth surface. This average kinetic energy is given by the temperature only. The average path of the molecule in this two-dimensional gas is shortened by the participation of the surface atoms.

67. The hopping molecule

Apart from the fluctuations caused by the thermal movement one may find structural fluctuations of the adsorption energy on a surface of an adsorbent caused by the structural arrangement of the constituent surface atoms in the surface. These fluctuations are mostly greater and of more importance than those caused by the thermal movement. Owing to the regular pattern of crystalline matter the surface of crystalline adsorbents will show periodical fluctuations. There will be a regular alternation of spots where the adsorption energy is somewhat greater than the average and others where the value is lower. If, for instance, the adsorption is caused by non-polar van der Waals' forces, the magnitude of the heat of adsorption is given mainly by the number of surface atoms which are in direct contact with any atom of the adsorbed molecule. Let us suppose the surface atoms to form a regular square pattern, the surface being the boundary of a crystal with a cubic arrangement of its atoms. Let us suppose an atom to be adsorbed at a point A above the centre of a square of four surface atoms (see Fig. 13 a). The atom is in direct contact with these four atoms. In order to move this adsorbed atom to the next site, A', where it will be bound in exactly the same manner as in the first one, we have to pass a point

B where the adsorbed atom is only in direct contact with two surface atoms. Roughly speaking the heat of adsorption at this intermediate point B is only about half that in the sites just over the squares, A or A'. If we consider a hexagonal pattern (see Fig. 13b), the heat of adsorption in a point B half-way between sites just

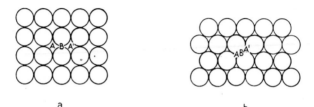

a   b

FIG. 13. Fluctuations of adsorption energy due to the periodical
structure of the surface.

over the centres of triangles of surface atoms A and A' will be about two-thirds. In such cases one may expect that a move from one spot to another will only take place if the adsorbed atom or molecule picks up such an amount of energy from the thermal energy fluctuations that it may overcome the difference between the heat of adsorption at spots A and B. The molecule, therefore, has to assemble an amount of activation energy to enable it to pass over the energy hill ABA'. If we indicate the difference of heat of adsorption at A and at B by ΔQ_a, the probability of acquiring this amount will be proportional to

$$e^{-\Delta Q_a/RT}.$$

We may describe the process in a similar way to that used for the time of adsorption itself, and we shall arrive then at the following picture. The adsorbed molecule at A vibrates with respect to the surface atoms. After an average time, τ', it will pick up an amount of energy ΔQ_a or more. It will then make a hop to another adsorption spot. There it will vibrate again until once more, after an average halting time, τ', it will hop again. The halting time, τ', is related to ΔQ_a and to the temperature, by an equation

$$\tau' = \tau_0' e^{\Delta Q_a/RT}. \tag{27}$$

This equation is very similar to equation (13) for the time of adsorption. The constant τ_0' is again related to the time of oscillation of surface atoms. It will be of the same order of magnitude as the constant τ_0 in equation (13). If the surface atoms were completely isotropic in all their properties it would be exactly the same. A surface atom will, however, because it is bound asymmetrically, be anisotropic. We will nevertheless also take the order of magnitude of 10^{-13} sec. for the constant τ_0'.

ΔQ_a is, as we have seen above, the difference in adsorption energy which has to be taken up as an energy of activation in order to enable the molecule to move. We may expect that ΔQ_a in all practical cases will be smaller than Q_a, the energy of adsorption itself. We saw in the rough considerations above, that ΔQ_a may be of the order of magnitude of half to one-third of Q_a. In cases where the adsorbed molecules are bound by chemical forces, the difference between ΔQ_a and Q_a may be smaller. When the atoms or molecules are adsorbed on metal surfaces, however, ΔQ_a may be a smaller fraction of Q_a. We may also expect that with adsorption of molecules at surfaces of liquids, ΔQ_a may be relatively small with respect to Q_a itself. In any case ΔQ_a will be smaller than Q_a. In many cases it may be smaller than the energy of the thermal movement, RT; the movements of the adsorbed molecules may then be described by the picture of the previous section. In other cases it will be greater than RT. The halting time τ', in this latter case, though greater than the time of oscillation τ_0 (order of magnitude 10^{-13} sec.) will be definitely smaller than τ, the time of adsorption.

To give an example we will assume Q_a to be 10 k.cal./mole and ΔQ_a to be 5 k.cal./mole. The time of adsorption τ at room temperature is then roughly 3×10^{-6} sec. whilst the halting time τ' is roughly 5×10^{-10} sec. This means that during the very short time of adsorption the molecule nevertheless will make an average of 6,000 hops from one spot to another. If every hop is only of the distance of two surface atoms (roughly 3 A) the molecule would cover a distance of roughly 2×10^{-4} cm. $= 2\mu$ in this time. It does not mean, of course, that its total displacement is 2μ, because the directions of the successive hops are arbitrarily distributed so that the displacement of the molecule is far smaller than the total length of all the hops together.

Translated into the language of the gas of super bees (§ 12) the above example means that during the adsorption time of somewhat more than $1\frac{1}{2}$ minutes the super bee is far from at rest, making a hop roughly every one-hundredth of a second vibrating with a

851916   H

frequency of a few hundred thousand times per second all the time. Even in our slow-motion film when we take a whole year for showing the happenings in one second (factor 32 million), one can still not follow the movements of the super bee.

68. The energy of activation for surface migration

There are only a few estimates known of the activation energy ΔQ_a and hardly any in cases of purely physical van der Waals' adsorption. The temperature coefficient of the diffusion of ethane and propane through porous charcoal suggests that the activation energy for surface migration of these gases on the surface of charcoal is about 3 k.cal./mole. This is roughly half as much as the heat of adsorption.

In many cases the energy of activation for surface migration may be negligibly small or sufficiently small with respect to the energy of thermal movement to guarantee an unrestricted movement of the molecules over the surface. In such cases the behaviour of the molecules is comparable with the picture described in § 66, the molecules making sliding rather than hopping movements. The study of the entropy of the adsorbed state may give us valuable information about the degrees of freedom of an adsorbed molecule and we shall discuss in § 82 some of the conclusions which may be drawn from entropy considerations.

There are a few more estimates of the energy of activation for surface migration in cases where the atoms are adsorbed by chemical forces. The activation energy ΔQ_a for caesium atoms on the surface of tungsten is about 14 k.cal./mole, whilst the heat of evaporation Q_a from the same surface is 55 k.cal./mole. Still higher figures are found for thorium atoms on a tungsten surface, namely, 67 k.cal./mole for the heat of activation ΔQ_a and 178 k.cal./mole for the heat of evaporation (heat of adsorption).

69. Equilibrium between a two-dimensional and a three-dimensional gas

However scarce the experimental evidence is, the figures point out that ΔQ_a is essentially smaller than the heat of adsorption Q_a; one can hardly imagine it to be otherwise. Such a statement, however, brings us to a very important conclusion. As long as there is a dynamic equilibrium between adsorbed molecules and a gas

involving numerous molecules adsorbing and desorbing every moment, there must be an equally active movement along the surface.
We cannot expect the molecules to establish a dynamic equilibrium
with the gas, involving a great probability of any individual adsorbed
molecule escaping from the surface without there being an even
greater probability of the same molecule's moving along the surface.

We can *not* expect the molecules to be adsorbed at definite sites
from which they cannot move as long as we expect them to evaporate
after a relatively short time of adsorption τ. We mention at this point
that the lateral migration will be restricted as soon as a two-dimensional condensation takes place. We will discuss this phenomenon
later. When, however, the surface density, and hence the number
of molecules, σ, adsorbed per cm.^{2} is not too great, we are dealing
with singly adsorbed molecules and they behave as a two-dimensional gas. Referring, therefore, to those parts of the adsorption
isotherm which correspond to the lower regions of pressure, we can
make the statement that the beginning of any equilibrium of gas
adsorbed is an equilibrium *between a three-dimensional gas and a two-
dimensional gas.*

70. The two-dimensional gaseous state and the entropy of adsorption

The two-dimensional movement is very important for the occurrence of adsorption phenomena generally. Like any other phenomenon, adsorption can only take place spontaneously if the free enthalpy
of the system decreases. This means that either the heat of adsorption must be positive (heat liberated by the adsorption) or that the
entropy of the system increases (more freedom for the adsorbed
molecules), or both. If a three-dimensional gas is in equilibrium
with a two-dimensional one, the molecules have less freedom in the
latter. Adsorption of molecules from a gas on to a surface therefore
always means a decrease in entropy. (See § 80 where the estimation
of this decrease from experimental data will be discussed.) Adsorption from gases can consequently only take place if the heat of
adsorption is positive. The process of adsorption of gases is essentially exothermic (see also § 143).

When we consider, however, a liquid state (or solid) and we compare the freedom of the molecules in that state with the freedom
they enjoy in a two-dimensional gaseous state on a surface, at which

they are adsorbed, then we see that bringing the molecule from the liquid phase to an adsorbed phase will in most cases mean an increase in entropy. It is possible, therefore, that even in cases where the heat of adsorption is smaller than the heat of evaporation (water on charcoal, iodine on various surfaces, see § 42) adsorption may nevertheless take place at pressures lower than the saturation pressure. It is the higher entropy in the adsorbed state which makes this possible.

When we consider the adsorption of molecules at a surface of solids or liquids from a solution we may expect roughly the same relation as in adsorption from gases. As, however, solute and solvent molecules both compete at the surface of the adsorbent the movements of the molecules there will be restricted. The movements in the solution itself are also more restricted than in the gas. Where, however, the molecules can move in three dimensions when dissolved and in two only when adsorbed, there is every likelihood of the entropy's being lower in the adsorbed state. The entropy of mixing of solvent and solute molecules will work in the same direction. We may expect, therefore, the adsorption at surfaces of solids or liquids from solutions to be governed by the heat of adsorption which in this case is the difference of the energy content per molecule in the adsorbed and in the dissolved states.

If the surface of a solution is not in contact with the surface of a solid but in contact with air or with its own vapour only, we may expect either an increase or a decrease of concentration of the dissolved molecules at the surface. We may expect the freedom of movement, hence the entropy, to be greater at such a 'free' surface. We will see (§ 72) that many examples of two-dimensional gases can be found under those circumstances. If the heat of solution, i.e. the heat liberated when the free molecule is brought into the dissolved state is high, it would need much energy to bring the molecule to the surface where it is surrounded by fewer solvent molecules. In such a case a possible increase in entropy is not great enough to induce the molecules to come to the surface. The surface concentration will then be lower than the concentration in the solution. We have a so-called *negative* adsorption at the free surface of the solution. Solutions of inorganic salts show this behaviour; the solvation energy of ions is large.

If, however, the heat of solution for a single molecule is not great it does involve far less energy to bring the molecule to the surface and the increase of entropy then causes a higher concentration at the surface. These are the cases where a two-dimensional gas of adsorbed molecules forms spontaneously at the surface of the solution.

71. Spontaneous spreading and entropy

The increase of entropy may be the direct cause of the spontaneous spreading of various substances when a crystal of them is brought into contact with a liquid (see § 64). The phenomenon of this spontaneous spreading is directly comparable with the phenomenon of evaporation. A two-dimensional gas of adsorbed molecules 'evaporates' from the spreading crystal over the surface of the liquid. There will be a negative heat of two-dimensional evaporation (spreading) in some cases. Just as in three-dimensional evaporation we have to supply a certain amount of heat in such a case; the phenomenon is endothermic.

The heat of spreading, however, is the difference between the heat of evaporation and the heat of adsorption. We can easily see this if we imagine the molecules to evaporate first from the crystal; this costs us the heat of evaporation. When we now adsorb them from the vapour on to the surface, the heat of adsorption will be liberated. We can also reach the same state of affairs by the direct spreading from the crystal on to the surface. The heat involved in this act is the heat of spreading. If the heat of evaporation is smaller than the heat of adsorption (a state of affairs which, as we have seen already several times, is quite a normal one) then the spreading is accompanied by liberation of heat: the process is exothermic. One might now expect that there would be a complete unlimited spreading in such a case and that perhaps a multimolecular layer of adsorbed molecules would form on the surface. Whether or not multimolecular layers of finite or infinite thickness are formed, depends entirely on the relative magnitudes of p_0 and q in equations (21) and (22).

Those cases where the spreading absorbs heat, i.e. in which the act of spreading is endothermic, are the cases where the heat of adsorption on the surface is smaller than the heat of evaporation or, what is the same thing, the heat of condensation on to the liquid or solid phase. We have already mentioned that we find this behaviour with water on charcoal and with iodine on several inorganic surfaces. The adsorption of mercury on charcoal is also an example which may be mentioned here. The heat of adsorption of mercury atoms at the surface of activated coco-nut charcoal was measured in 1927 by Coolidge;[†] he found a heat of adsorption of 8·9 k.cal./mole. This is an appreciably high figure but nevertheless lower than the heat of evaporation of liquid mercury which is 13·6 k.cal./mole. Subtracting the two we may derive the conclusion that the heat of spreading of the endothermic process of the two-dimensional evaporation of normal liquid mercury to the two-dimensional gas of adsorbed mercury atoms on the charcoal surface is 4·7 k.cal./mole. The amount of adsorbed atoms which is in equilibrium with liquid mercury and consequently also with the saturation pressure of mercury will therefore increase with temperature. Table 4 shows a few figures for this maximal amount σ_{max} in mg. per g. charcoal for a few temperatures, whilst the values of the saturation pressure are also indicated for the same temperatures. The increase of p_0 is quicker than the increase of σ_{max} because the heat of evaporation is greater than the heat of spreading.

TABLE 4

Temp. °C.	p_0 mm. Hg	σ_{max} in mg./g. charcoal
20	0·0013	0·3
100	0·28	2·5
180	9·2	10·0
220	33·7	16·0

A similar relationship is found for the sorption of mercury in chabazite. The heat of adsorption as found by Barrer and Woodhead[‡] is 5·8 k.cal./mole, the heat of spreading, therefore, 7·8 k.cal./mole. The difference between the heat of evaporation and the heat of adsorption is often called the *net heat of adsorption*, an expression which may however lead to confusion. This 'net heat of adsorption' is related to the phenomenon of wetting, which of course depends directly on spontaneous spreading (see § 64).

72. Establishing a two-dimensional gas on the surface of a liquid

We will now study the behaviour of the two-dimensional gases. We want to emphasize, however, at this point that the gas is of

† A. S. Coolidge, *J. Am. Chem. Soc.* **49** (1927), 1949.
‡ R. M. Barrer and M. Woodhead, *Trans. Faraday Soc.* **44** (1948), 1001.

course not strictly two-dimensional. The molecules first have three dimensions themselves. Secondly, as we saw in §§ 66 and 67, the atoms of the adsorbent participate in establishing the lateral movement, which means that the two-dimensional gas molecules are pushed by forces originating in the third dimension. We shall nevertheless see that many important conclusions, which can be verified by experiment, may be derived from the conception of a two-dimensional gas. We imagine, therefore, an energetically smooth surface, we bring on to this surface a great number of adsorbed molecules, and we provide them with the two-dimensional kinetic energy to establish the chaotic movement of the two-dimensional gas. We have mentioned already that the surface of a liquid may be considered to be one of the best approximations to such an ideal surface. Experimentally most of the studies have been done with adsorbed molecules on liquid surfaces.† There are three ways in which such a system can be realized.

First, one may adsorb the molecules from the gas phase on to the liquid surface. Many studies of the adsorption of fatty acids, alcohols, etc., with relatively short hydrocarbon chains have been made on water surfaces, the adsorption of carbon tetrachloride or of water molecules, etc., has been studied on the surface of liquid mercury.

Secondly, we can reach this state from inside the solution. As we mentioned in § 70, the 'free' surface of a solution may show a higher concentration of the molecules which are dissolved in the solvent. These molecules float more or less on the surface of the solution. They are in exactly the same adsorbed state as if they had been brought there from the gas phase. Numerous studies have been made of the surfaces of aqueous solutions of many organic substances. As has been mentioned in the previous section, solutions of inorganic salts which are dissociated into ions, mostly show a so-called 'negative' adsorption. It must be understood that the adsorption is only negative with respect to ions. The concentration of the solvent (water) is of course then higher. It is especially on the salt side of the system, hence with concentrated solutions, that the positive adsorption of water on these very concentrated solutions or rather relatively dilute solutions of water in molten salts can be studied.

† For good surveys see N. K. Adam, *The Physics and Chemistry of Surfaces*, Oxford Univ. Press, 1941, and also the book by E. K. Rideal mentioned in a footnote in § 65.

A third method of reaching this two-dimensional gaseous state is the spontaneous spreading of crystals. This procedure may be applied to substances which are hardly soluble or not soluble at all and which are also hardly volatile.

73. The two-dimensional pressure, F

We may expect a two-dimensional gas to exert a pressure as a three-dimensional gas does. It can very easily be shown that such a property exists if the surface of water on which talcum powder is strewn is touched with a crystal of a spontaneously spreading substance. The talcum powder is pushed aside by the act of spreading and blown away by the two-dimensional gas which evaporates from the crystal. This blowing away of talcum powder is analogous to the blowing away of a cloud of smoke in the three-dimensional space.

As early as 1890 Miss Pockels discovered that a strip of paper, wood, or metal placed on the surface of a rectangular trough, completely filled with water, could serve as a barrier to show this pressure. A layer of spread molecules on the one side of this barrier could be pushed together by it, or its surface could be extended by drawing the barrier aside. This barrier, therefore, is completely analogous to a piston in a cylinder with gas. A normal three-dimensional gas can be compressed by pushing this piston in and it can be expanded by pulling the piston out. A three-dimensional gas exerts a pressure on the piston, or, as a matter of fact on any wall, and we may express the magnitude of this pressure in dynes/cm.^{2} Similarly, the two-dimensional gas will exert a pressure on the barrier and we may express this two-dimensional pressure in dynes/ cm., hence as a force per cm. of length of the barrier. We will denote this two-dimensional force by the letter F. Langmuir and his collaborators in 1917, followed by others (e.g. N. K. Adam), developed the device of Miss Pockels further and constructed ingenious balances[†] with which one can exert a force on the barrier to compensate the pressure F. The two-dimensional pressure, therefore, can be directly measured.

74. F and the 'surface tension'

There is also an indirect way in which this pressure can be estimated. Suppose we have a barrier of length l cm. On the one side

† See the books by E. K. Rideal, footnote, § 65, and N. K. Adam, footnote, § 72.

of the barrier we have a two-dimensional gas exerting a pressure of F dynes/cm. We have balanced this pressure by an external force. Let us now increase the surface of the two-dimensional gas by pushing the barrier aside over a distance dx. A certain amount of work is performed by the two-dimensional gas, the amount being $Fl\,dx$ ergs. In doing this we have taken away a certain area of surface of pure water, namely, the area $l\,dx$ cm.², and we have created the same area of water contaminated with the two-dimensional gas. When creating a new surface one has to work against the cohesion forces. This is the so-called surface energy. When a certain area of surface is taken away, work is done by these forces. The surface energy is caused by the fact that the molecules in the surface are only one-sidedly attracted by the molecules of the liquid. It costs energy to create a new surface because more molecules have to be brought into the surface, which means that they have to be partially freed from the attraction by the other molecules. If foreign molecules are adsorbed at a surface, the one-sided attraction of the surface molecules by those inside is partly compensated. The adsorption of foreign molecules on to the surface of a liquid therefore decreases the surface energy.

If we denote the specific surface energy of pure water by γ_0 and of the contaminated surface (that is the surface with the adsorbed molecules on it) by γ_1, the total work done can be expressed easily. γ_0, expressed in ergs/cm.², is the work which we have to perform when we create 1 cm.² of new clean water surface. In our experiment $l\,dx$ cm.² of clean water surface had disappeared. The amount of work done by the system, therefore, was $\gamma_0 l\,dx$ ergs. Simultaneously $l\,dx$ cm.² of contaminated surface was created. In order to do that we have to perform an amount of work $\gamma_1 l\,dx$ ergs. By doing both these things an amount of work equal to $(\gamma_0 - \gamma_1)l\,dx$ ergs has therefore been done. This amount must be the same as the work which, as we saw above, was done by the two-dimensional gas on the barrier, hence

$$Fl\,dx = (\gamma_0 - \gamma_1)l\,dx$$

or
$$F = \gamma_0 - \gamma_1. \tag{28}$$

The magnitude of F in dynes/cm. therefore equals the magnitude of the difference between the two surface energies.

The surface energy is expressed in ergs/cm.², which are of course the same dimensions as dynes/cm. One often says that the two-dimensional pressure is equal to the difference of the two 'surface tensions'. There is a controversy whether there is a physical reality connected with the conception of surface tension. This question, however, is irrelevant for our purpose. The above-mentioned difference between the two surface tensions γ_0 and γ_1 certainly has a physical significance. It is the two-dimensional pressure of the two-dimensional gas which forms the contamination of the contaminated surface.

75. Gibbs' adsorption equation

The great importance of equation (28) is that it enables us to formulate a relationship between the surface concentration σ (number of adsorbed molecules/cm.²), the two-dimensional pressure F exerted by these molecules, and the concentration of the molecules in the three-dimensional phase which is in equilibrium with this two-dimensional gas. In 1878 Gibbs derived an equation giving such a relationship. The adsorption equation of Gibbs can be derived from purely thermodynamical considerations. As this derivation can be found in many textbooks we will abstain from giving it here.† The equation may be arranged in a form suitable for our purpose as

$$\sigma = -\frac{c}{RT}\left(\frac{\partial\gamma}{\partial c}\right)_\omega \qquad (29)$$

where σ is the number of molecules/cm.², c the concentration of the molecules in the three-dimensional phase, R the gas constant per molecule, T the absolute temperature, and $(\partial\gamma/\partial c)_\omega$ the partial differential quotient of the surface energy with respect to the three-dimensional concentration at a constant value of the surface ω. If we express the surface energy in ergs/cm.², we have to express the molecular gas constant R in ergs/°K. ($R = 1\cdot38\times10^{-16}$ ergs/°K.). It does not matter in what units the three-dimensional concentration c is expressed, as its dimensions appear in numerator and denominator.

Instead of the surface energy we can now introduce the two-dimensional pressure F with the aid of equation (28). The variable in equation (28) is γ_1. A decrease of surface energy means an increase in the two-dimensional pressure F, hence

$$\left(\frac{\partial F}{\partial c}\right)_\omega = -\left(\frac{\partial\gamma}{\partial c}\right)_\omega$$

† See, for example, the book by N. K. Adam, footnote, § 72.

and therefore $$\sigma = \frac{c}{RT}\left(\frac{\partial F}{\partial c}\right)_{\omega}. \tag{29 a}$$

If we are dealing with adsorption from solutions with, for instance, the positive adsorption of molecules on the free surface of a solution, we may conveniently take for c the concentration of the solute molecules in that solution. If, however, the equilibrium of the adsorbed molecules on the surface of a liquid is established from the gas side, it is more convenient to use the pressure p, and we write

$$\sigma = \frac{p}{RT}\left(\frac{\partial F}{\partial p}\right)_{\omega}. \tag{29 b}$$

76. A few examples of a linear relationship F versus p (or c)

As early as 1891 Traube found experimentally that the decrease of surface tension of water in which organic substances were dissolved was directly proportional to the concentration. This statement holds at least in the region of small concentrations.

We can formulate this experimental fact as

$$F = \gamma_0 - \gamma_1 = k'_s c$$

where k'_s is a constant. We will just mention one example. Propyl alcohol in water at 15° C. decreases the surface energy and we find

$$F = \Delta\gamma = 96c,$$

where c is expressed in moles/litre. A solution of 0·01 mole/litre forms, therefore, an adsorbed layer of molecules on its surface and the two-dimensional pressure of these molecules is 0·96 dyne/cm. At greater concentrations there are deviations from this law and the decrease of surface energy is less than that given by a strictly linear formula. The surface energy of water at 15° C. is 73·4 ergs/cm.² This figure is therefore decreased to practically 72·4 ergs/cm.² by the influence of this two-dimensional pressure of roughly 1 dyne/cm. This looks quite an insignificant effect, the two-dimensional pressure being a difference of two surface energies which are far greater in magnitude. In reality, however, a pressure of 1 dyne/cm. is not a small one, as we will see later.

As long as the proportionality between F and c holds, the differential coefficient in equation (29 a) is constant and has the value 96 in this case. Equation (29 a) then gives us immediately the value

$$\sigma = 2 \cdot 4 \times 10^{13} \text{ molecules/cm.}^2$$

for the surface concentration in equilibrium with the concentration in the solution of 0·01 mole/litre. As every molecule of propyl alcohol will occupy an area of roughly 25 A^2, this means that already about 6 per cent. of the surface is covered. We can easily calculate from the concentration in the solution that we would find only $3·3 \times 10^{12}$ molecules/cm.^{2} if there were not a positive adsorption on the surface.

We will mention a similar example for the equilibrium of the adsorbed layer with the gas phase. Cassel and Neugebauer[†] estimated the adsorption of xenon at the surface of mercury by measuring the decrease of surface energy as a function of the pressure of the gas. In Table 5 some of their data are given for 0° C. and for 20° C.

TABLE 5

$T = 273°$			$T = 293°$		
Pressure of xenon, p mm. Hg	$\gamma_0 - \gamma_1 = F$ dynes/cm.	F/p	Pressure of xenon, p mm. Hg	$\gamma_0 - \gamma_1 = F$ dynes/cm.	F/p
69	0·80	$1·16 \times 10^{-2}$	40	0·35	$8·7 \times 10^{-3}$
93	1·10	$1·18 \times 10^{-2}$	91	0·70	$7·7 \times 10^{-3}$
146	1·75	$1·20 \times 10^{-2}$	149	1·20	$8·0 \times 10^{-3}$
227	2·75	$1·21 \times 10^{-2}$	205	1·60	$7·8 \times 10^{-3}$
278	3·35	$1·20 \times 10^{-2}$	280	2·00	$7·2 \times 10^{-3}$
			355	2·80	$7·9 \times 10^{-3}$
		$1·19 \times 10^{-2}$			$7·9 \times 10^{-3}$

Owing to the proportionality of the two-dimensional pressure F and the three-dimensional pressure, p, we may apply equation (29 b) with a constant value for the differential quotient of F with respect to p. At a pressure of xenon of 278 mm. Hg and 0° C. we see that $8·8 \times 10^{13}$ molecules/cm.^{2} are adsorbed on the mercury surface. This means that roughly 17 per cent. of the surface is covered with xenon atoms which even at this rather high surface density behave as an ideal two-dimensional gas (see also §§ 78 and 110).

77. The linear relationship F versus p and the linear part of an adsorption isotherm

The proportionality of the two-dimensional pressure F with either the concentration in the solution or with the pressure in the gas (both at relatively small concentrations or at relatively small pres-

† H. M. Cassel and K. Neugebauer, *J. Phys. Chem.* **40** (1936), 523.

sures) leads to a few important conclusions. If we insert $F = k_s p$ in Gibbs' adsorption equation (29 b) we get

$$\sigma = \frac{p}{RT} k_s.$$

At a constant temperature, therefore, we get

$$\sigma = k_1 p,$$

an equation identical with equation (14 a) although it is not so very easy to see at first glance that the constant k_1 is indeed the same as k_1 in equation (14 a). Similarly we find for the equilibria with solutions

$$\sigma = k'c,$$

which is identical with equation (14 a').

We see therefore that the region of the linear relationship between the two-dimensional pressure and the concentration in the three-dimensional phase is the same as the region where the adsorption isotherm is linear with the pressure or with the concentration. It is the beginning of every adsorption isotherm.

78. The ideal gas law

Another and even more important conclusion may be drawn from the above proportionality between the two-dimensional pressure and the three-dimensional concentration or pressure. The proportionality means that

$$p\left(\frac{\partial F}{\partial p}\right)_\omega = F.$$

Inserting this in equation (29 b) gives us

$$\sigma = \frac{F}{RT}.$$

We divide both sides by Avogadro's number N ($N = 6{\cdot}023 \times 10^{23}$)

$$\frac{\sigma}{N} = \frac{F}{RT},$$

where R is now the molar gas constant ($8{\cdot}31_5 \times 10^7$ ergs/°K.). σ/N in this expression is the number of moles adsorbed per cm.^{2} If we denote the surface area in cm.^{2} occupied by 1 mole by the letter A, we have the relation

$$\frac{\sigma}{N} = \frac{1}{A}.$$

Inserting this in the above equation we obtain

$$\frac{1}{A} = \frac{F}{RT}$$

or
$$FA = RT. \tag{30}$$

This is the expression of the equation of state for an ideal two-dimensional gas, completely comparable with Boyle–Gay Lussac's

$$pV = RT,$$

the equation of state for an ideal three-dimensional gas.

We have arrived here at the very important conclusion that in that region of the three-dimensional pressure or of the three-dimensional concentration where the adsorption isotherm is linear, the behaviour of the adsorbed molecules is that of an ideal two-dimensional gas. Right at the beginning of every adsorption isotherm, therefore, the ideal gas law holds on the surface, the two-dimensional pressure is proportional to the three-dimensional concentration, and the number of molecules which are adsorbed also has the same proportionality.

As soon as the behaviour of the two-dimensional gas starts to deviate from that of an ideal one we observe that this affects the shape of the adsorption isotherm. We shall discuss some of these deviations in Chapter VII.

79. The molar area and the magnitude of the pressure F

Before discussing deviations from the ideal two-dimensional gases, however, it is worth while to calculate the molar surface area A. We want to have more or less an equivalent to the molar volume of 22·4 litres, which is the volume of a mole at 0° C. and 1 atmosphere of pressure ($1·013 \times 10^6$ dynes/cm.²). If we again choose 0° C. and assume arbitrarily a two-dimensional pressure of 1 dyne/cm., we obtain for A

$$A = \frac{RT}{F} = \frac{8·31_5 \times 10^7 \times 273}{1} = 227 \times 10^8 \text{ cm.}^2$$

The molar area is therefore 227 hectares (558 acres).

This area of nearly a square mile (0·885 sq. mile) looks very large and we may wonder whether this is because of a rather low pressure of 1 dyne/cm. which we have chosen. As we have already stated in previous sections, the pressure of 1 dyne/cm. is not a low pressure at all. It is a bit difficult to compare a two-dimensional pressure with a three-dimensional one. Various comparisons have been made in literature. Adam, in his well-known book,† leaves the two-dimensional space when he makes a comparison and he argues that the pressure of 1 dyne/cm. is after all exerted by a layer of molecules of molecular thickness. Imagine that the thickness is 3 A, the pressure of 1 dyne/cm. is then in reality exercised on a surface area of $3 \times 10^{-8} \times 1$ cm.^{2}, corresponding to a three-dimensional pressure of $3 \cdot 34 \times 10^7$ dynes/cm.^{2}, hence about 33 atmospheres.

Rideal, in his well-known work,† follows another argument and derives the conclusion that 1 dyne/cm. is roughly analogous to $47 \cdot 7$ atmospheres.

Kemball and Rideal‡ defining a standard state of the adsorbed layer for use in entropy calculations (see next section) again assign a thickness to this layer. Let us denote this thickness by δ. The two-dimensional pressure, F_s dynes/cm., of this standard state is then exerted on a surface area of δ cm.^{2}, and it corresponds, therefore, with a three-dimensional pressure of F_s/δ dynes/cm.^{2} Kemball and Rideal take arbitrarily $\delta = 6 \times 10^{-8}$ cm. and in order to define the standard two-dimensional pressure corresponding to the three-dimensional pressure of 1 atmosphere ($= 1 \cdot 013 \times 10^6$ dynes/cm.^{2}), they take $F_s/\delta = 1 \cdot 013 \times 10^6$ dynes/cm.^{2}, hence $F_s = 0 \cdot 0608$ dynes/cm. The molar area, A_s at 0° C. (corresponding to the standard volume of $22 \cdot 4$ litres in the three-dimensional state) is then 3,735 hectares ($14 \cdot 6$ sq. miles).

Without leaving the two-dimensional space we can immediately see that 1 dyne/cm. must be a high pressure if we calculate the mean distance of the molecules at that pressure. We have just seen that the molar area at this pressure and 0° C. is 227 hectares. There are $N = 6 \cdot 023 \times 10^{23}$ molecules in that area, which means an area of 377 A^2/molecule, a mean distance therefore of $19 \cdot 4$ A.

If we compare this with the three-dimensional case of 1 atmosphere and 0° C., we derive the conclusion that every molecule occupies an average space of 37,190 A^3 and that the mean distance is $33 \cdot 4$ A. In order to get the same mean distance in a three-dimensional gas, as we have in the two-dimensional gas at a pressure of 1 dyne/cm., we must compress the three-dimensional gas to $5 \cdot 1$ atmospheres.

† See footnote in § 72.
‡ C. Kemball and E. K. Rideal, *Proc. Roy. Soc.* A **187** (1946), 53.

If, therefore, we make a comparison in this way we come to the conclusion that the three-dimensional pressure corresponding to a pressure of F dynes/cm. equals $5 \cdot 1 \times F^{\frac{3}{2}}$ atmospheres.

Instead of the standard state defined by Kemball and Rideal, and without making use of an arbitrarily chosen thickness of the adsorbed layer, we might introduce the standard state of the two-dimensional gas as that state where at $0°$ C. the average distance between the molecules is the same as in the three-dimensional standard state ($0°$ C., 1 atm.). We arrive then at the value $F_s = 0 \cdot 338$ dynes/cm. for the pressure in that state, and we obtain $A_s = 672$ hectares ($2 \cdot 62$ sq. miles) for the molar area.

One can measure two-dimensional pressures up to 50 dynes/cm. experimentally with the barrier balance instruments constructed by Langmuir and others. According to the above considerations this would correspond to measurements in the high pressure region of gases. 50 dynes/cm. would correspond to 1,800 atmospheres. At these high figures of two-dimensional pressures, two-dimensional gases have generally ceased to exist: condensation has taken place and with that condensation a reorientation of the molecules with respect to the surface may have taken place. It is hardly allowable to continue our comparison of two- and three-dimensional pressures when such fundamental changes take place. We will discuss this phenomenon in the next chapter.

80. Evaluation of the entropy of adsorption from experimental data

As stated in § 70 adsorption of molecules from a gas on to a surface is always accompanied by a fall in entropy. The study of the magnitude of this decrease may enable us to draw some very important conclusions about the freedom of movement of the adsorbed molecules. It is largely due to the work of Kemball† that this line of attack has come to the fore. We may start, as Kemball does, by estimating the change in free energy in transferring at constant temperature a molecule from a standard gaseous state to a standard adsorbed state. The choice of the standard states of the gas is such that the pressure is kept constant (1 atmosphere) independent of temperature, whilst also for the adsorbed states the two-dimensional

† C. Kemball and E. K. Rideal, *Proc. Roy. Soc.* A **187** (1946), 53; C. Kemball, ibid. p. 73; A **190** (1947), 117. See also C. Kemball in *Advances in Catalysis*, ii. 233, Academic Press, New York, 1950.

pressure is a constant at any temperature. This constant two-dimensional pressure is—arbitrarily—chosen to be 0·0608 dynes/cm. (see section 79). Starting from the gaseous state and keeping the temperature constant at T_1, we first change the pressure from the standard value ($p_s = 760$ mm. of mercury) to the value p_1 which is in equilibrium with the chosen standard adsorption state keeping the temperature constant at T_1; the change in free enthalpy is given by

$$\Delta G_1 = -RT_1 \ln \frac{p_s}{p_1}. \tag{31}$$

The adsorption of the molecules from the gas at equilibrium pressure p_1 to the standard adsorption state is not accompanied by a change in free enthalpy, as in equilibrium

$$G_{\text{gas}} = G_{\text{ads}}.$$

The whole transfer, therefore, is given by expression (31). The pressure p_1 is obtained from Gibbs' adsorption equation (equation 29 b, § 75)

$$\sigma = \frac{p}{RT} \left(\frac{\partial F}{\partial p} \right)_\omega,$$

hence $$p = \sigma RT \frac{\partial p}{\partial F} = F \frac{\partial p}{\partial F} \quad \text{(see § 78)}.$$

If we insert $F = F_s$, the chosen two-dimensional standard pressure, we obtain p_1, provided we use the value of $\partial p/\partial F$ valid at the temperature T_1

$$p_1 = F_s \left(\frac{\partial p}{\partial F} \right)_{T_1}.$$

Inserting this in equation (31) and putting $p_s = 760$ and $F_s = 0·0608$ we obtain

$$\Delta G_1 = -RT_1 \ln \left(\frac{760}{0·0608} \frac{\partial F}{\partial p} \right);$$

hence $$\Delta G_1 = -RT_1 \ln \left(12{,}500 \frac{\partial F}{\partial p} \right). \tag{31 a}$$

The change in entropy, ΔS, and the change in enthalpy (heat of adsorption), ΔH, may be derived from ΔG by means of the relation

$$\Delta G = \Delta H - T \Delta S. \tag{32}$$

Estimating ΔG at two temperatures T_1 and T_2 we may derive ΔH and ΔS for the mean temperature

$$\frac{T_1 + T_2}{2}$$

from the two equations of the type (32)

$$\Delta G_1 = \Delta H - T_1 \Delta S,$$
$$\Delta G_2 = \Delta H - T_2 \Delta S.$$

We will take as an example the adsorption of xenon on mercury, mentioned in § 76. From the data given in that section we see that at $T_1 = 273 \cdot 1°$ K. we have

$$\frac{\partial F}{\partial p} = \frac{F}{p} = 1 \cdot 19 \times 10^{-2}.$$

Substituting this in equation (31 a) gives

$$\Delta G_1 = -2711 \cdot 4 \text{ cal./mole.}$$

Similarly we obtain at $T_2 = 293 \cdot 1°$ K.

$$\Delta G_2 = -2671 \cdot 7 \text{ cal./mole.}$$

Application of equation (32) gives the following results at $T = 283 \cdot 1°$ K.

$$\Delta H = -3255 \text{ cal./mole,}$$
$$\Delta S = -2 \cdot 0 \text{ cal./mole.degree (entropy units).}$$

The value for ΔH gives the change in heat content in this adsorption process; it must be compared with the heat of adsorption. We will discuss this relationship in the next section. ΔS gives the change in entropy and hence the difference of the entropy of the gas and the adsorbed layer when both are in their standard states.

The entropy of a rare gas, like xenon, at atmospheric pressure, is only given by the translation entropy in three directions as expressed by the equation

$$S_t = R \ln(M^{\frac{3}{2}} T^{\frac{5}{2}}) - 2 \cdot 30 \qquad (33)$$

where M is the molecular weight; the entropy S is expressed in cal./degree.mole (entropy units). Applying equation (33) to xenon at $T = 283 \cdot 1°$, we obtain

$$S_t = 40 \cdot 2 \text{ entropy units.}$$

As in the standard state of adsorption (characterized by $F_s = 0 \cdot 0608$ dynes/cm.) the entropy of the two-dimensional gas xenon, adsorbed on mercury, is only 2 entropy units lower, we arrive at the result that the entropy

$$S_{\text{ads}} = 38 \cdot 2 \text{ entropy units.}$$

If xenon were adsorbed as an ideal two-dimensional gas, having unrestricted freedom of movement in two directions and no freedom of movement in a direction perpendicular to the surface, its entropy would be given by an equation given by Kemball

$$_2S_t = R\ln(MTA_s)+65\cdot80, \tag{34}$$

where A_s is the area available for a molecule in the standard state. As we are dealing with ideal gases (two-dimensionally and three-dimensionally) A_s may be derived from the relation

$$A_s = \frac{RT}{F_s} = \frac{1\cdot38\times10^{-16}T}{0\cdot0608} = 22\cdot70T\times10^{-16} \text{ cm.}^2$$

For xenon at $283\cdot1°$ K., we obtain for the two-dimensional translation entropy in the standard state

$$_2S_t = 2\cdot30\times1\cdot98\log(MT^2\times22\cdot70\times10^{-16})+65\cdot80 = 31\cdot0$$

entropy units.

If we compare this with the experimental figure of $38\cdot2$ entropy units the adsorbed xenon has a higher entropy, viz., $7\cdot2$ entropy units higher. This difference is most probably an entropy of vibration with respect to the surface. We will discuss this problem in § 82.

81. The standard state and the heat of adsorption

We mentioned in the previous section that in defining the standard state for adsorption the constant two-dimensional pressure $F_s = 0\cdot0608$ dynes/cm. was arbitrarily chosen. It was originally derived from an arbitrarily chosen thickness of 6 A for the adsorbed layer (§ 79). The figures obtained for the free energy and also for the change in entropy depend on the choice of the standard state. As the changes in entropy are, however, to be compared with theoretical figures which (equation (34)) also depend on this choice (value for A_s), in the same way, the actual choice is not important. It can, moreover, be proved thermodynamically that the figures of ΔH are independent of this choice.

Nevertheless, it seems more logical to accept as a standard the state already discussed in § 79 which is linked with the three-dimensional standard state by the condition that the average distance of the molecules in both states is the same at $0°$ C.† In adopting this, we derive for the standard pressure $F_s = 0\cdot338$ dynes/cm. (as already mentioned in § 79) and for the standard area, to be used in equation

† J. H. de Boer and S. Kruyer, *Proc. K. ned. Akad. Wet.* B **55** (1952), 451.

(34): $A_s = 4 \cdot 08 T \times 10^{-16}$ cm.^{2} Introducing this value for F_s in equation (31 a) we obtain for ΔG

$$\Delta G = -RT \ln\left(\frac{760}{0 \cdot 338} \frac{\partial F}{\partial p}\right);$$

hence
$$\Delta G = -RT \ln\left(2247 \frac{\partial F}{\partial p}\right). \qquad (31\,b)$$

Applying this equation in the case of the adsorption of xenon on mercury, as we did in the previous section, we obtain, at 273·1° K.

$$\Delta G_1 = -1780 \cdot 3 \text{ cal./mole}$$

and at 293·1° K.

$$\Delta G_2 = -1673 \cdot 3 \text{ cal./mole}.$$

Equation (32) then gives the following data for 283·1° K.:

$$\Delta H = -3255 \text{ cal./mole},$$

$$\Delta S = -5 \cdot 4 \text{ entropy units}.$$

The figure for ΔH is the same as that found with the standard state of adsorption in the previous section. ΔS must be subtracted again from the entropy of xenon at 283·1° K. and one atmosphere, viz. $S_t = 40 \cdot 2$ entropy units and we obtain the result that the entropy of xenon adsorbed on mercury at the standard state as defined in this section is

$$S_{\text{ads}} = 34 \cdot 8 \text{ entropy units}.$$

Applying equation (34) and inserting $A_s = 4 \cdot 08 T \times 10^{-16}$ cm.^{2} gives us for the two-dimensional translation entropy in this state:

$$_2 S_t = 27 \cdot 6 \text{ entropy units}.$$

The experimental figure is again 7·2 entropy units higher than the translation entropy (see § 82).

The figure calculated for ΔH is independent of the choice of the standard state as long as the definition of this state is such that it involves a constant two-dimensional pressure, F_s, independent of temperature. It can be proved thermodynamically† that ΔH derived in this way is numerically equal to the differential heat of adsorption defined in § 39. ΔH is, therefore, smaller than the isosteric heat of adsorption, also defined in § 39, the difference being RT. We may, in order to check this, calculate the isosteric heat of adsorption from the data of the adsorption of xenon on mercury in § 76. Let us make

† J. H. de Boer and S. Kruyer, loc. cit.

the calculation for the case when 10^{13} atoms of xenon are adsorbed per cm.² of mercury. The equilibrium pressures p_1 and p_2 to obtain $\sigma = 10^{13}$ atoms/cm.² at the temperatures T_1 and T_2 is given by Gibbs' adsorption equation (29 b)

$$\sigma = \frac{p}{RT}\left(\frac{\partial F}{\partial p}\right).$$

We obtain, at $T_1 = 273\cdot1°$ K., $p_1 = 31\cdot67$ mm. of mercury and at $T_2 = 293\cdot1°$ K., $p_2 = 51\cdot20$ mm. of mercury. Equation (15) of § 38,

$$\ln p = -\frac{Q}{RT} + B_a,$$

gives us $$\log p = -\frac{3817}{4\cdot57T} + 4\cdot559.$$

The isosteric heat of adsorption, therefore, is 3,817 cal./mole, and so is 562 cal./mole higher than the value of ΔH, calculated in this section and in the previous one. This difference is indeed equal to RT at $T = 283\cdot1°$, viz. 560 cal./mole.

82. The various modes of motion

Xenon, adsorbed on mercury, is very mobile. In addition to un-restricted freedom of movement in two directions along the surface, it shows a vibration with respect to the surface. The entropy of this vibration is, as we saw in § 80 and confirmed in § 81, rather high, viz. 7·2 entropy units. The corresponding frequency, ν, of this vibration may be calculated from the entropy by means of the equation

$$S_{\text{vibr}} = R\left[\frac{h\nu}{kT}\frac{1}{e^{h\nu/kT}-1} - \ln(1-e^{-h\nu/kT})\right] \qquad (35)$$

which, when $h\nu$ is small with respect to kT, may be simplified to

$$S_{\text{vibr}} = R\left(1 - \ln\frac{h\nu}{kT}\right). \qquad (35\,\text{a})$$

R, in these equations, is the molar gas constant, which, in this case, may conveniently be expressed in cal./degree.mole, hence in the same units as S (entropy units) ($R = 1\cdot987$ cal./degree.mole). h stands for Planck's constant, $h = 6\cdot625\times10^{-27}$ erg.sec. and k for the gas constant per molecule, i.e. for R/N, conveniently expressed in ergs/degree ($k = 1\cdot38\times10^{-16}$ ergs/degree). Equation (35 a) with $S_{\text{vibr}} = 7\cdot2$ entropy units and $T = 283\cdot1°$ K. gives

$$\nu = 4\cdot3\times10^{11}/\text{sec.}$$

Such a vibration, superimposed on the gliding movement of the molecules along the surface, results in an undulatory motion, a vibratory flight of the molecules over the surface. The wavelength of this undulatory motion may be calculated from the velocity of the xenon atoms at $10°$ C., $\bar{u} = 2 \cdot 14 \times 10^4$ cm./sec. (equation (5) in Chapter II), to be

$$\lambda = \frac{\bar{u}}{\nu} = \frac{2 \cdot 14 \times 10^4}{4 \cdot 3 \times 10^{11}} = 5 \times 10^{-8} \text{ cm.}$$

and so is a distance somewhat greater than the atomic distances of the adsorbent. Rather than gliding or sliding over the surface, as described in § 66, the xenon atoms dance gracefully over the surface with a relatively low rhythm. The word 'low' must not be misunderstood; the frequency is only low in comparison with the frequencies which we shall encounter with other molecules. In reality the frequency is high, and we may visualize it if we translate it again into the language of the gas of super bees (§ 12) where all dimensions of length and time are 32×10^6 times greater than in the molecular world. The super bee, in this case, moving with a speed of 214 metres/sec. over the surface, dances up and down during this movement, making waves of $1 \cdot 6$ cm. length, 13,400 times per second, giving a very high pitched hum.

This mode of movement is an example of the behaviour of a two-dimensional gas which is only slightly bound to the surface. There is little restriction in the freedom of movement and, though they cannot move freely in a direction perpendicular to the surface, the freedom of the vibratory or rather undulatory movement of the molecules in that direction is great. The entropy of this movement is great, which means that a great number of molecules are in higher vibration levels and so vibrate with great amplitudes. Kemball[†] introduced the name 'supermobile' adsorption for cases like this. There are not many cases known at present; krypton or acetone on mercury may be mentioned and there are, probably, also examples in the adsorption of gases on mica.

In many other cases the loss of entropy on adsorption, found experimentally, is roughly equal to the entropy change which may be expected theoretically, assuming that the translational degree of freedom perpendicular to the surface is completely lost. This does

† C. Kemball in *Advances in Catalysis*, ii. 233, Academic Press, 1950.

not mean that no vibration with respect to the surface exists. It only means that the strength of the adsorption is so great that practically all molecules are compelled to vibrate in the ground level of this vibration. If the frequency ν of this vibration is so high that the energy $h\nu$ is great with respect to the energy of the temperature movement kT, only a few molecules will vibrate in higher levels. This means that the freedom of vibration is negligibly small, hence that its contribution towards entropy is practically zero. Equation (35) shows that at room temperature (25° C.) and for a vibration of frequency

$$\nu = 10^{13}/\text{sec.}, \qquad S = 1{\cdot}25 \text{ e.u.},$$

$$\nu = 5 \times 10^{13}/\text{sec.}, \qquad S = 0{\cdot}011 \text{ e.u.},$$

$$\nu = 10^{14}/\text{sec.}, \qquad S = 0 \text{ e.u.}$$

Kemball mentions many cases where the entropy of the two-dimensional adsorbed gas, calculated from experimental data in the way described in previous sections, equals roughly the theoretical value for a two-dimensional gas with two degrees of unrestricted translational freedom. We may mention carbon monoxide or nitrogen on silver at low temperatures (90° K.), argon, oxygen, and nitrogen on potassium chloride at about 80° K., carbon tetrachloride on silica gel or ferric oxide at room temperature, ethane or propane on chabazite at about 150° to 160° C. Many gases, like CO, CH_4, C_2H_6, C_3H_8, C_4H_{10}, C_2H_4, C_2H_2, etc., adsorbed on active charcoal at temperatures between 50° and 150° C. also behave in this manner.[†] In all these cases we have to do with two-dimensional gases behaving according to the picture of the gliding and sliding molecules of § 66. If, to mention an example, the velocity of these molecules along the surface is about 5×10^4 cm./sec. and the frequency of their undulatory motion is 5×10^{13}/sec., the corresponding wavelength will be 10^{-9} cm., which means that during their motion over the surface they make fifteen to thirty vibrations for every atomic distance of the surface which they cover.

If the strength of the adsorption is still greater the movements of the molecules will become more restricted. They will then linger at spots of higher potential as given by the periodic structure of the surface (§ 67) and pass more quickly over intermediate spots. Simul-

† J. H. de Boer and S. Kruyer, *Proc. K. ned. Akad. Wet.* B **56** (1953), 415; B **57** (1954), 92.

taneously any rotary motion they have may be restricted. Kemball, studying the adsorption of benzene on mercury, concludes that the benzene molecules lose all rotation except that in the plane of the ring and also lose the translational freedom perpendicular to the surface. The picture of this adsorption, therefore, is that the benzene molecules are adsorbed in a flat position on the surface, the rings rotating about an axis perpendicular to the surface, whilst they move rather freely over the surface, this motion, of course, being accompanied by a vibration of high frequency, probably of a frequency of about 10^{13} to 10^{14} per sec.

The majority of substances, bound on surfaces by physical adsorption (§ 27), belong to this class, showing restricted translational and rotational freedom of movement.

If the strength of the adsorption is still higher, and the interaction energy sufficiently great with respect to the kinetic energy of the temperature movement, the time of lingering at the periodic spots of higher potential will be such that the molecule comes virtually to a standstill apart from its vibrations. After an average but well defined short time of lingering it jumps to a neighbouring spot, etc.; we get the picture of the hopping molecule of § 67. Far from being at rest over a sufficiently long time interval, the molecule seems to be at rest—or perhaps it is better to describe it as localized— over very short intervals of time. The entropy of the adsorbed molecules may, therefore, be low, showing no freedom of motion at all. This is why Kemball describes this state as immobile or localized adsorption. The term immobile, however, may be somewhat misleading, the hopping motion of the molecules still makes them behave as a two-dimensional gas, exercising a two-dimensional pressure F and obeying, if dilute enough, the two-dimensional ideal gas law. The entropy of such an assembly of molecules is given by the number of ways they may be distributed over a given number of adsorption sites, irrespective of their hopping motion, viz.

$$S = R\ln\left(\frac{1-\theta}{\theta}\right).$$

The adsorption of water molecules on charcoal may serve as an example of such a localized adsorption;† the entropy is still high

† J. H. de Boer and S. Kruyer, loc. cit.

enough to cause this adsorption to take place, although the transfer of a water molecule from liquid water to the surface of charcoal is not an exothermic process (see § 42).

83. The nature of the constant τ_0

Whenever we are dealing with an equilibrium between a gas and an adsorbed layer, and so whenever there is a vivid dynamical exchange of molecules between the gas and the adsorbate, there is an even more active motion along the surface (§ 69). In Chapter III, when we were discussing the time of adsorption, τ, we did not examine what the molecule was going to do during this time. We introduced an equation (13) for τ, namely,

$$\tau = \tau_0 \, e^{Q/RT},$$

and we defined τ_0 as the time of oscillation of the molecules in the adsorbed state, referring especially to vibrations perpendicular to the surface, which is valid for the picture which Frenkel originally had in mind. In Frenkel's concept, the molecules were bound only loosely in the adsorbed state, and from all their movements they had only partly lost one freedom of translation. Instead of moving freely in three directions, as they do in the gaseous state, they now move in two directions along the surface as a two-dimensional gas, whilst the movement in the third direction, perpendicular to the surface, has been reduced to an excited vibration perpendicular to the surface. In this case of adsorption, where the molecules are bound to the surface only rather weakly, τ_0 is indeed the time of oscillation perpendicular to the surface. This case is identical to the so-called super-mobile adsorption of Kemball (§ 82).

This super-mobile adsorption, however, is only one of the possible ways in which the molecules can be bound to the surface. In most of the cases with which we are concerned in this book, the molecules are bound more strongly to the surface. The vibration frequency of the molecule perpendicular to the adsorbing surface is then of the order of 10^{13} per sec. or higher, and does not contribute significantly towards the entropy.

As already stated in § 29, in this case τ_0 equals h/kT; hence, the molecules are still free to move unhindered in two directions along the surface, while still retaining all their degrees of freedom of rotation and of internal vibration. In § 143 a more complete description, based on statistical mechanics, will be given of the calculation of τ_0 for different cases of adsorption. There we shall show that a more detailed study of the connexion between τ_0 and the loss of entropy by the act of adsorption indicates that much lower values for τ_0 than 10^{-13} sec. may be found when the molecule is further restricted in its freedom of translation, rotation, or internal vibration. The less freedom of movement the molecules have, the smaller the corresponding value of τ_0 is. This is often accompanied by an increase in the value of the heat of adsorption Q. The experimental figures for τ_0 may be derived from measurements at various temperatures and application of equation (14) of § 35. A caution may be given, however, that Q in this equation is neither the differential nor the isosteric heat of adsorption whilst also Q, in many cases, may be dependent on temperature.

We may end this chapter with the remark that all the variations in modes of motion which we studied are caused by the interaction of the adsorbed atoms with the atoms of the adsorbent, not by mutual interaction between adsorbed molecules. We have, in all the cases described, to consider the adsorbed two-dimensional gas as an ideal gas, giving a linear relationship between F and p (see §§ 76 and 78). In the example of xenon on mercury which we used in §§ 80, 81, and 82 such a linear relationship exists over the whole range of pressures which is examined experimentally. In many other examples mentioned in § 82 this linear relationship holds only for regions of low pressures and small amounts of adsorbed molecules. The mutual interaction of adsorbed molecules leads to deviation from the ideal gas law for the two-dimensional gas. This will be considered in the next chapter.

NON-IDEAL TWO-DIMENSIONAL GASES:
TWO-DIMENSIONAL CONDENSATION

84. A two-dimensional pressure F corresponding to the Langmuir adsorption isotherm

THE linearity between the two-dimensional pressure and the concentration, mentioned in §§ 76, 77, and 78, will only hold for small concentrations. From a certain concentration onwards, depending on the substance which is dissolved, deviations set in.[†] von Szyszkowski found in 1908 that a decrease of surface energy with many solutions could be represented over large regions of concentrations, by an empirical equation

$$\Delta \gamma = F = a \ln \frac{b+c}{b},$$

where a and b are empirical constants. If we differentiate F with respect to the concentration c, we get, for the differential coefficient in Gibbs' adsorption equation, the expression

$$\frac{dF}{dc} = \frac{a}{b+c}.$$

Introducing this in equation (29 a) we obtain

$$\sigma = \frac{c}{RT} \frac{a}{b+c}.$$

If we call $\qquad \dfrac{a}{RT} = \sigma_0 \quad \text{and} \quad \dfrac{1}{b} = k'_u$

and rearrange the terms, we obtain

$$\frac{\sigma}{\sigma_0} = \theta = \frac{k'_u c}{1+k'_u c} \tag{18 a}$$

an equation very similar to equation (18) but for the fact that here it is written for concentrations instead of for pressures. von Szyszkowski's empirical relationship leads therefore to an adsorption equation of the same form as that of Langmuir.

---

† Apart from the books of Adam and of Rideal, mentioned in §§ 65 and 72, a good survey may be found in H. Freundlich, *Kapillarchemie*, Ak. Verl. Ges., Leipzig, 1930.

85. Introducing the 'surface area correction' b_2

A linear relationship between F and c corresponds to a linear adsorption isotherm and to the ideal gas law for the two-dimensional gas (§§ 77 and 78). The empirical relationship between F and c found by von Szyszkowski corresponds to the Langmuir adsorption isotherm. The question arises what correction this will involve for the gas law of the two-dimensional gas, in other words, which equation of state will hold for the two-dimensional gas.

The Langmuir adsorption isotherm is derived by introducing the condition that the molecules can only be adsorbed on those spaces of the surface which are not yet occupied. The underlying idea is therefore that every molecule occupies a certain space. This space, in the conception leading to the Langmuir isotherm, is predetermined by the structure of the surface; it is assumed that adsorption occurs at definite adsorption sites (§§ 43, 61, and 67).

Starting from the conception of a two-dimensional gas one might expect a correction term for the space occupied by the adsorbed molecules determined by the dimensions of the molecules themselves. It is therefore logical to try to introduce a molecular area into equation (30) as a correction term, similar to the volume correction b, in the well-known van der Waals equation of state. Attempts have been made to derive the Langmuir equation from that conception. Attractive forces between the molecules which were not introduced by Langmuir, are, therefore, not introduced in the two-dimensional equation of state in such an attempt.

We start, therefore, from an equation of state, given by Volmer†

$$F(A - b_2) = RT \tag{36}$$

where b_2 is the two-dimensional correction term analogous to the three-dimensional b in the van der Waals equation.

86. A wrong way to derive the Langmuir equation

If the two-dimensional pressure F were still proportional to the three-dimensional pressure, hence (i.e. $F = k_s p$), the Langmuir adsorption isotherm would immediately follow from this relationship. We could write

$$k_s p = \frac{RT}{A - b_2}.$$

† M. Volmer, *Z. physikal. Chem.* **115** (1925), 253.

Introducing
$$\frac{1}{A} = \frac{\sigma}{N}$$

as we did in § 78 and similarly

$$\frac{1}{b_2} = \frac{\sigma_0}{N},$$

expressing in this way that the maximum number of molecules in a molecular layer is determined by the surface area which each molecule occupies, we obtain

$$p = \frac{RT\sigma\sigma_0}{k_s N(\sigma_0 - \sigma)}$$

or
$$p = \frac{RT\sigma_0}{k_s N} \frac{\theta}{1-\theta}.$$

This is one of the forms in which the Langmuir adsorption equation can be expressed. We can immediately see that if we solve the pressure p from equation (18); we then get

$$p = \frac{1}{k_u} \frac{\theta}{1-\theta}. \tag{18b}$$

The difficulty, however, in using the proportionality between F and p is that we completely ignore Gibbs' adsorption equation. If this proportionality is introduced in Gibbs' adsorption equation we automatically get the two-dimensional ideal gas law, equation (30), while we had just started from a correction on that. We also know experimentally that the proportionality does not exist in the region of concentrations or pressures which we are considering here. We have nevertheless given this argument because attempts similar to this can be found in the literature; we will show one of them later (§ 111).

87. Relations between the Langmuir equation and Volmer's equation of state

It is therefore better to apply Gibbs' adsorption equation to equation (36) as Volmer did. To do this we write equation (29 b) in the following form

$$\frac{\sigma}{N} = \frac{1}{A} = \frac{p}{RT} \frac{dF}{dp} = \frac{p}{RT} \frac{dF}{dA} \frac{dA}{dp},$$

where R is now the molar gas constant. The differential coefficient dF/dA can be obtained by differentiating equation (36). It is

$$\frac{dF}{dA} = -\frac{RT}{(A-b_2)^2}.$$

Introducing this in the above form of Gibbs' adsorption equation, we obtain

$$\frac{1}{A} = -\frac{p}{RT}\frac{RT}{(A-b_2)^2}\frac{dA}{dp}$$

or

$$\frac{dp}{p} = -\frac{A}{(A-b_2)^2}\,dA.$$

Before integrating this equation Volmer† assumes $b_2^2 \ll 2Ab_2$, which is reasonable for rather dilute two-dimensional gases where A is still great. We obtain

$$\frac{dp}{p} = -\frac{dA}{A-2b_2}$$

or

$$\ln p = -\ln(A-2b_2)+\text{constant.}$$

Introducing
$$A = \frac{N}{\sigma} \quad \text{and} \quad 2b_2 = \frac{N}{\sigma_0},$$

arranging terms and eliminating the logarithms, we obtain

$$p = k\frac{\theta}{1-\theta}$$

which is the form (18 b) of the Langmuir equation.

If we do not introduce Volmer's simplification however, but if we integrate the original form

$$\frac{dp}{p} = -\frac{A}{(A-b_2)^2}\,dA,$$

we obtain

$$\ln p = -\left\{\ln(A-b_2)-\frac{b_2}{A-b_2}\right\}+\text{constant.}$$

If we now introduce

$$A = \frac{N}{\sigma} \quad \text{and} \quad b_2 = \frac{N}{\sigma_0}\ \text{instead of}\ 2b_2 = \frac{N}{\sigma_0},$$

re-arrange terms and eliminate the logarithms, we obtain

$$p = k_b''\frac{\sigma\sigma_0}{\sigma_0-\sigma}\,e^{\sigma/(\sigma_0-\sigma)}$$

or

$$p = k_b'\frac{\theta}{1-\theta}\,e^{\theta/(1-\theta)}. \tag{37}$$

† M. Volmer, loc. cit.

This equation must be compared with the Langmuir equation, preferably when written in the form (18 b). In a graph representing σ or θ as a function of the pressure p, equation (37) shows a stronger saturation character than the Langmuir equation proper as is shown

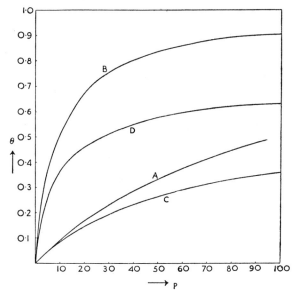

FIG. 14. Comparison between the Langmuir adsorption isotherm and the isotherm of equation (37).

in Fig. 14. Curves A and B in this figure represent the Langmuir curves

$$p = k\frac{\theta}{1-\theta}$$

with $k = 100$ and $k = 10$ respectively. C and D are curves according to equation (37) with the same values for the constant k'_b.

Equation (37) has been derived on the assumption that no forces are present which make the molecules attract each other mutually. It would appear that under the practical circumstances where the Langmuir equation is obeyed some influence is already noticeable from attraction forces, compensating the influence of the e power in equation (37). We come back to this problem in § 113.

88. Mutual attraction forces

In discussing two-dimensional gases we have so far completely ignored the mutual attraction forces between the molecules in the adsorbed layer.

The best way to discuss the influence of these mutual forces will be via the equation of state of the two-dimensional gas. It is the deviation from the ideal gas law in the two-dimensional gas which will provide us with the first knowledge of these forces. Like a three-dimensional gas, a two-dimensional gas may only be considered to obey the ideal gas law if we may consider the molecules to behave as bodies without a volume or a surface and without influencing each other. This conception may hold as long as the molecules are far enough apart, which means for two-dimensional gases at low surface concentrations. We have already learned in the previous chapter, however, that surface concentrations in practical cases are such that the two-dimensional gases with which we are dealing may be considered to be in a more highly compressed state. Therefore in the study of two-dimensional gases, we are really far more concerned about the deviations of the ideal gas laws than in many studies of three-dimensional gases.

If the deviations of the ideal gas law were still small, one might try to describe them in the same way as in the case of three-dimensional gases by putting

$$\frac{FA}{RT} = 1 + \frac{B}{A}$$

where B might be compared with the second virial coefficient for gases. This coefficient depends on the mutual potential of the molecules when they are in each other's neighbourhood and it is therefore dependent on the mutual attraction forces as well as on the repulsion forces. At a given distance these forces balance each other, thus determining the dimensions of the molecule, which they assume in their mutual influencing of each other, hence the volume of the molecules in the three-dimensional gas and their surface in the two-dimensional gas. It is, however, customary to introduce separate correction coefficients for the attraction forces on the one hand and for the dimensions of the molecules on the other hand. In the previous sections we have already introduced a correction term b_2 for the surface area occupied by the molecules. In the following sections a correction for the mutual attraction will be introduced.

89. FA versus F diagrams

The deviations of the ideal gas law may conveniently be studied in a way which is very similar to the method which is in use with three-dimensional gases. The product FA is plotted against F. FA

is equal to RT when the ideal gas law holds, and so is a constant given by the temperature only when there are no deviations. Studies of this kind have been made by several investigators, notably by Adam and collaborators† and by Rideal and collaborators.† In previous sections we have introduced A as the molar area and we obtained large areas (§ 79). For the following sections it is more

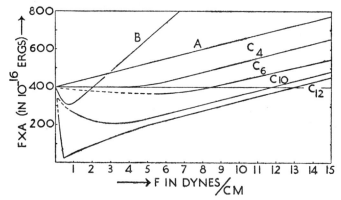

Fɪɢ. 15. Diagram of FA against F.

convenient to take A to be the *molecular* area. We have to divide both sides of equation (30) by N, Avogadro's number, which means that we take R as the molecular gas constant again ($R = 1 \cdot 38 \times 10^{-16}$ ergs/degree). If we then express A the area per molecule in cm.² and F in dynes/cm., we obtain the product in ergs.

In Fig. 15 we have plotted FA (in 10^{-16} ergs) against F in dynes/ cm. The horizontal line drawn at $FA = 400 \times 10^{-16}$ ergs is the constant line for RT at a temperature of 17° C. ($T = 290°$ K.).

If the dimensions of the molecules are not negligible we may try to introduce the correction discussed already in a previous section (§ 85), namely, the correction comparable with the volume correction of the constant b of the van der Waals equation. If we assume the molecules to have, for instance, such a size that each of them occupies 25 A², when the unimolecular layer is closely packed, we can introduce this correction by putting

$$b_2 = 25 \times 10^{-16} \text{ cm.}^2$$

in the equation $\qquad F \times (A - b_2) = RT.$

Curve A in Fig. 15 is the curve representing this equation for the

† See the books mentioned in §§ 65 and 72.

K

temperature $T = 290°$ K. We may write the equation in the form $FA = RT + Fb_2$, and from this we see that the correction b_2 always gives an increase of the product FA, the slope of the line gives the correction b_2, and hence the 'real surface' of the molecules.

Curves of this character are not very frequently found experimentally. The behaviour of butyric acid in the interface between water and benzene obeys curve A in Fig. 15. Curves of the same character are also found for the behaviour of cane sugar in the interface between water and mercury and for pyridine in the same interface.

Mostly, however, one finds curves that start at the right value of FA, show a decreasing value of FA with increasing value of F, then pass through a minimum, whereupon a more or less steep increase follows. In many cases the curves are straight lines for the higher pressures. Curve B in Fig. 15 for instance shows the behaviour of the ethyl ester of a two-basic acid $C_2H_5OOC.(CH_2)_{10}.COOC_2H_5$ as studied by Adam. The molecules of this ester, when spread on water, behave completely as a gas, but as a gas in a highly compressed state. The slope of the right part of the curve suggests a surface area of 85 A^2 for each molecule. Curves C_4, C_6, C_{10}, and C_{12} are curves for mono-basic fatty acids, having the number of carbon atoms which are indicated, spread on water. These acids, adsorbed on the free surface of their solutions, have been studied by Rideal and collaborators. An acid like caproic acid, for instance (curve C_6), is completely gaseous in its behaviour on the water surface and so is capric acid (C_{10}). The deviations from the ideal gas law in both cases are of course great. A curve like that drawn for C_{12} shows a sharp decrease and a discontinuity. Such a behaviour indicates that the two-dimensional state not only deviates from the ideal gases but that a two-dimensional condensation has set in. We will discuss this two-dimensional condensation later in this chapter. The fatty acids up to say C_{10}, however, do not show such a discontinuity; they do not show the phenomenon of two-dimensional condensation. They behave as a gas up to the highest pressures. Caproic acid, for instance, has been investigated at pressures up to 40 dynes/cm. The area A which is available for each molecule at that pressure is only 28·6 A^2. They are rather closely packed and we see that this gaseous state is indeed highly compressed. The whole behaviour of all these acids, and many more substances which behave similarly, resembles that of three-dimensional gases compressed to very high pressures *above* their critical temperatures. We will return to this important phenomenon later.

It is a remarkable fact that all the curves of the fatty acids tend to have the same slope at higher temperatures, hence they all show the same molecular area correction b_2, namely, roughly 25 A^2. The explanation of this is that in the highly compressed two-dimensional state, all the molecules with their carboxyl group in the water surface, have erected each other into parallel positions pointing away from the surface. In this highly oriented state it is therefore the surface area of the carboxyl group which roughly determines the constant b_2.

As already stated at the beginning of this section, butyric acid (C_4) shows the same correction constant b_2 when spread in the interface between water and benzene. Also in this interface the molecules are highly oriented. It is a remarkable fact that in this interface the horizontal part which is shown by curve C_4 is not present, but that curve A represents the behaviour here. It looks as if the correction for the size of the molecule is sufficient to describe their behaviour in such an interface.

90. Schofield and Rideal's equation

The decrease of the product FA in the region of lower pressures indicates strongly that it is not the correction b_2, the correction for the size of the molecules, which is the most important one. The decrease is caused by the mutual attraction of the molecules. The deeper the dip the stronger the lateral attraction between the molecules.

The straight parts of the curves at higher pressures also reflect this. They are the lower the stronger the attraction is. The straight parts of some of the curves shown in Fig. 15 may be represented by

C_4-acid (*n*-butyric acid): $FA = 24 \cdot 3F + 0 \cdot 73RT$

C_6-acid (*n*-caproic acid): $FA = 24 \cdot 3F + 0 \cdot 43RT$

C_{10}-acid (*n*-capric acid): $FA = 24 \cdot 3F + 0 \cdot 3RT.$

In 1925 Schofield and Rideal introduced an empirical equation, viz.
$$F(A - b_2) = iRT,$$
where b_2 is, as above, the surface area occupied by each molecule

when the layer is closely packed, compressed together by an infinitely high pressure F, and i is a measure for the attraction forces. The smaller i is, the stronger the mutual attraction between the molecules becomes. In the cases of n-butyric acid in the interface between water and benzene $i = 1$: it is as if no attraction forces can make themselves felt there. The curve has been determined up to 25 dynes/cm. in this case, the value of A being about 41 A². The molecules are certainly not far apart. We shall see in §§ 92 and 107 that there are particular reasons for the attraction forces being small in cases like this.

91. The two-dimensional van der Waals equation

.It seems logical to try and describe the deviations from the two-dimensional ideal gas law by a two-dimensional analogue of the van der Waals equation. Instead of the three-dimensional form

$$\left(p+\frac{a}{V^2}\right)(V-b) = RT$$

we, therefore, write

$$\left(F+\frac{a_2}{A^2}\right)(A-b_2) = RT, \tag{38}$$

where a_2 and b_2 are the two-dimensional analogues of the van der Waals a and b respectively. We will discuss their significance and magnitude later.

We may write equation (38) in the form

$$FA = RT+Fb_2-\frac{a_2}{A}+\frac{a_2 b_2}{A^2}$$

or

$$FA = RT+Fb_2-\frac{a_2}{A}\left(1-\frac{b_2}{A}\right).$$

The effect of the last term is to decrease FA, even over-compensating the increase by Fb_2 at relatively small values of F. When F increases and, consequently, A decreases, Fb_2 grows and

$$\frac{a_2}{A}\left(1-\frac{b_2}{A}\right)$$

decreases. The result is that the FA versus A curve passes through a minimum and rises again.

92. The correction term a_2

The van der Waals attraction forces which are responsible for the correction term a may be ascribed to three causes. There is first the non-polar part (London attraction; dispersion forces) caused by the mutual polarization by the alternating dipoles which are present at any moment, because of the movement of the electrons in the atoms. This first cause is the general one, always present, even in non-polar spherical atoms, such as those of the rare gases. There is, secondly, a polarization effect when permanent dipoles are present in the molecules. The dipole of one molecule induces a dipole in another molecule—and vice versa. Dipole and induced dipole attract each other. The same holds for any permanent electrical asymmetry in the molecules (Debye effect). There is, thirdly, a mutual influence by permanent dipoles in molecules possessing this asymmetry. Permanent dipoles either attract or repel each other, depending on their mutual orientation. In three-dimensional gases the molecules rotate; this rotation is influenced by the dipole-forces and results in a general mutual attraction (Keesom effect).

In two-dimensional gases the first effect (London effect) works qualitatively in the same way as in the three-dimensional case, it always gives an attraction. So does the second effect (Debye effect). The third cause, however, may lead to mutual repulsion in the case of two-dimensional gases. If dipole-containing molecules are adsorbed in such a way that their dipoles are oriented with respect to the surface, two such molecules may find each other in such positions that their dipoles are parallel orientated. Those dipoles will then repel each other. This repulsion may be of appreciable magnitude, comparable with, or even greater than, the attraction caused by the other effects.

It is especially in those cases when molecules with peripheral dipoles are bound to polar or metallic surfaces that such mutual repulsion forces may be expected to be of dominant importance, but the effect may also be noticeable in many other cases. Magnus applied a two-dimensional van der Waals equation in 1929 to the adsorption phenomena of many gases. He considered a mutual dipole repulsion only, and so did not introduce attraction forces at all. This is certainly too much of a simplification; moreover, the equation derived by Magnus is not correct. We will come back to this in § 111.

If we separate a mutual dipole-repulsion from the other effects which cause a mutual attraction, we may introduce a third correction constant (a_2') in conjunction with the constant a_2 representing the van der Waals attraction forces

$$\left(F+\frac{a_2-a_2'}{A^2}\right)(A-b_2) = RT \tag{39}$$

or
$$FA = RT+Fb_2-\left(\frac{a_2-a_2'}{A}\right)\left(1-\frac{b_2}{A}\right).$$

The behaviour of the lower representatives of the aliphatic mono-basic fatty acids is as if the last terms of this equation compensate each other practically completely when the molecules are spread on water. As is shown in Fig. 15 the curve for n-butyric acid is horizontal up to a pressure of about $F = 4$ dynes/cm. All fatty acids up to n-valeric acid (5 C atoms) behave in this way. Even up to relatively high pressures they behave as ideal gases. The parallel orientated dipoles of the COOH-groups may well diminish the mutual attraction forces from the hydrocarbon-chains to such an extent that the total attraction forces balance the influence of the correction term b_2. In the interface between water and benzene the normal attraction, moreover, is so weakened that nothing compensates b_2 and the behaviour is represented by curve A of Fig. 15. When the hydrocarbon chains are longer than those in the n-valeric acid molecules, their mutual attraction becomes dominant and a dip is seen in the curves, and the longer the hydrocarbon chain is, the deeper it becomes.

In many instances we may expect the adsorbent to polarize adsorbed atoms or molecules, providing them with dipoles which may be all at the same position to the surface, and parallel to each other. In such cases molecules not possessing dipoles of their own may nevertheless suffer a decrease of a_2. We shall see later that adsorption of gases on mercury or on charcoal point to the existence of such an effect (§ 110).

93. Two-dimensional condensation phenomena

If the attractive forces between the molecules are large enough we must not only expect serious deviations from the ideal gas law, but from certain surface concentrations onward we may expect condensation phenomena to set in. Two-dimensional condensation phenomena are well-known and have been studied extensively for molecules spread on a water surface. Again, the adsorption can be brought about by molecules hitting the surface from a gas phase: they can come from within the solution, or they may have been brought on to the surface of the water by means of the spontaneous spreading of an insoluble and not volatile crystal. The pressure-area relations have been studied, either by measuring the pressure directly, for instance with the aid of the barrier balance, or by studying a change in surface energy.

The two-dimensional equation of van der Waals (equation (38)) will, for certain values of the correction terms a_2 and b_2, lead to a curve with a maximum and a minimum. Just as in the three-dimensional van der Waals equation, three values of the area A will then correspond to the same pressure F. The middle one represents a labile situation, the other two are stable. In Fig. 16 we have calculated a few curves giving F as a function of A using equation (38). In all the curves in this figure we have chosen $b_2 = 25$ A^2. F is expressed in dynes/cm., A in A^2, hence 10^{-16} cm.^{2}, for R we take the gas constant per molecule: $R = 1{\cdot}38 \times 10^{-16}$ ergs/ °K., whilst we have chosen $T = 290°$ K., hence $RT = 400 \times 10^{-16}$ ergs. It is only the correction term a_2 which we have varied for the various curves of Fig. 16.

In curve A we have chosen

$$a_2 = 10{,}000 \times 10^{-32} \text{ ergs.cm.}^2$$

This curve is identical with that of an ideal gas for all practical purposes, at least up to a pressure of 3 dynes/cm. The influence of the correction terms a_2 and b_2 compensate each other, as can also be seen from Fig. 17, where the product FA is plotted as a function of F. Curve A, in this figure, corresponding to curve A in Fig. 16 is very similar to that which is found in practice for butyric acid or valeric acid on the surface of their solutions (see Fig. 15).

For curve B we have chosen

$$a_2 = 20{,}000 \times 10^{-32} \text{ ergs.cm.}^2$$

It represents the case of a two-dimensional gas deviating from the ideal gas law, but where the attraction forces are not strong enough to give two-dimensional condensation at the temperature which we have chosen. In the FA versus F diagram of Fig. 17 we see that curve B resembles the case of caproic acid in Fig. 15.

Curve C is drawn for a value

$$a_2 = 35,000 \times 10^{-32} \text{ ergs . cm.}^2$$

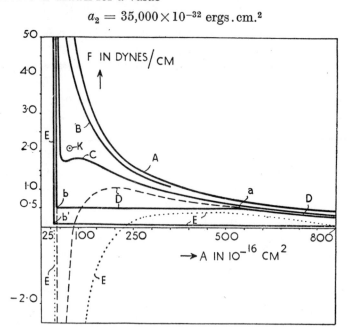

FIG. 16. F–A curves for various values of a_2.

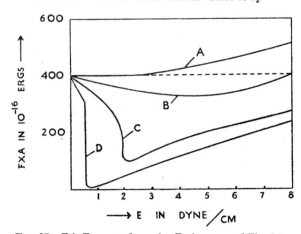

FIG. 17. FA–F curves from the F–A curves of Fig. 16.

This is a curve corresponding to a gas just under its critical temperature. At a pressure of 1·75 dynes/cm. there is an indication
of condensation. The corresponding curve C in Fig. 17 shows a
slight vertical part in reaching the deepest point of the dip.

Curve D has been drawn for

$$a_2 = 50,000 \times 10^{-32} \text{ ergs.cm.}^2$$

The actual curve, as given by equation (38) is drawn as a full line from the higher values of A, up to the point a. From there onward the curve is shown by dashes: it passes through a very deep minimum at surface areas between 50 and 75 A^2, where the pressure according to the equation would even be strongly negative, whilst for still smaller surface areas the curve shows a steep rise, and from point b onwards it is shown in full again. Points a and b are to be considered as coexisting surface phases, a being the gas, b being the condensed phase. The parts enclosed by the curve D, as shown by dashes, and the horizontal line ab, lying over and under this horizontal line respectively, are equal in area. The part of the curve shown in dashes represents the metastable and labile parts of the curve. When we start from a very dilute two-dimensional gas and compress it either by a barrier or by increasing the three-dimensional pressure or the three-dimensional concentration, and we reach a pressure of 0·55 dynes/cm., where the surface area per molecule is 550 A^2, condensation sets in and a two-dimensional condensed phase with a surface area of about 40 A^2 per molecule is formed. Bringing more molecules into the adsorbed layer or compressing it means condensation of more molecules, whilst the pressure F remains constant. The corresponding curve D in Fig. 17 is also shown.

If the attractive forces are still greater and we take for instance, as we have done in curve E,

$$a_2 = 100,000 \times 10^{-32} \text{ ergs.cm.}^2,$$

such condensation sets in at a very large surface area, which is greater than that shown in Fig. 16 and the corresponding pressure F is only of the order of magnitude of 0·1 dynes/cm. or lower. Curve E is shown as a dotted curve apart from the nearly vertical part starting at point b' at a surface area of about 35 A^2 per molecule. The dotted parts of the curve are metastable or labile.

If we had chosen a higher temperature the substance having a value for a_2 of, for instance, $50,000 \times 10^{-32}$ ergs.cm.^{2}, which shows curve D at 17° C., would show curve C, whilst the substance which shows curve C would show a curve the behaviour of which was like curve B, etc. (see also § 108).

94. The two-dimensional saturation pressure, F_0, and the spreading force, F_s

Curves of the types derived in Fig. 16 by means of the two-dimensional van der Waals equation (38) are known experimentally for many substances. In Fig. 18 we give experimental curves for tridecylic acid, myristic acid, and pentadecylic acid, determined at

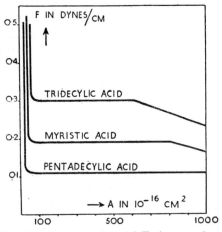

Fig. 18. Some experimental $F–A$ curves for a few acids.

14° C. The difficulty of making such measurements has prevented determinations at other temperatures. The two-dimensional saturated gas pressures, F_0, of the two-dimensional condensed phases, are only known, therefore, for one single temperature, 14° C. in this case: some of the figures are:

TABLE 6

Substance	Two-dimensional saturation pressure
C_{13} tridecylic acid	0·30 dynes/cm.
C_{14} myristic acid	0·19 dynes/cm.
C_{15} pentadecylic acid	0·11 dynes/cm.
C_{16} palmitic acid	0·04 dynes/cm.

Adam expects this pressure to rise by 0·01 dynes/cm. for every degree of temperature.

It is not easily possible to make measurements at pressures lower than 0·02 dynes/cm. There are, however, numerous substances which show lower saturated surface pressures than this figure, substances therefore which condense two-dimensionally at pressures lower than 0·02 dynes/cm. As the corresponding surface area A is very big in such cases, we may expect condensation to occur at very low surface concentrations.

A direct comparison with calculated curves or calculated values is not easily possible. In the gaseous state molecules of fatty acids and similar substances lie flat on the surface whilst in the condensed state they have mutually erected each other to unimolecular condensed sheets of parallel molecules pointing away from the surface. During the condensation phenomenon, therefore, the constant b_2 and also a_2 alter their values. A comparison, however, of Figs. 16 and 18 shows us that the phenomenon is well enough described qualitatively by a two-dimensional van der Waals equation.

The surface pressures, F_0, must not be confused with the pressures shown when a three-dimensional crystal of the same substance spreads on water. It is easier to take a molecule from a three-dimensional crystal and to adsorb it at the water surface than to bring a molecule from the two-dimensional condensed phase into the two-dimensional gas phase. In both cases we have to do work against the mutual cohesion forces holding the molecules together. In the first case our process, however, is facilitated by the fact that we gain the heat of adsorption; but in the second case the two-dimensional condensed phase is itself adsorbed and that part of the heat of adsorption arising from the mutual attraction of molecule and surface is substantially unaltered. Consequently, the equilibrium pressure, F_s, between the three-dimensional crystal and the two-dimensional gas, hence the spreading force, will be far higher than the two-dimensional gas pressure of the equilibrium between the two-dimensional condensed and the gaseous phases. In Table 7 we show the spreading forces of some fatty acids at 20° C.

TABLE 7

Substance	Spreading force
C_{11} undecylic acid	35 dynes/cm.
C_{12} lauric acid	21 dynes/cm.
C_{14} myristic acid	11 dynes/cm.
C_{15} pentadecylic acid	15 dynes/cm.
C_{16} palmitic acid	$8\frac{1}{2}$ dynes/cm.
C_{18} stearic acid	$1\frac{1}{2}$ dynes/cm.

We see that, indeed, these forces are far larger than the forces of Table 6. They are all so large that as a result of the spreading from the three-dimensional crystal a two-dimensional condensed film is formed.

It may be observed that the spreading forces of these crystals show an alternation similar to that shown for so many physical properties of the crystals of the fatty acids. The spreading forces of the acids with an odd number of carbon atoms are higher than those of the acids with an even number. Alternation of physical properties is caused by the crystal structure of the three-dimensional crystals.

95. Other two-dimensional phases

Although the two-dimensional van der Waals equation (38) may give a satisfactory qualitative or sometimes semi-quantitative description of the condensation phenomena, we must not forget that it depends only on a rough approximation according to which two separate correction terms are introduced in the equation of state. One of these correction terms accounts for the attraction forces (a_2) and the other for the dimensions of the molecule (b_2)—its surface—and these dimensions are determined by the mutual distances of the molecules where the attraction and repulsion forces balance each other (see also § 88).

There are, according to this equation, therefore, only two states, two phases, in which we may find the assembly of molecules, namely, the gaseous state and the condensed state. Whether this condensed state is a two-dimensional solid or crystalline state, comparable with the three-dimensional crystal, or whether it is a two-dimensional liquid is immaterial for this description.

Experimentally there are numerous phases known in two-dimensional unimolecular films. Sometimes there can be more than one solid phase, depending on the relative freedom of movement of the molecules in them (free or restricted rotation). This relative freedom depends on their mutual orientation and on their orientation with respect to the surface on which they are adsorbed. Transitions between these phases are often not connected with a heat of transition, the transition being not of the first order. There is, however, always a change in the partial derivatives of the entropy. In an F–A diagram a transition of the first order is characterized by a constant value of F over a long range of areas A; it is the horizontal region in the diagram, where

$$\left(\frac{\partial F}{\partial A}\right)_T = 0.$$

In a second-order transition there is only a discontinuity in the curve, whilst in a third-order transition there is a discontinuity in

$$\left(\frac{\partial^2 F}{\partial A^2}\right)_T.$$

Especially in the case of long-chain molecules with a polar group in an end position, as, for instance, the fatty acids, many more possibilities of mutual arrangement arise. The long hydrocarbon chains lie flat on the surface in the gaseous phase. When the surface density increases the molecules attract each other so strongly that they may lift their hydrocarbon chains mutually from the water surface, giving a small agglomeration of molecules, the polar heads of which are in the water surface and not condensed yet, or the polar heads may already be closely packed whilst the hydrocarbon tails are not yet mutually arranged, making chaotic movements. Such an arrangement of parts of the long molecules, whilst other parts are not closely packed, gives rise to a limited number of molecules forming aggregates or micelles on the surface. Phenomena of this kind seem to be responsible for those two-dimensional films described as expanded films, which may be subdivided again into vapour expanded and liquid expanded films. They form intermediates between the gaseous and the condensed phases. We will not, however, discuss this part of surface chemistry, interesting as it may be.† These phenomena are restricted to molecules of special shape and construction. It is, for the purposes of our present considerations, sufficient to know that there are condensation phenomena in two-dimensional films, transitions from a gaseous phase into a condensed phase and vice versa.

96. Critical phenomena

The experimental evidence gained from the investigation of unimolecular films, spread on water, points to the existence of a critical temperature above which no discontinuous condensation phenomena can take place. It is true that there are no investigations on the temperature dependence of the two-dimensional condensation

† See the books of N. K. Adam and E. K. Rideal mentioned in §§ 72 and 65 respectively.

phenomena. The results obtained with the homologous series of many organic substances show that the F–A curves or the FA–A curves of the lower members (with the fatty acids of chain lengths, for instance, up to 12 C atoms) all show the behaviour of substances above this critical temperature, whilst the substances of longer chain length show the coexistence of two phases.

The two-dimensional van der Waals equation (38) enables us to express the critical data in terms of the constants a_2 and b_2 in just the same way as can be done for the three-dimensional case. At the critical temperature the curve according to this equation does not show a separate maximum and a minimum. These are just united at an inflexion point. At this point in the F–A diagram the first and second derivations of F with respect to A must be zero. Taking

$$\frac{dF}{dA} = 0 \quad \text{and} \quad \frac{d^2F}{dA^2} = 0,$$

equation (38) gives us, just as in the three-dimensional case, the following relations for the critical data:

$$\left.\begin{aligned} F_c &= \frac{a_2}{27b_2^2} \\ A_c &= 3b_2 \\ T_{c2} &= \frac{8a_2}{27Rb_2} \end{aligned}\right\}. \tag{40}$$

We have denoted the critical two-dimensional pressure by F_c and the critical molecular area by A_c. Their dependence on the constants a_2 and b_2 is exactly the same as in the case of three-dimensional gases. We denoted the critical temperature for the two-dimensional gas by T_{c2} to distinguish it from the normal critical temperature of a three-dimensional gas, T_c. We shall see in the following sections that these temperatures are not identical.

Turning back to the set of curves for $T = 290°$ K. and $b_2 = 25$ A^2 in Fig. 16 we can now calculate at which value of a_2 a two-dimensional gas would just be at its critical temperature. Putting $T_{c2} = 290°$ K. and $A_c = 3b_2 = 75$ A^2, we obtain $F_c = 2.05_5$ dyne/cm. and $a_2 = 34,750 \times 10^{-32}$ ergs.cm.^{2} Point K in Fig. 16 gives the coordinates of the inflexion point of the F–A curve for this case. We see, therefore, that if at constant temperature we study a series of substances, the molecules of which all have the same values of b_2, we pass from two-dimensional gases showing the character of an ideal gas, via gases deviating strongly from the ideal gas law and gases showing a behaviour of being just above their critical temperature, to gases under their critical temperature and thence to gases which show predominant condensation phenomena. This is exactly what is found for homologous series of, for instance, fatty acids, fatty alcohols, and similar substances.

97. Non-ideal two-dimensional gases on solid surfaces

Up till now we have discussed the two-dimensional gases and their equation of state for substances whose molecules were adsorbed on a liquid interface. The pressure F is measured either directly or indirectly via the decrease of surface energy. The molecular area, A (or the amount of molecules which are adsorbed, $\sigma = 1/A$), is again either measured directly—when we know how much of an insoluble substance is spread on the surface—or it is estimated indirectly by calculating it from the relationship between σ, F, and the three-dimensional concentration c, or pressure p, with the aid of Gibbs' adsorption equation (29).

The same two-dimensional gas laws and the same condensation phenomena may be expected when molecules are adsorbed at surfaces of solid adsorbents. As we have stated already in Chapter VI (see especially §§ 69 and 83), every time that we can speak of a dynamic equilibrium between a gas (or a solution) and an adsorbed layer, we must expect lateral movements of the adsorbed molecules along the surface, i.e. we must expect the behaviour of a two-dimensional gas. In studying adsorption phenomena of this class one measures experimentally the amount of molecules which are adsorbed as a function of the pressure, p, or the concentration, c, keeping the temperature constant (adsorption isotherm). Again with the aid of Gibbs' adsorption equation, the two-dimensional pressure, F, may be derived from the data of an experimental adsorption isotherm, when we take Gibbs' equation in the integrated form

$$F = RT \int_0^p \sigma \, d\ln p \quad \text{or} \quad F = RT \int_0^c \sigma \, d\ln c, \qquad (29\,\text{c})$$

where R is the gas constant per molecule ($R = 1.38 \times 10^{-16}$ ergs/degree) if σ is expressed in molecules per cm.² It does not matter in what units p or c are expressed. F is then obtained in dynes/cm.

The integration may be done graphically. The molecular area A is known when we know σ, because

$$\sigma = \frac{1}{A}.$$

F–A curves, therefore, may be calculated from adsorption isotherms.

The difficulty arises here that, while in all examples of adsorption at liquid surfaces we know the size of the surface, this quantity is not known in the case of the surfaces of solid adsorbents. There are numerous methods suggested and in use for determining the area of the surface of a solid adsorbent. A discussion of these methods and their merits is not contemplated here. Some very reliable methods are possible in special cases. All methods for general use, however, are based on certain assumptions, which in many cases may hold for all practical purposes, but which will not hold in other cases. If the actual size of the surface is f times the figure which is used experimentally, in a special case, the figure for σ which is used is f times too large, the figure for A, which one then uses is f times too small, and the figure for F, calculated with (29 c) is f times too large.

98. Experimental evidence

In 1944 Miss Marion H. Armbruster and J. B. Austin published some F–A curves of CO and of N_2 on steel surfaces at low temperatures.[†] Their curves indicate, as the authors remark, phase-transformations similar to those occurring in unimolecular layers on water.

In a beautiful series of experimental studies, Jura, Loeser, Basford, and Harkins,[‡] of the University of Chicago, applying the method just discussed to adsorption isotherms of n-heptane on various surfaces, found F–A relationships strikingly resembling those of fatty acids and similar substances when spread on water. Their F–A diagrams closely resemble Figs. 16 and 18. Whilst no experimental studies have been made on the temperature dependence of the behaviour of substances spread on water, the Chicago workers determined a complete set of curves for n-heptane adsorbed on ferric oxide. All curves at temperatures lower than 29° C. show a horizontal part in the F–A diagrams, this horizontal part being longer,

† M. H. Armbruster and J. B. Austin, *J. Am. Chem. Soc.* **66** (1944), 159.

‡ G. Jura, E. H. Loeser, P. R. Basford, and W. D. Harkins, *J. Chem. Physics*, **14** (1946), 117. See also ibid. **13** (1945), 535, and **14** (1946), 344.

the lower the temperature is. 29° C. has all the features of a critical temperature.

Similar results are obtained with n-heptane on other substances. Older publications of adsorption isotherms indicate that similar phenomena occur in the adsorption of, for instance, A, N_2, and O_2 on ionic surfaces in the neighbourhood of 77° K., and also of CO on a steel surface in the region of 78–93° K.

As already remarked, if the actual size of the surface is not known, the values for F and for A as calculated from adsorption data are only proportional to the real values. Fortunately this does not influence the value for the critical temperature derived from the data.

99. The two-dimensional critical temperature

It is a striking experimental fact that the various indications of critical temperatures in two-dimensional condensation phenomena all point to figures far lower than the three-dimensional critical temperatures of the same substances. In § 94 we found that an acid of, for instance, 6 carbon atoms behaves as a substance far above its critical temperature, when adsorbed on a water surface. The normal three-dimensional critical temperatures of some of the lower fatty acids are:

(C_2)	acetic acid	321·6° C.
(C_3)	n-propionic acid	339·5° C.
(C_4)	n-butyric acid	355° C.
(C_5)	n-valeric acid	379° C.

Notwithstanding this, all these acids and even acids of longer chain length behave as if they were above their critical temperature when spread on water at room temperature.

The experiments of Jura, Harkins, and collaborators, discussed in the previous section, point to a two-dimensional critical temperature of n-heptane of 29° C. when adsorbed on ferric oxide. The normal critical temperature of n-heptane is 266·8° C.

The F–A curves found for the adsorption of CO on steel surfaces (see previous section) indicate that CO shows a critical temperature at about 93° K. (−180° C.). Its three-dimensional critical temperature is 134° K. (−139° C.). Nitrogen, adsorbed on an unreduced steel surface at −195° C. (78° K.) shows an F–A curve indicating that it is just below its critical temperature under these circumstances; the normal critical temperature of nitrogen is −147·1° C. (126° K.).

We saw in § 96 that the critical temperatures are related to the van der Waals constants a and b, or a_2 and b_2 respectively. The van der Waals equation will enable us to understand why this two-dimensional critical temperature, T_{c2}, is so much lower than the normal critical temperature T_c. We have to go somewhat deeper into the significance of the constants a and b.

100. The relations of a_2 and b_2 with a and b

Restricting ourselves for the moment to spherical isotropic molecules the three-dimensional van der Waals constant b can be expressed in terms of the dimensions of the molecule,

$$b = \frac{2\pi}{3} N d^3, \qquad (41)$$

where N is the number of Avogadro and d is the diameter of the molecule. The constant b, therefore, is $4N$ times the volume of a sphere with a diameter d. It is the sphere inside which the centres of other molecules cannot penetrate, divided by 2, because in adding these 'volumes' together we should count them twice. Similarly, we define the two-dimensional constant b_2 as

$$b_2 = \frac{\pi}{2} N d^2, \qquad (42)$$

hence $2N$ times the area of the circle with diameter d.

If we also restrict ourselves to molecules which show no electrical asymmetries, the mutual attraction arises from the dispersion forces only (London forces, § 92). We may then write, as a first approximation, for the potential of attraction of two molecules at the distance r

$$\epsilon = -\frac{C}{r^6},$$

where C is related to the polarizability α by the expression

$$C = \tfrac{3}{4}\alpha^2 E,$$

where E is a characteristic energy.[†] The van der Waals constant a is directly proportional to C, viz.,

$$a = \frac{N^2}{2} \int_d^\infty \frac{C}{r^6} 4\pi r^2 \, dr = 2\pi C N^2 \int_d^\infty \frac{dr}{r^4},$$

† Cf. the article 'Atomic forces and adsorption' by J. H. de Boer in *Advances of Colloid Chemistry*, vol. iii, Interscience Publ., New York, 1950.

hence
$$a = \frac{2\pi C}{3d^3} N^2.$$
(43)

Similarly, the two-dimensional van der Waals constant a_2 is

$$a_2 = \frac{N^2}{2} \int_d^\infty \frac{C}{r^6} 2\pi r \, dr = \pi C N^2 \int_d^\infty \frac{dr}{r^5},$$

hence
$$a_2 = \frac{\pi C}{4d^4} N^2.$$
(44)

If we want to express the various data of the two-dimensional gases per molecule, instead of per mole, we have to divide b_2 of equation (42) by N and a_2 of equation (44) by N^2.

The two-dimensional correction term b_2 may be expressed in terms of the three-dimensional one by using equations (42) and (41)

$$b_2 = \frac{3b}{4d}.$$
(45)

Similarly, for a_2 from equations (43) and (44)

$$a_2 = \frac{3a}{8d}.$$
(46)

The normal three-dimensional critical temperature, T_c, can be expressed in terms of a and b (cf. § 96 and equation 40):

$$T_c = \frac{8a}{27Rb}.$$

In equation (40) we derived for T_{c2}

$$T_{c2} = \frac{8a_2}{27Rb_2}.$$

Inserting the figures from equations (45) and (46), we obtain

$$T_{c2} = \tfrac{1}{2}T_c.$$
(47)

The rigorous application, therefore, of van der Waals' equation leads to the result that the two-dimensional critical temperature is only half the normal three-dimensional one. Qualitatively, however, similar results will be obtained if other formulations of the equation of state are used. Lennard-Jones and Devonshire[†] in discussing a more general form come to similar conclusions. A special model for instance gives $T_{c2} = 0.53T_c$.

† J. E. Lennard-Jones and A. F. Devonshire, *Proc. Roy. Soc.* A **163** (1937), 53 and 132.

We will in our discussions adhere to the van der Waals equation (38). Meanwhile it must be stated here that equation (47) is derived for spherical, isotropic molecules. Only the molecules of the rare gases can be treated in this way. We shall see in later sections that all other gases may deviate considerably in this respect. We will see that the two-dimensional critical temperature may be higher or lower than the figure given by equation (47). It is an outstanding fact, however, that, generally speaking, the critical temperature T_{c2} is substantially lower than the normal critical temperature T_c.

101. Numerical values for light gases

In Table 8 we have collected some data of van der Waals' constants a and b as given in the *Handbook of Chemistry and Physics*,[†] re-calculated in ergs.cm.^{3} and cm.^{3} respectively. From these figures the diameter d can be calculated; d is shown in the last column of the Table. With the known values of a, b, and d, the two-dimensional data a_2 and b_2 may then be calculated by means of equations (45) and (46). We have shown the figures per mole, as well as per molecule, the latter figures being more useful in the calculation of F–A relationships.

TABLE 8

	Per mole				Per molecule		
	Three-dimensional		Two-dimensional		Two-dimensional		
	a in 10^{12} ergs.cm.^{3}	b in cm.^{3}	a_2 in 10^{20} ergs.cm.^{2}	b_2 in 10^8 cm.^{2}	a_2 in 10^{-32} ergs.cm.^{2}	b_2 in 10^{-16} cm.^{2}	d in 10^{-8} cm.
He	0·034	23·7	0·0048	6·68	132	11·1	2·66
Ne	0·212	17·1	0·0333	5·38	920	8·9^5	2·39
A	1·35	32·2	0·172	8·20	4,740	13·6	2·95
Kr	2·33	39·8	0·276	9·5	7,600	15·7	3·17
Xe	4·34	51·0	0·475	11·2	13,100	18·5	3·43
H_2	0·245	26·8	0·0331	7·28	915	12·1	2·77
N_2	1·39	39·2	0·166	9·4	4,570	15·5^5	3·15
O_2	1·36	31·8	0·174	8·15	4,800	13·5	2·93
CO	1·49	39·8	0·176	9·5	4,860	15·7	3·17
CH_4	2·26	42·8	0·272	9·9	7,500	16·4	3·24
H_2O	5·5	30·5	0·71	7·6^5	19,600	13·1	2·89
NH_3	4·2	37·0	0·51	9·0	14,100	14·9^5	3·08

† Published by Chemical Rubber Publishing Co., Cleveland, Ohio, 32nd ed., 1951.

We have included in the Table, besides the rare gases, the gases, hydrogen, nitrogen, carbon monoxide, and methane also. The figures calculated for the two-dimensional constants a_2 and b_2 for these gases, must be considered as a first approximation only. These gases are neither spherical nor isotropic and small deviations from these two properties show clearly in the behaviour of two-dimensional gases. This is still worse with the molecules water and ammonia, also included in Table 8, which show an electrical asymmetry.

102. Values of a_2 and b_2 simulating the behaviour of an ideal gas

It is worth while considering which values of a_2 and b_2 will compensate each other at room temperature sufficiently well for the behaviour of the two-dimensional gas to simulate that of an ideal one. Writing the equation of state in the form

$$FA = RT + Fb_2 - \frac{a_2}{A}\left(1 - \frac{b_2}{A}\right)$$

we see that for small values of b_2/A the two last terms compensate each other if a_2/A is somewhat greater than Fb_2. In order to simulate an ideal gas behaviour, a_2 should be somewhat greater than RTb_2.

Table 8 shows us that whilst the values of b_2 do not vary very much, the values of a_2, for instance for the rare gases, vary by a factor 100 when we pass from helium to xenon. Taking an average value for b_2 of 15×10^{-16} cm.², and restricting ourselves to room temperature ($RT = 400 \times 10^{-16}$ cm.²) we derive the conclusion that a_2 should be $6,000 \times 10^{-32}$ ergs.cm.² or somewhat larger in order to compensate the influence of b_2. Table 8 shows us that the lighter gases like nitrogen, oxygen, carbon monoxide, argon, and certainly neon, helium, and hydrogen, have lower a_2 values than this. We may therefore expect their behaviour as two-dimensional gases to be such that they will show the influence of b_2 more than of a_2. These are the gases for which we may expect the Langmuir adsorption equation to be more or less useful. In many circumstances these gases will show an adsorption isotherm of the Langmuir type (see also §§ 87 and 113).

If we make the same comparison for three-dimensional gases, similar reasoning may lead us to the conclusion that in order to simulate an ideal gas behaviour at room temperature, assuming an average value for b of 35 cm.^{3}, the value for a should be in the neighbourhood of 0.85 to 1.0×10^{12} ergs.cm.^{3} A glance at Table 8 shows us that the same gases as discussed above already have in general, *larger a* values than this.

103. Heavier gases

TABLE 9

	Per mole		Per molecule		
	Three-dimensional		Two-dimensional		
	a in 10^{12} ergs.cm.^{3}	b in cm.^{3}	a_2 in 10^{-32} ergs.cm.^{2}	b_2 in 10^{-16} cm.^{2}	d in 10^{-8} cm.
Acetic acid . . .	17.7	107	41,700	30.2	4.4
n-propionic acid . .	20.6	119	46,500	32.3	4.5^5
Methyl propionate . .	20.0	134	43,600	35.0	4.7^5
Methyl butyrate . .	24.0	157	49,800	39.0	5.0
Methyl valerate . .	29.0	185	57,000	44.0	5.2^8
n-heptane . . .	31.6	205	55,000	47.0	5.4^5

In Table 9 similar calculations have been made for some larger molecules. We have only shown the values for the two-dimensional constants a_2 and b_2 as they are per molecule. The figures of Table 9 may only be considered as a very rough first approximation. Molecules of this kind are far from spherical and certainly not isotropic. Again, this shows itself far more dominantly in the field of the two-dimensional gases than it would do in a three-dimensional gas.

We see, however, that the figures for a_2 are in the neighbourhood of those which we used for constructing Fig. 16. We may, however, remark immediately that the figures shown in Table 9 will prove to be too high. If these figures were right, acetic acid would have a critical temperature, T_{c2}, of 297° K. It would, therefore, at room temperature, be just under its critical point. In reality its behaviour is of a two-dimensional gas, far above its critical point. We shall see the reason for this deviation in § 108.

104. Anisotropic molecules; orientation

Apart from those of the rare gases the molecules of most other substances deviate from the conception of isotropic spheres. In three-dimensional gases these deviations do not have such a great influence, because the molecules rotate in all directions and show an average value of their 'diameter' and of their polarizability, causing b and a of the van der Waals equation to be an average value. When adsorbed on surfaces they may, in some circumstances, still be considered as rotating in all directions. They roll over the surface as marbles do. In other cases, however, they will slide over the surface with one of their axes more or less perpendicular to it, making vibratory movements only (see § 82). In their sliding movements they still may be able also to rotate two-dimensionally around the axis which is perpendicular to the surface.

Let us consider a two-atomic molecule. The 'diameter' in the direction of the line connecting the centres of the two atoms will be greater than the 'diameters' in the two directions perpendicular to the long axis of the molecule. In the three-dimensional gas state an average diameter is shown. If adsorbed at a surface and lying flat on it, with both atoms in direct contact with the surface, the diameter shown in directions along the surface will be greater than if the molecule is adsorbed in a position with its long axis perpendicular to the surface. The value of b_2 will be smaller in the case of adsorption perpendicular to the surface.

Such a two-atomic molecule generally has its greatest polarizability in a direction parallel to its long axis. It tends to attract other molecules more strongly in that direction.† Other molecules, however, may come nearer to it in directions perpendicular to the long axis. This over-compensates the influence of the polarizability, the net result being that the mutual potential of the two molecules in close contact is always greatest when their long axes are parallel. Since the van der Waals forces are additive in character, they always tend to place long molecules parallel to each other, and make flat molecules have their flat planes parallel, so that as many constituent atoms as possible come into contact with each other. This plays an important role in the normal condensation of these substances to liquids or solids.

The same properties make the adsorbed molecules lie flat on the surface when adsorbed singly. It is true that the axis of greatest polarizability is parallel to the surface in such a position. The fact that the molecule is nearer to the surface when lying flat, however, is dominant. As many atoms as possible are then in contact with

† For a more detailed discussion see J. H. de Boer, 'Atomic forces and adsorption', in *Advances in Colloid Science*, vol. iii, Interscience Publ., New York, 1950.

the surface. Single adsorbed molecules, therefore, whether they are
of nitrogen, pentane, or of palmitic acid all lie flat on the surface[†]
at sufficiently low temperatures. If the temperature is high enough
to allow the molecule to rotate freely over the surface, every difference between flat or perpendicular positions disappears.

This is what happens when there are few molecules present when
σ is small. If they come together and influence each other, it may
be more advantageous for them to erect themselves mutually from
the surface and to combine in groups with their long axes mutually
parallel, directed away from the surface. In such a position every
molecule can be surrounded by more of its own kind than when
lying flat on the surface. The heat of combining mutually in vertical
positions is greater than the heat of combining when lying flat on
the surface; the heat of adsorption, however, will be greater in the
flat positions. There will most probably be a difference of entropy
between the two possibilities. Whether or not the molecules will
mutually erect themselves when two-dimensional condensation sets
in depends on the change in free enthalpy which will take place (compare equation (32) in § 80)

$$\Delta G = \Delta H - T \Delta S.$$

If ΔG decreases when the molecules erect each other mutually, then
the condensed state will consist of such a layer of parallel molecules
with their long axis pointing away from the surface. We will discuss
the influence of ΔH and ΔS more specifically in § 108.

Such behaviour is known experimentally for long-chain molecules
with a polar group at the end. When adsorbed on a water surface
or on a surface of a metal or an ionic adsorbent, they lie flat when
σ is small, but they erect each other when they come close together.
Whether such a state of affairs also occurs with, for instance, normal
pentane or nitrogen, is not so easy to say. In some cases they may
stay flat on the surface when two-dimensional condensation takes
place. Other molecules may then be adsorbed on top of them, thus
leading to multimolecular adsorption. It has been shown, by means
of absorption spectra, that p-nitro-phenol molecules, adsorbed on
ionic adsorbents, behave in this way.[‡] Ortho-nitrophenol, fatty
acids, and similar substances, on the other hand, erect each other.

[†] J. H. de Boer and G. Heller, *Physica* 4 (1937), 1045.
[‡] J. H. de Boer and J. F. H. Custers, *Z. physikal. Chem.* B **25** (1934), 238; B **16**
(1932), 403; *Physica*, **3** (1936), 407.

The attraction forces emanating from their hydrocarbon ends, which form a new surface, are very small and other molecules have no tendency to be bound on top of them.

If such a mutual erection takes place, we may expect the value of b_2 to be smaller and of a_2 to be greater than the average value. The direct result would be that a two-dimensional critical temperature, T_{c2}, would be increased (see equation (40)) and would be greater than $\frac{1}{2}T_c$. We will make a rough estimation of the magnitude of this effect in the case of nitrogen.

105. Nitrogen as an example

A molecule of nitrogen has a greater dimension in the direction of the line connecting the centres of the atoms than in a direction perpendicular to this axis. The centres of the two atoms are 1·1 A apart, and we may expect the value of d to be 3·3 A when the molecule is lying flat on the surface and 2·8 A if it is adsorbed with its long axis perpendicular to the surface. The average value of d, as shown in Table 8, is 3·15 A.

The average polarizability of a nitrogen molecule is $1·76 \times 10^{-24}$ cm.³ The polarizability in the direction of the long axis, however, is $2·38 \times 10^{-24}$ cm.³, whilst the polarizability in the two other directions at right angles is $1·45 \times 10^{-24}$ cm.³

If we calculate C (equation (43)) from the three-dimensional a, and the average value of d, we obtain

$$C = 57·2 \times 10^{-60} \text{ ergs.cm.}^6$$

C is proportional to the square of the polarizability α (§ 100). We may, therefore, expect the average C, acting in the direction along the surface to be

$$C_{\text{flat}} = 68·0 \times 10^{-60} \text{ ergs.cm.}^6,$$

when the molecule is lying flat on the surface, and

$$C_{\text{perp}} = 41·2 \times 10^{-60} \text{ ergs.cm.}^6$$

when its position is such that its long axis is perpendicular to the surface.

We can now calculate the values of a_2 and b_2 in the two positions using these figures for C and with the corresponding figures for d

$$d_{\text{flat}} = 3·3 \times 10^{-8} \text{ cm.}$$

and $$d_{\text{perp}} = 2·8 \times 10^{-8} \text{ cm.}$$

With the aid of equations (42) and (44) we obtain:

(a) for the position flat on the surface:

$$(a_2)_{\text{flat}} = \frac{\pi C_{\text{flat}}}{4d_{\text{flat}}^4} = 4{,}500 \times 10^{-32} \text{ ergs.cm.}^2,$$

$$(b_2)_{\text{flat}} = \frac{\pi d_{\text{flat}}^2}{2} = 17 \cdot 1 \times 10^{-16} \text{ cm.}^2$$

and the critical temperature would be

$$(T_{c2})_{\text{flat}} = \frac{8(a_2)_{\text{flat}}}{27 R(b_2)_{\text{flat}}} = 56 \cdot 8° \text{ K.}$$

(b) for the position with its long axis perpendicular to the surface:

$$(a_2)_{\text{perp}} = \frac{\pi C_{\text{perp}}}{4d_{\text{perp}}^4} = 5{,}250 \times 10^{-32} \text{ ergs.cm.}^2$$

$$(b_2)_{\text{perp}} = \frac{\pi d_{\text{perp}}^2}{2} = 12 \cdot 3 \times 10^{-16} \text{ cm.}^2$$

$$(T_{c2})_{\text{perp}} = 92° \text{ K.}$$

For comparison the figures calculated from the average values for C and d may be given:

$$a_2 = 4{,}570 \times 10^{-32} \text{ ergs.cm.}^2$$

$$b_2 = 15 \cdot 5^5 \times 10^{-16} \text{ cm.}^2$$

as already mentioned in Table 8 with a critical temperature, $T_{c2} = 63°$ K., this being exactly half the value of $T_c = 126°$ K.

106. Influence of orientation on the two-dimensional critical temperature

If the molecules, therefore, erect each other when condensing on the surface, the two-dimensional critical temperature goes up. We have seen in § 99 that there are indications that the critical temperature of nitrogen on a steel surface is above 78° K., that is higher than 63° K. The same holds for CO. There are indications that its two-dimensional critical temperature, when adsorbed on steel, is at 93° K.; half the value of the three-dimensional critical temperature would be 67° K. Heptane on ferric oxide shows a two-dimensional critical temperature of 29° C. $= 302°$ K.; half the value of the three-dimensional critical temperature would be 270° K. $= -3°$ C. Long-chain molecules, however, of which n-heptane is an example, offer more possibilities. In the three-dimensional gas state they form spiral-shaped molecules and their a and b are averages for that shape. When n-heptane molecules, adsorbed at a solid surface, attract each other to form a condensed state, the spirals may be converted into stretched molecules. Even if these stretched molecules lie flat on the surface, their a_2 values will be higher than shown in Table 9. It may be that their b_2 value is also somewhat larger than shown there, when they lie flat but stretched. The critical temperature, T_{c2}, however, is likely to be higher than when calculated with the data of Table 9.

There are, moreover, other reasons why in some cases the critical temperature may be higher than half the three-dimensional one. We will discuss this later in § 123 in the next chapter.

107. Dipoles and the two-dimensional critical temperature

We discovered above that a mutual erection of molecules when condensing increases the value of a_2 and decreases the value of b_2, causing the two-dimensional critical temperature to be higher than half the value of the three-dimensional one. We know experimentally that fatty acids and similar substances do erect each other mutually, but we also know that despite the above expectation their two-dimensional critical temperature is certainly lower than half the value of the three-dimensional one. This is caused by another factor which over-compensates the above-mentioned one. This factor is the existence of permanent dipoles in these molecules which are directed parallel to each other by the influence of the surface.

We have discussed the influence of such parallel dipoles in § 92 and we saw that their mutual repulsion may lead to a term (a_2'), substantially lowering the mutual attraction caused by the dispersion forces (equation (39)). Their contribution is given by the expression

$$a_2' = -\tfrac{1}{2} \int_d^\omega \frac{\mu^2}{r^3} 2\pi r \, dr = -\frac{\pi \mu^2}{d} \tag{48}$$

where μ is the dipole moment, r is the variable distance between the dipoles, and d is again the diameter of the molecules. We see that for $\mu = 1 \times 10^{-18}$ e.s.u. $\times$ cm. (1 Debye) and $d = 3$ A such a contribution amounts to roughly $10{,}000 \times 10^{-32}$ ergs.cm.^{2}, a value of a substantial magnitude when compared with the values shown in Tables 8 and 9.

In three-dimensional gases dipoles lead to an increase of the attraction forces, as already discussed in § 92. The procedure which we followed in § 100 in calculating a_2 from a (equation (46)) is only valid for molecules which show no electrical asymmetries (see §§ 92 and 100). The experimental a values for the fatty acids, as mentioned in Table 9, however, are rather high because their dipoles restrict the rotation and lead to a contribution to attraction (the Keesom alinement effect). This contribution can, as a first approximation, be given by the following expression

$$a_\mu = \frac{N^2}{2} \int_d^\infty \frac{2\mu^4}{3RT} \frac{1}{r^6} 4\pi r^2 \, dr = N^2 \frac{4\pi\mu^4}{3RT} \int_d^\infty \frac{dr}{r^4},$$

hence

$$a_\mu = \frac{4\pi\mu^4}{9RTd^3} N^2, \tag{49}$$

where μ is the dipole moment, r is the distance between the molecules, and d is the diameter, as used in the van der Waals theory. If we use the value for d of acetic acid mentioned in Table 9, $d = 4\cdot4$ A, and use for the dipole moment of acetic acid, $\mu = 1\cdot7 \times 10^{-18}$ e.s.u. × cm. then this contribution at room temperature amounts to about 2×10^{-12} ergs.cm.^{3}, and this is somewhat more than 11 per cent. of the experimental value for a.

The calculated value for a_2 would, therefore, be about 11 per cent. lower than the figure mentioned in Table 9. This, however, would give us only the value caused by the dispersion forces of free rotating molecules. When acetic acid molecules are adsorbed to a layer of parallel orientated molecules, the effect of this orientation will be similar to that which we discussed in § 105. In this vertical position we may expect the C value of equation (44) to be roughly 25–30 per cent. smaller than the average figure whilst the value for d will be about 10 per cent. smaller (with $b_2 = 25$ A^2 we obtain $d = 4$ A), hence d^4 will be roughly 40 per cent. smaller; and so a_2 in this vertical position will be 10–15 per cent. higher than the average value. As a result of such very rough and approximate calculations we may expect the a_2 value for acetic acid as caused by dispersion forces only to be about $40,000 \times 10^{-32}$ ergs.cm.^{2} and the values for the higher fatty acids to increase by approximately $5,000 \times 10^{-32}$ ergs.cm.^{2} for every addition of one CH$_2$ group. Butyric acid would then have an a_2-value of roughly $50,000 \times 10^{-32}$ ergs.cm.^{2}

A comparison of Figs. 16 and 17 (see § 93 and also Fig. 15) shows us that butyric acid has in reality a value of roughly $10,000 \times 10^{-32}$ ergs.cm.^{2} The parallel orientated dipoles repelling each other strongly seem therefore to have caused a decrease in the a_2 value of roughly $40,000 \times 10^{-32}$ ergs.cm.^{2} Such a decrease could be (equation (48)) caused by parallel dipoles having a dipole moment of $2 \cdot 25 \times 10^{-18}$ e.s.u. $\times$ cm., using a value for b_2 of 25 A^2, which means $d = 4 \times 10^{-8}$ cm. It is not unlikely that the dipole moments of the fatty acids, when adsorbed on water, are increased by the orientation of the water dipoles underneath them.

108. A further examination of the phenomenon of two-dimensional condensation

We have mentioned already in § 104 that the heat of adsorption will be different for molecules which lie flat and molecules which take up positions perpendicular to the surface. The total heat of adsorption will be composed of two contributions, the heat of adsorption proper, due to the interaction with the surface of the adsorbent, and the heat of combining, resulting from the mutual van der Waals attraction forces. We will see later (§ 132 in Chapter IX) that we can write

$$Q_t = Q_s + \frac{2a_2}{A}, \tag{50}$$

where Q_t is the total heat of adsorption, Q_s the contribution due to the interaction with the surface, a_2 the two-dimensional van der Waals attraction correction, and A the area available per molecule. As we saw in preceding sections (§§ 105 and 107) the a_2 value in the perpendicular position will mostly be somewhat greater than in the flat position because the decrease of d^4 in equation (44) is usually stronger than the decrease of C.

In order not to complicate matters too much, however, we will assume in the calculations of this section that a_2 does not alter when the molecules change from the flat to the perpendicular position.

In the flat position A cannot decrease further than $(b_2)_{\text{flat}}$; in the vertical position, however, they come closer together. Consequently an additional amount of heat of two-dimensional condensation may be liberated, amounting to

$$\left\{ \frac{2a_2}{A} - \frac{2a_2}{(b_2)_{\text{flat}}} \right\}.$$

The difference in the total heat of adsorption between the closely packed arrangement of flat-lying molecules and of an assembly of perpendicularly arranged molecules may, therefore, be written as

$$(Q_t)_{\text{perp}} - (Q_t)_{\text{flat}} = (Q_s)_{\text{perp}} - (Q_s)_{\text{flat}} + \left\{ \frac{2a_2}{A} - \frac{2a_2}{(b_2)_{\text{flat}}} \right\} = \Delta Q_t$$

(51)

where A is the space per molecule in the arrangement of perpendicular molecules.

During the process of erection there will be, at any moment, molecules lying flat and molecules already in vertical positions. If we denote the number (per unit area) of molecules which are in vertical position by n_{perp} and the number of flat-lying molecules by n_{flat}, we may write

$$\frac{n_{\text{perp}}}{n_{\text{flat}}} = \frac{f_{\text{perp}}}{f_{\text{flat}}} e^{\Delta Q_t/RT} = f e^{\Delta Q_t/RT},$$

(52)

where f_{perp} and f_{flat} are the partition functions for vertically arranged and flat-lying molecules respectively. These partition functions bear a direct relationship to the entropy, which we will discuss later. From equation (52) we obtain for the fractions of flat and vertical molecules, respectively,

$$\frac{n_{\text{flat}}}{n_{\text{perp}} + n_{\text{flat}}} = \frac{1}{1 + f e^{\Delta Q_t/RT}} = \phi,$$

$$\frac{n_{\text{perp}}}{n_{\text{perp}} + n_{\text{flat}}} = 1 - \frac{1}{1 + f e^{\Delta Q_t/RT}} = 1 - \phi.$$

The effective value for b_2 may be calculated from these fractions by the equation

$$(b_2)_{\text{eff}} = (b_2)_{\text{flat}} \phi + (b_2)_{\text{perp}} (1 - \phi).$$

(53)

$(b_2)_{\text{eff}}$ depends, therefore, on the difference in heat of adsorption, ΔQ_t, and hence on A (equation (51)) and on temperature and entropy difference (equation (52)). If we know ΔQ_t as a function of A and if we know the difference in entropy $(b_2)_{\text{eff}}$ may be evaluated for any value of A (and for any temperature). Substituting these values for $(b_2)_{\text{eff}}$ and the value of a_2, which we assumed to be constant, in the two-dimensional van der Waals equation (38)

$$\left(F + \frac{a_2}{A^2} \right)(A - (b_2)_{\text{eff}}) = RT,$$

(38 a)

we may calculate F as a function of A.

We may illustrate this procedure by a few examples.

I. We assume the following data:

(1) $(b_2)_{\text{flat}} = 100 \times 10^{-16}$ cm.²

(2) $(b_2)_{\text{perp}} = 25 \times 10^{-16}$ cm.²

(3) $a_2 = 50,000 \times 10^{-32}$ erg.cm.²

(4) $\Delta Q_s = (Q_s)_{\text{perp}} - (Q_s)_{\text{flat}} = -2,000 \times 10^{-16}$ ergs/molecule.

(5) $T = 298°$ K.

(6) $f = 1$.

Assumptions (1) and (3) mean that the molecules, in their flat positions, would not give a two-dimensional condensation (the critical temperature according to equation (40) would be 107° K.), but assumptions (2) and (3) mean that they would condense if they were in their vertical positions. Assumption (4) means that the erection of the molecules would require work to be done against the attraction forces of the surface. This would amount to about 2·9 k.cal./mole. Assumption (6) means that we do not assume a difference in entropy between the flat and the vertical arrangements.

ΔQ_t, according to equation (51), is negative until with decreasing values of A we reach $A = 33$ A²; there is no possibility of reaching this value, however, because in the neighbourhood of $A = 100$ A² the work to be done against the attraction forces of the surface is far higher than the kinetic energy of temperature (RT at $T = 298°$ is 411×10^{-16} ergs/molecule compared with $\Delta Q_t = -2,000 \times 10^{-16}$ ergs/molecule for $A \geqslant 100$ A²). Presumably the erection of the molecules will not take place. This is revealed when $(b_2)_{\text{eff}}$ is calculated from equation (53). Even at $A = 90$ A² one would still find $(b_2)_{\text{eff}} = 100$ A², which is impossible. With $(b_2)_{\text{eff}} = (b_2)_{\text{flat}} = 100$ A² for all values of $A > 100$ A² we may calculate F and we obtain an F versus A curve as given by curve I in Fig. 19; the curve is a normal one for a substance far above its critical temperature, no condensation taking place. We see that we could only come to erection of the molecules at infinitely high pressures F.

II. Let us now assume that far less work is required for the erection of the molecules; we assume

$$\Delta Q_s = (Q_s)_{\text{perp}} - (Q_s)_{\text{flat}} = -500 \times 10^{-16} \text{ ergs/molecule.}$$

This is an amount of the same order of magnitude as RT and even at 0° C. there are, at large values of A, already several molecules

in the vertical position: their fraction $(1-\phi)$ can be calculated with
the aid of equation (52) to be 21 per cent.; the value for $(b_2)_{\text{eff}}$, therefore, is 84 A. When A decreases and becomes smaller than $A = 100$ A^2

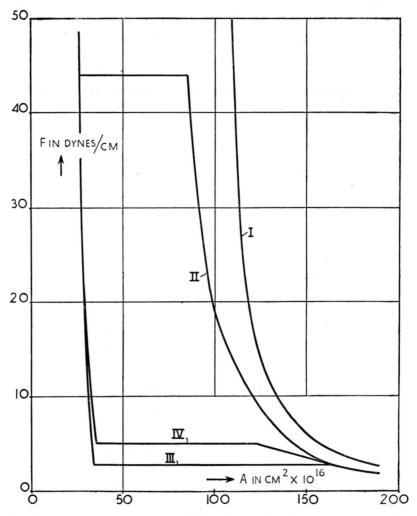

Fig. 19. $F\text{–}A$ curves for various possibilities of assemblies of molecules erecting each
other mutually.

some heat is liberated by the mutual attraction, more erection then
takes place, $(b_2)_{\text{eff}}$ decreases, still more heat is liberated, and when
$A \leqslant 67$ A^2 this heat even overcompensates ΔQ_s. Erection of all the

molecules and consequently two-dimensional condensation will take place.

The F versus A curve reflects this; it is curve II of Fig. 19 (given also in Fig. 20 as the curve for $0°$ C.). The equilibrium pressure, F_0 (see § 94), is found to have a high value.

III. If we had assumed $\Delta Q_s = 0$, an appreciable number of molecules would always be in the vertical position at large values of A, the fraction being $(1-\phi) = 50$ per cent. at all temperatures. When A is decreased extra heat of condensation is liberated for smaller values than $A = 100$ A^2, $(b_2)_{\text{eff}}$ being 62.5 A^2 at the beginning decreases further; all molecules will be erected easily. The corresponding curve is shown as curve III in Fig. 19. A low value for F_0 results.

IV. In example I we assumed $f = 1$. This quotient of partition functions (see equation (52)) is directly related to the difference in entropy, ΔS, between the perpendicular and flat arrangements:

$$\Delta S = R\left\{\ln f + T\frac{\partial \ln f}{\partial T}\right\}. \tag{54}$$

We may expect the molecules to have a higher entropy in the vertical position. They occupy less surface space, they have probably more freedom to oscillate or vibrate in directions perpendicular to their own axis, they will have more freedom to rotate, whilst in addition vibrations of parts of these molecules with respect to other parts come into the picture (see also § 95).

In order to investigate the effect of such an entropy difference we will assume ΔS to be roughly 10 entropy units. We take $f = e^5$, but at the same time we choose the other assumptions of example I to be valid again. Despite the high value of ΔQ_s, there are at $25°$ C. and at values of $A \geqslant 100$ A^2 many molecules in the vertical position, the fraction $(1-\phi)$ being 53 per cent. This means that they can approach each other sufficiently close to start condensation; the extra heat of condensation helps then to complete this process. The corresponding curve is given as curve IV in Fig. 19.

109. The influence of temperature on two-dimensional condensation

Investigation into the influence of temperature on the condensation phenomena discussed in the previous section leads to very interesting results. In the two-dimensional condensation phenomena of examples II and III heat is liberated, ΔQ_t (equation (51)) being positive. Consequently we find that the equilibrium pressure, F_0,

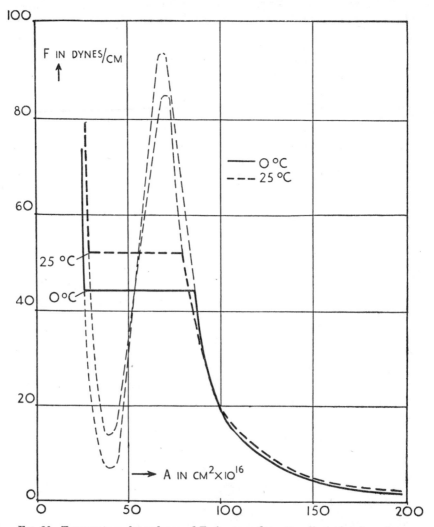

FIG. 20. Temperature dependence of F–A curves for a two-dimensional condensation which is exothermic in its last stage.

increases with temperature, just as in the case of normal condensation of three-dimensional gases, where the equilibrium pressure also rises with temperature, because there is liberation of heat connected with the condensation phenomenon (§ 40, equation (16)).

Fig. 20 shows the effect of temperature on example II, the curve for 0° C. is the same as curve II of Fig. 19. The only difference shown by a similar set of curves for a normal two-dimensional condensation, without erection of molecules being necessary, is that the curves intersect twice. When A is still in the neighbourhood of $A = 100$ A² there is no liberation of heat yet; ΔQ_s is still dominating. The erecting of molecules by temperature movement is just capable of starting the condensation process. An increase in temperature favours this starting process, the 25° C. curve, therefore, intersects that of 0° C. When condensation sets in heat is liberated and the Clapeyron relation (§ 40) shows that the equilibrium pressure, F_0, rises as the temperature increases, and hence a second intersection takes place. Fig. 21 shows the influence of temperature on the case of example III of the previous section. ΔQ_t is positive, right from the beginning. The curves for higher temperatures are all higher over their entire region than the curves for lower temperatures. The set of curves shows that in raising the temperature we shall reach a critical temperature; the curve for 100° C. is already a super-critical one.

In examples IV and I the value for ΔQ_t is negative over the whole range of A values which fall in the condensation range. If the entropy did not increase (example I) no condensation would set in. As already stated in the previous section (example I) we could only succeed in bringing the molecules into vertical positions and therefore into close enough contact to give condensation if we could overcome an infinitely high two-dimensional pressure barrier in the region of A values between 100 A² and 33 A². In applying equation (32) (§§ 80 and 104) for the difference in free enthalpy

$$\Delta G = \Delta H - T \Delta S,$$

we may assume here that

$$\Delta H = -\Delta Q_t.$$

ΔH, therefore, is positive, and as $\Delta S = 0$ we see that (at any temperature) ΔG will be positive, hence the process does not occur.

In example IV of the previous section, however, ΔG is negative, because we chose ΔS to be positive, namely, about 10 entropy units. If we make a rough estimation of ΔQ_t from equation (51), putting $A = 35$ A² (the left end of the horizontal part of curve IV in Fig. 19) we obtain

$$\Delta Q_t = -140 \times 10^{-16} \text{ ergs/molecule} = -0.2 \text{ k.cal./mole.}$$

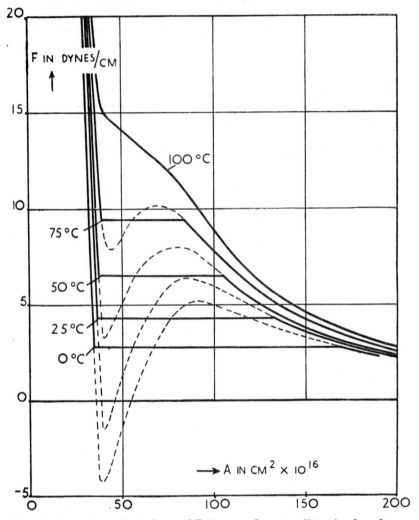

FIG. 21. Temperature dependence of F–A curves for a two-dimensional condensation which is exothermic over the whole range.

Substituting $\Delta S = 10$ cal./degree and $\Delta H = -\Delta Q_t = 200$ cal./mole in the equation for the difference in free enthalpy, we obtain

$$\Delta G = 200 - 10T.$$

This would mean that ΔG would be negative for all temperatures higher than $T = 20°$ K. Long before such a low temperature is reached, however, two-dimensional condensation will in practice fail to set in. Fig. 22 shows that starting from the curves at 0° C. (which

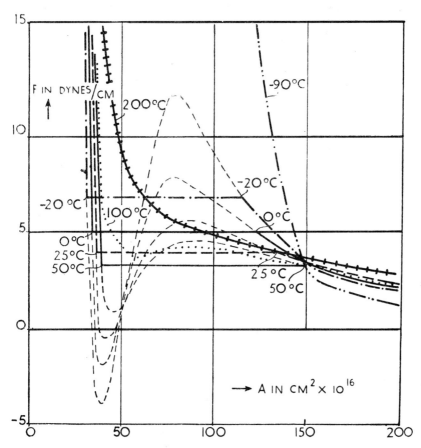

Fig. 22. Temperature dependence of $F–A$ curves for an endothermic two-dimensional condensation.

is the same as curve IV of Fig. 19), a decrease of temperature gives a curve, starting at lower F values when A is large, intersecting (see the $-20°$ C. curve) the 0° C. curve, before condensation sets in (indicating that the decrease of $(b_2)_{\text{eff}}$ is more difficult at lower temperatures) and giving a higher value for F_0, the two-dimensional pressure of condensation. This result is in accordance with the Clapeyron equation because ΔQ_l is negative. At lower A values the curves intersect again.

At still lower temperatures the condensation will not be able to set in because at those lower temperatures the effect of the increase of entropy is not strong enough to overcome the rather high $\Delta Q_s = 2,000 \times 10^{-16}$ ergs/molecule (about $2 \cdot 9$ k.cal./mole) with the result that too few molecules will be erected to give a sufficiently high contribution of two-dimensional condensation energy to support the process. A more detailed analysis would probably reveal that the erection process is accompanied by an energy of activation.

Application of equation (38 a) (§ 108) gives for $-90°$ C. a curve, shown in Fig. 22, which bears a close resemblance to curve I of Fig. 19; no condensation takes place, the curve is a supercritical one for a substance having $a_2 = 50,000 \times 10^{-32}$ erg.cm.^{2} and $b_2 = 100 \times 10^{-16}$ cm.^{2} At still lower temperatures ($T < 107°$ K. $= -166°$ C.) condensation phenomena would set in for the flat-lying molecules.

Starting again from the curve for $0°$ C. of Fig. 22, we obtain the $25°$ C. and $50°$ C. curves as indicated. The equilibrium pressure F_0 decreases with temperature. At still higher temperatures, however, this process is reversed, as may be seen from the $100°$ C. curve. At such high temperatures, apparently, the number of molecules which are already erected at any high value of A ($A > 100$ A^2) is so large, that we approach the normal behaviour of a substance with $a_2 = 50,000 \times 10^{-32}$ erg.cm.^{2} and $b_2 = 25 \times 10^{-16}$ cm.^{2} The equilibrium pressure, F_0, will increase again with increasing temperature and at still higher temperatures we shall have a critical curve; the $200°$ C. curve which is shown in Fig. 22 is a supercritical one.

In all our examples of this and of the previous section a_2 was kept constant. Generally there is an increase in a_2 when the molecules are brought into positions perpendicular to the surface (see e.g. § 105). Such an increase in a_2 would not alter the character of the curves derived; it only facilitates the condensation, as at values for $A > 100$ A^2 an extra amount of interaction energy will be available. An increase in a_2, therefore, will have the tendency to shift the character of the curves from those of Fig. 20 to those of Fig. 21, if there is no increase of entropy in the process. Usually, however, the entropy will also increase and we may expect also that in some cases curves of the character of those of Fig. 22 may be found.

There are hardly any experimental data about the influence of temperature on the equilibrium value, F_0, available. The curves published by Jura, Loeser, Basford, and Harkins[†] for n-heptane on silver and on ferric oxide show an increase of F_0 with temperature, comparable with the increase of the saturation pressure of normal

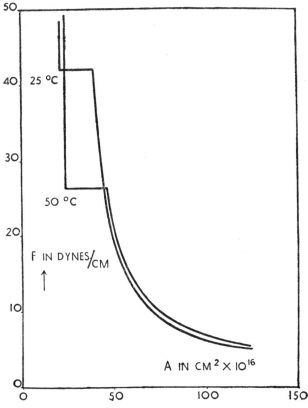

FIG. 23. $F-A$ curves for butyl alcohol on mercury (Kemball).

liquids with temperature. Kemball[‡] published results of two-dimensional condensation of some lower aliphatic alcohols on mercury, where the pressure, F_0, decreases with temperature. In Fig. 23 his curves of butyl alcohol on mercury are shown at 25° C. and at 50° C.; they show the character of the curves of Fig. 20 as far as the high

† G. Jura, E. H. Loeser, P. R. Basford, and W. D. Harkins, *Jour. Chem. Physics*, **13** (1945), 535; **14** (1946), 117.

‡ C. Kemball, *Proc. Roy. Soc.* A **190** (1947), 117.

level of F_0 is concerned, but the temperature dependence is that of Fig. 22, showing that increase in entropy is the governing factor in this process.

110. The influence of the nature of the adsorbent

We may expect that in future far more experimental data will be found, so that we may be able to judge the mutual relations between adsorbed molecules in the way discussed in this chapter. Mutual orientation will, generally speaking, occur if the attraction forces from the adsorbent tending to keep the molecules in flat positions can be overcome. The increase in mutual van der Waals attraction and possibly an increase in entropy tend to counterbalance this influence of the substrate. They facilitate erection and consequently mutual orientation. Mutual orientation in itself tends to increase the two-dimensional critical temperature, and tends to favour condensation. Mutual parallel orientation of dipoles, however, has the reverse effect: it lowers the mutual attraction and the critical temperature, and it hinders condensation. When, however, the dipoles are parallel but alternating in direction, a high critical temperature may be expected and also very favourable conditions for condensation.

Polar surfaces may be expected to add small contributions to these dipole effects, by introducing small dipole moments in dipole-free molecules, or by increasing or decreasing permanent dipoles. Even the behaviour of rare gas atoms may be modified by a surface which induces dipoles in them. The formation of dipoles in rare gas atoms —and, of course, in any other molecule—seems even to be possible when they are adsorbed on metal surfaces[†] or on charcoal. Presumably these dipoles are also parallel orientated and tend to lower the value of a_2; even negative values of a_2 may result.[‡] This may, just to mention one example, explain why xenon, when adsorbed on mercury, behaves as an ideal gas (§ 76), whereas, according to Table 8 in § 101, its a_2 value, calculated from the three-dimensional a, amounts to $13,100 \times 10^{-32}$ ergs.cm.^{2} which together with $b_2 = 18.5 \times 10^{-16}$

[†] J. C. P. Mignolet, in 'Heterogeneous catalysis', *Discussions of the Faraday Soc.*, No. 8 (1950), p. 105.

[‡] J. H. de Boer and S. Kruyer, *Trans. Faraday Soc.* **54** (1958), 540. Investigations by Sidney Ross and J. P. Olivier have shown that a lowering of a_2 may also be simulated by an unhomogeneous surface: see their book, *On Physical Adsorption*, Interscience, New York, 1964, p. 142.

cm.^{2} should result in a noticeable deviation of the ideal behaviour. According to the considerations of § 102 its ideal behaviour suggests an a_2 value of about $8,000 \times 10^{-32}$ ergs.cm.^{2}, hence a decrease of about $5,000 \times 10^{-32}$ ergs.cm.^{2}, which may be understood if dipoles of $\mu = 0.74 \times 10^{-18}$ e.s.u. cm. (0.74 Debyes) were induced. These induced dipoles may, in many cases, assume rather high values; they lower the a_2 values considerably and, consequently, often prevent two-dimensional condensation when molecules are adsorbed on metal surfaces or on charcoal. The two-dimensional condensation of polar molecules, such as fatty acids or fatty alcohols, when adsorbed on metals may be facilitated by this effect. This is caused by the fact that the induced dipoles are pointing with their positive poles away from the metal surfaces, thus decreasing the effect of the orientated permanent dipoles of these molecules.

THE ADSORPTION ISOTHERM IN THE CASE OF TWO-DIMENSIONAL CONDENSATION

111. Adsorption isotherm with van der Waals' attraction forces

WE now study the relation between the pressure p (or concentration c) and the two-dimensional condensation phenomena which we discussed in the previous chapter. Instead of calculating F and A from an experimental adsorption isotherm (§ 97) we start our considerations from the two-dimensional van der Waals equation and translate it into the language of an adsorption isotherm. We again need Gibbs' adsorption equation to perform this translation.

As in § 87 we use Gibbs' adsorption isotherm in the form

$$\sigma = \frac{p}{RT}\frac{dF}{dp} = \frac{p}{RT}\frac{dF}{dA}\frac{dA}{dp}.$$

σ being the number of molecules adsorbed per cm.², R must be taken as the gas constant per molecule ($R = 1{\cdot}38 \times 10^{-16}$ ergs/°K.). For σ we write

$$\sigma = \frac{1}{A},$$

where A is the area per molecule; hence

$$\frac{1}{A} = \frac{p}{RT}\frac{dF}{dA}\frac{dA}{dp},$$

$$d\ln p = \frac{A\,dA}{RT}\frac{dF}{dA}.$$

dF/dA now may be derived from the two-dimensional van der Waals equation

$$\left(F+\frac{a_2}{A^2}\right)(A-b_2) = RT,$$

$$\frac{dF}{dA} = -\frac{RT}{(A-b_2)^2}+\frac{2a_2}{A^3}.$$

We therefore obtain

$$d\ln p = \left\{-\frac{ART}{(A-b_2)^2}+\frac{2a_2}{A^2}\right\}\frac{dA}{RT},$$

i.e.

$$d\ln p = -\frac{A\,dA}{(A-b_2)^2}+\frac{2a_2\,dA}{RTA^2}.$$

Integrating this equation gives us

$$\ln p = -\ln(A - b_2) + \frac{b_2}{A - b_2} - \frac{2a_2}{RTA} + \text{constant.}$$

Hence
$$p = \frac{k_b'}{A - b_2} e^{b_2/(A - b_2)} e^{-2a_2/RTA}, \tag{55 a}$$

where k_b' is a constant.

Reintroducing
$$\sigma = \frac{1}{A}$$

and putting
$$\sigma_0 = \frac{1}{b_2},$$

where σ_0 is the maximum number of adsorbed molecules/cm.^{2} in a unimolecular layer, we obtain

$$p = \frac{k_b' \sigma \sigma_0}{\sigma_0 - \sigma} e^{\sigma/(\sigma_0 - \sigma)} e^{-2a_2\sigma/RT}. \tag{55 b}$$

Writing, as usual, $\sigma/\sigma_0 = \theta$ and putting $k_b' \sigma_0 = k_b$, we obtain

$$p = k_b \frac{\theta}{1 - \theta} e^{\theta/(1-\theta)} e^{-2a_2\sigma/RT}. \tag{55}$$

If there were no lateral attraction forces, hence no constant a_2, equation (55) would reduce to equation (37), already discussed in § 87, where we remarked that this equation gives a stronger saturation character than the Langmuir adsorption isotherm.

The two-dimensional van der Waals equation and its influence on adsorption phenomena has been a subject of discussion by various authors. Mostly these discussions went no further than establishing a few general qualitative remarks.[†] Magnus[‡] derived an equation for the adsorption isotherm, basing his work on the two-dimensional van der Waals equation. He assumed, however, that the two-dimensional pressure F was proportional to the three-dimensional pressure p. We have shown in § 86 that such an assumption leads to erroneous results; it is not compatible with Gibbs' adsorption equation. Magnus' equation will, therefore, not be discussed. There are two authors who just mention an equation of the form (55), namely, Hückel[§] and Cassel.[||] They do not examine the equation, however,

† See the articles cited in the books by E. K. Rideal, mentioned in § 65, by N. K. Adam, mentioned in § 72, and by S. Brunauer, mentioned in § 48.

‡ A. Magnus, Z. Physikal. Chem. A **142** (1929), 401; Trans. Faraday Soc. **28** (1932), 386.

§ E. Hückel, discussion remark in Trans. Faraday Soc. **28** (1932), 442.

|| H. Cassel, Jour. Phys. Chem. **48** (1944), 195.

and unfortunately there is a small misprint in the equation in both cases. Only Terrell L. Hill,† in the course of studies already mentioned in § 61, derived the same equation. We shall discuss equation (55) fully in this chapter.

112. The choice of σ_0

Before discussing equation (55) we want to say something about our choice of σ_0. We have put $\sigma_0 = 1/b_2$. This seems strange at first sight; b_2, as we discussed in § 100, is twice the surface area of a

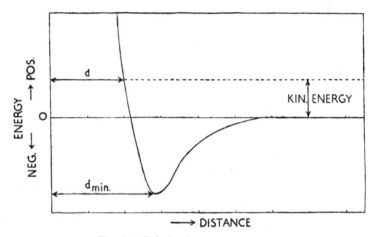

Fig. 24. Relation between d and d_{min}.

molecule, the diameter of which is d. In the conception of the van der Waals equation, where the molecules are given dimensions, they are considered to be rigid spheres with a diameter d, which in the three-dimensional case have a volume of $\frac{1}{6}\pi d^3$ and which in the two-dimensional case have a surface area of $\frac{1}{4}\pi d^2$. When the molecules collide their centres approach each other up to the distance d. This diameter d is determined by the point where the energy of the mutual attraction forces, together with the kinetic energy of their thermal movement, equals the energy of their mutual repulsion forces.

When, however, the molecules are condensed, for instance in a liquid phase, the average distance which they observe is determined by the balance of the attraction and the repulsion forces. This distance is greater than the distance entering into the van der Waals equation. The relationship may be illustrated by Fig. 24, where the

† Terrell L. Hill, *Jour. Chem. Physics*, **14** (1946), 441.

energy content of the system of two molecules is shown as a function of their distance. We arbitrarily call the energy content zero when the molecules are far apart. If they approach each other, their attraction forces come to work and the energy content of the system decreases. The closer the molecules approach the more the energy content decreases, until from a certain moment work has to be done against the repulsion forces to bring the molecules still nearer to each other. The energy content which had become negative increases again, passes zero, and increases further to positive values. At the minimum of the so-called potential curve which we obtain in this way the depth gives the heat of combination, while the distance at this point, which we have called $d_{\min}$, is the equilibrium distance which the molecules observe with respect to each other in a combined state, for instance in a liquid phase.

If, however, the molecules approach each other possessing kinetic energy of a certain positive value, they can approach to that distance where the horizontal line indicating their kinetic energy crosses the potential curve of the two molecules. $d_{\min}$ is therefore essentially greater than the value of d derived from the van der Waals equation.

In our figure $d_{\min}$ is roughly $1\cdot4\times d$. This proportion is not an uncommon one. We can calculate $d_{\min}$ from the density of the liquids. Assuming the molecules to be packed as closely as possible (hexagonal packing), their spheres, having a volume of $\frac{1}{6}\pi d_{\min}^3$ each, occupy 74 per cent. of the available space. If the molecular weight is M and the density D, $d_{\min}$ is therefore given by the relation

$$\tfrac{1}{6}\pi d_{\min}^3 = \frac{0\cdot74M}{ND}.$$

In Table 10 we have calculated the values for $d_{\min}$ for the same gases as were mentioned in Table 8. In the third column of Table 10 the values for d are shown; they are the same as the ones shown in Table 8 and are derived from the van der Waals constant b. In the last column of Table 10 we see that the quotient of $d_{\min}$ and d is somewhere between $1\cdot35$ and $1\cdot4$. We take

$$d_{\min} = 1\cdot37d.$$

If the molecules are packed again in a two-dimensional closely packed hexagonal arrangement the surface area that each of them occupies is
$$\tfrac{1}{2}d_{\min}^2\sqrt{3} = 0\cdot865d_{\min}^2 = 1\cdot62d^2.$$

As $$b_2 = \tfrac{1}{2}\pi d^2 = 1\cdot57 d^2$$

we see that the surface area which the molecules really occupy if (both in the three-dimensional phase as well as in the two-dimensional phase) their packing is as close as possible is given reasonably by b_2. Hence we may write

$$\sigma_0 = \frac{1}{b_2}.$$

This relation has, empirically, already been found by Terrell L. Hill[†] and by Livingston.[‡]

TABLE 10

	d_{min} in A	d in A	d_{min}/d
He	4·25	2·66	1·59
Ne	3·40	2·39	1·42
A	4·05	2·95	1·37
Kr	4·22	3·17	1·33
Xe	4·65	3·43	1·35
H_2	4·07	2·77	1·47
N_2	4·34	3·15	1·38
O_2	4·03	2·93	1·38
CO	4·36	3·17	1·38
CH_4	4·48	3·24	1·39
H_2O	3·48	2·89	1·21
NH_3	3·95	3·08	1·28

113. Relations between the Langmuir adsorption isotherm and the equations of state

Equation (55 a) of § 111,

$$p = \frac{k_b'}{A-b_2}\, e^{b_2/(A-b_2)}\, e^{-2a_2/RTA}, \tag{55 a}$$

may, for large values of A, be written approximately as

$$p = \frac{k_b'}{A-b_2}\left(1+\frac{b_2}{A-b_2}\right)\left(1-\frac{2a_2}{RTA}\right), \tag{56}$$

which may be transformed into

$$p = \frac{k_b'}{A-[2b_2-2a_2/RT-(b_2-2a_2/RT)^2/A]} \tag{56 a}$$

[†] Terrell L. Hill, appendix to article, *Jour. Chem. Physics*, **16** (1948), 181.
[‡] H. K. Livingston, *Jour. of Colloid Science*, **4** (1949), 447.

or, if A is sufficiently large,

$$p = \frac{k_b'}{A-[2b_2-2a_2/RT]}. \tag{56 b}$$

These expressions take the form of a Langmuir adsorption isotherm, which we can see if we replace the term between square
brackets in the denominator of (56 a) or (56 b) by $1/\sigma_L$. Substituting
also

$$A = \frac{1}{\sigma}$$

we obtain

$$p = \frac{k_b' \sigma \sigma_L}{\sigma_L-\sigma}.$$

Solving for σ from this equation and putting

$$\theta_L = \frac{\sigma}{\sigma_L}$$

and

$$k_L = \frac{1}{k_b' \sigma_L},$$

we obtain

$$\theta_L = \frac{k_L p}{1+k_L p}, \tag{18 c}$$

which is equation (18) (§ 43) of Langmuir's adsorption isotherm but
for the fact that instead of σ_0 we have used a symbol σ_L (consequently we denoted the degree of occupation as θ_L and the constant
as k_L instead of θ and k_u respectively).

As stated already in § 43 the picture leading to Langmuir's adsorption isotherm involves the conception that the molecules are
bound to definite adsorption sites on which they are adsorbed directly
from the gas phase and from which they return to the gas phase.
In Chapter VI, however, we have repeatedly stated that if there is
a dynamic equilibrium with the gas phase there is unavoidably an
intense migratory movement along the surface either in the form of
sliding or gliding molecules or in the form of hopping molecules (see
§ 82). It is in the last mentioned mode of movement that the adsorption sites play a role, but only as temporary resting-places for the
hopping molecules, which still retain their two-dimensional gas
character. Applying the two-dimensional van der Waals equation
to this gas we obtain equation (55), which as we saw above may, for
large values of A, be written in the approximate form (56). In the
Langmuir equation (18) of § 43, σ_0 does not have, therefore, the

physical meaning which we ascribed to it. It has to be replaced by σ_L, which is defined by

$$\frac{1}{\sigma_L} = 2b_2 - \frac{2a_2}{RT} - \frac{(b_2 - 2a_2/RT)^2}{A}$$

or, for sufficiently large values of A, by

$$\frac{1}{\sigma_L} = 2b_2 - \frac{2a_2}{RT}.$$

In this last approximation it is not dependent on A (hence on σ) and it is, therefore, a constant at constant temperature. Its value depends on a_2 and on b_2 and it is, therefore, not a direct measure for the maximum amount of adsorbed molecules in a molecular layer.

If there were no mutual attraction forces, that is if a_2 were zero, an adsorption isotherm written in the form of a Langmuir equation would give a value

$$\frac{1}{\sigma_L} = 2b_2 - \frac{b_2^2}{A}$$

or, when A is sufficiently great,

$$\frac{1}{\sigma_L} = 2b_2.$$

In such a case the equation of state of the two-dimensional gas would be the Volmer equation (36) (§ 85)

$$F = \frac{RT}{A - b_2}.$$

The constant b_2 in the Volmer equation is often called the co-area of the molecules; according to the previous section it is a good approximation for the real surface area which the molecules occupy when closely packed two-dimensionally. If the dimensions of the molecule are derived from the Langmuir isotherm we should obtain $2b_2$ for the surface area instead of b_2. (We have already obtained the same result in § 87.)

If, however, $a_2 \neq 0$, be it positive or negative, the co-area of the Volmer equation will fail to give the surface area of a molecule, though the F–A relationship may be represented pretty well by the form of this equation. The two-dimensional equation of van der Waals, written in the form

$$F = \frac{RT}{A - b_2} - \frac{a_2}{A^2},$$

may, when A is not too small, be written as

$$F = \frac{RT}{A-[b_2-a_2/RT+(a_2/RTA)(2b_2-a_2/RT)]}$$ (36 a)

or, if A is large enough,

$$F = \frac{RT}{A-[b_2-a_2/RT]}.$$ (36 b)

The 'co-area' in equation (36 b) is also dependent on a_2 and on T, whilst in (36 a) it would not be a constant but dependent on A. As soon, therefore, as a_2 becomes important the co-area found by evaluating the experimental results by means of a Volmer equation does not give a direct surface area of the molecules. This co-area will, moreover, be dependent on temperature. For positive values of a_2 the co-area will be smaller than b_2, whilst it will increase at higher temperatures. We have already seen that, for polar molecules or molecules which are polarized by the surface, a_2 may be negative; the co-area will then be greater than b_2 and it will decrease at higher temperatures. The van der Waals attraction term a_2 may (in the case of dipoles, for instance) also be itself dependent on temperature, and will mostly decrease with increasing temperatures.

Comparison of equations (36 b) and (56 b) shows that again $1/\sigma_L$, derived from the Langmuir isotherm, will have twice the value of the co-area, derived from the Volmer equation. If the experimental values of A are not large enough to warrant the use of equations (36 b) and (56 b), we may use (36 a) and (56 a); the value for $1/\sigma_L$ derived from the Langmuir isotherm will be less than twice the co-area derived from the Volmer equation, but it will still be appre ciably greater. This behaviour is often found in practical cases Neither of the figures gives the real surface area of the molecules.

The general results of this section are not dependent on the special form of the two-dimensional van der Waals equation. If we start from a general conception of an equation of state for the two dimensional gas, as already mentioned in § 88, viz.

$$\frac{FA}{RT} = 1+\frac{B}{A},$$ (57)

we may derive, for sufficiently large values of A,

$$F = \frac{RT}{A-[B-B^2/A]},$$ (57 a)

or even
$$F = \frac{RT}{A-B}.$$
(57 b)

If A is great enough (57 a) and (57 b) take the form of the Volmer equation.

We may also, following a line completely comparable with that followed in § 111, derive from (57) with the aid of Gibbs' equation

$$p = \frac{K}{A} e^{2B/A}.$$
(58)

As a first approximation for large A values this gives

$$p = \frac{K}{A}\left(1 + \frac{2B}{A}\right)$$

or at sufficiently large values of A

$$p = \frac{K}{A-[2B-4B^2/A]}$$
(58 a)

or even
$$p = \frac{K}{A-2B}.$$
(58 b)

(58 a) and (58 b) take the form of the Langmuir equation. Again, when the experimental data are moulded into the form of the Langmuir equation the figure for $1/\sigma_L$ ($1/\sigma_L = 2B$) is twice the co-area which will be found if the data are moulded into the form of the Volmer equation (B of (57 b)). If, again, the experimental data are such that (57 a) and (58 a) represent them rather than (57 b) and (58 b), the figure for $1/\sigma_L$ is still greater than, but less than twice, the co-area. Only if there are no attraction (or repulsion) forces does the co-area of the Volmer equation represent the real surface area.

We may remark that if the magnitude of the attraction forces is such that $a_2 = RTb_2$ the form of both the isotherm and the F–A diagram will be such that the behaviour of an ideal two-dimensional gas is simulated, as can be seen immediately from equations (56 b) and (36 b) respectively. This is, of course, in accordance with our considerations of § 102.

114. A reduced form of the isotherm equation and its constants

For a further discussion of the significance of the constants in equation (55) we will convert it to a more or less reduced state by dividing both sides by the saturation pressure, p_0, of the substance under investigation at the temperature T. If moreover we write

$$k_2 = \frac{k_b}{p_0} = \frac{k_b' \sigma_0}{p_0} = \frac{\sigma_0}{p_0} \frac{\sqrt{(MT)}}{3 \cdot 52 \times 10^{22} \tau_0} e^{-Q/RT}$$

and

$$k_1 = \frac{2a_2 \sigma_0}{RT},$$

we obtain from equation (55)

$$\frac{p}{p_0} = k_2 \frac{\theta}{1-\theta} e^{\theta/(1-\theta)} e^{-k_1 \theta}, \tag{59}$$

We must first discuss the constants k_1 and k_2. We have used the symbols k_1 and k_2 already before, namely, in equation (14). The k_1 and the k_2 used here have, of course, another significance from that implied there; although confusion will not be likely to occur a warning must be given not to mix up these symbols.

k_1 depends on temperature and on a_2 and σ_0, hence also on b_2; a_2 and b_2 both depend on temperature. Considering the constant for room temperature, however, we can estimate its order of magnitude from the figures of a_2 and b_2 given earlier. If we have a substance with an a_2 of $5,000 \times 10^{-32}$ ergs.cm.^{2} and $b_2 = 25 \times 10^{-16}$ cm.^{2}, the value of k_1 at room temperature ($RT = 400 \times 10^{-16}$ ergs) will be $k_1 = 1$. If the substance has a value of $a_2 = 50,000 \times 10^{-32}$ ergs.cm.^{2} and the same value of b_2, $k_1 = 10$. The constant k_1 depends only on the properties of the molecules which are adsorbed, it does not depend on the properties of the surface nor directly on the forces between the surface and the adsorbed molecules. For our further considerations we will vary k_1 from 0 or 1 (very weak inter-molecular forces) to $k_1 = 10$ (strong inter-molecular forces). We note that k_1 may have values higher than 10.

The constant k_2 measures mainly the strength of the adsorption on the surface. At very low values of the degree of occupation, k_2 gives the slope of the isotherm. At very low values of θ equation (59) reduces to

$$\frac{p}{p_0} = k_2 \theta;$$

hence

$$k_2 = \left(\frac{p/p_0}{\theta} \right)_{\theta \to 0}.$$

k_2, therefore, is the slope of the very first part of the adsorption isotherm. The stronger the adsorption the smaller k_2. If, for instance, at a value of $p/p_0 = 10^{-4}$, 1 per cent. of the surface is already covered with adsorbed molecules, the value of $k_2 = 10^{-2}$. The constant k_2 may well have far lower values than that. On the other hand, if the adsorption is very weak, and at the relative pressure $p/p_0 = 0.5$, only 5 per cent. of the surface is covered with adsorbed molecules, the value of $k_2 = 10$. It is of course possible that still larger values will be found, although in practical cases of adsorption k_2 will be 0·1 or lower.

One may easily derive the same conclusions if, with the definition for k_2 given above and with the aid of equations (14), (1), (6), and (13), one calculates the value for a few practical cases. Doing this we see that a value of $k_2 = 10$ at room temperature would roughly mean the adsorption of a substance with, for instance, a saturation pressure p_0 of 1,000 mm., and an adsorption energy of about 1 k.cal./mole, or of a substance having a saturation pressure of 10 mm., and an adsorption energy of about 4 k.cal./mole. Usually, however, substances with these values for the adsorption energy have higher saturation pressures at room temperature, and k_2 is more likely to be in the neighbourhood of 0·1 or lower. We will nevertheless start our discussion of equation (59) by assuming a value of $k_2 = 5$, assuming, therefore, very weak adsorption forces.

115. Various curves showing the characteristics of the equation

In Fig. 25 we have calculated a set of adsorption isotherms assuming the constant k_2 to be 5 and giving various values ranging from 1 to 10 to the constant k_1. A glance at Fig. 25 shows us that the line for $k_1 = 1$ is practically straight. At these weak inter-molecular forces and with the weak adsorption forces which we assumed ($k_2 = 5$), the two corrections of the van der Waals equation therefore compensate each other fully. For $k_1 = 5$, the adsorption isotherm shows a strong convex character towards the pressure axis. The isotherms for $k_1 = 6$ and $k_1 = 6.5$ are convex at first and then at higher pressures concave towards the pressure axis. They show the character of two-dimensional gases just above their critical temperature.

The curves for $k_1 = 7$, $k_1 = 7.5$, and $k_1 = 10$ have metastable and labile parts. Excluding supersaturation phenomena, these curves will therefore show a sudden jump of θ at a definite pressure. Referring to the curve of $k_1 = 10$, for instance, we see that at a relative pressure $p/p_0 = 0.15$ the amount of adsorbed molecules suddenly jumps from $\theta =$ roughly 0.05 to $\theta = 0.75$, whilst for the curve with $k_1 = 7$ the jump occurs at a relative pressure $p/p_0 = 0.4$ and is from

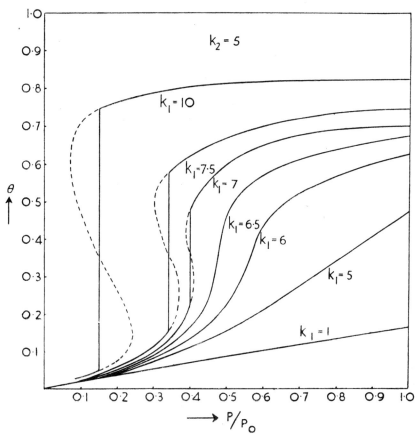

FIG. 25. Various isotherm curves according to equation (59); $k_2 = 5$, k_1 variable.

$\theta = 0.225$ to $\theta = 0.47$. These vertical jumps mean, just as in the discussion of Fig. 16 of the previous chapter, that condensation sets in. At those pressures where the jump occurs two surface phases are in coexistence, a two-dimensional gaseous phase and a two-dimensional condensed phase.

Fig. 26 shows the same set of curves for $k_2 = 10$, that is for still weaker adsorption forces. We see that the jumps for the various curves occur at exactly twice the pressure. The whole figure could be derived from the previous one by doubling the scale for p/p_0.

For any given k_1 the value of the relative pressure where the jump occurs is proportional to the constant k_2. The same set of curves,

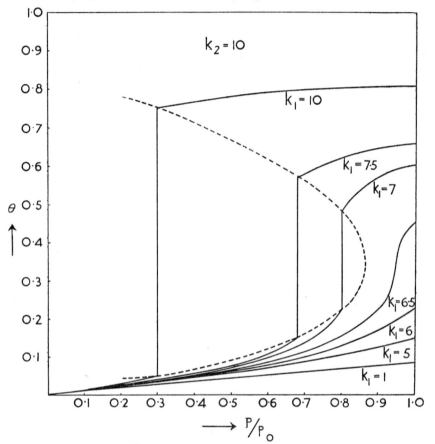

FIG. 26. As Fig. 25, but $k_2 = 10$.

therefore, as shown in Fig. 26 will also hold when, for instance, the constant $k_2 = 0.1$, provided we reduce the scale of p/p_0 by a factor 100. If, therefore, we are dealing with a substance showing a value for $k_1 = 10$, and we observe it at a surface on which it is strongly adsorbed, so that the value for k_2 is for instance 0.01, two-dimensional condensation sets in at a relative pressure of 0.0003.

Fig. 27 gives some of the curves, assuming stronger adsorption forces, namely, $k_2 = 0.1$. In the lower regions of p/p_0, which cannot

be distinguished at the scale at which we have drawn our figure, the
same phenomena occur as shown in the two previous figures. Fig. 27,
however, shows the character of the curves at the higher relative

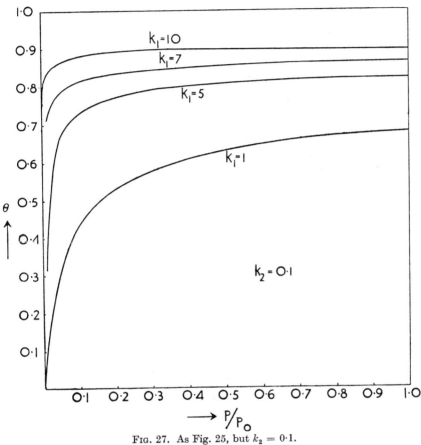

FIG. 27. As Fig. 25, but $k_2 = 0.1$.

pressures, and we see that all those curves show a tendency to saturation, quite independent of whether they have low values of k_1
($k_1 = 1$, $k_1 = 5$), and therefore do not show two-dimensional condensation phenomena, or whether they have had a sudden jump
in their curves in the region of low relative pressures ($k_1 = 7$, $k_1 = 10$).
The saturation part of the curve $k_1 = 5$ in Fig. 27 refers therefore
to a two-dimensional gas, highly compressed into a supercritical
state, whilst the curves $k_1 = 7$ and $k_1 = 10$ refer to two-dimensional
condensed states.

116. The pressure at which two-dimensional condensation occurs

In Fig. 28 a set of curves is shown for the same value $k_1 = 7$, but for different values of k_2. The proportionality of the point where

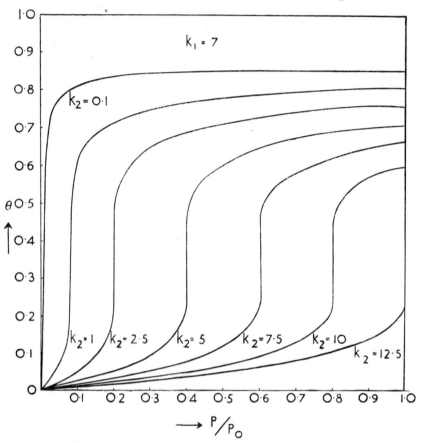

FIG. 28. Isotherm curves for $k_1 = 7$, various values for k_2.

the jump occurs and the constant k_2 is clearly shown. In every case the jump occurs as soon as the surface concentration has reached the point where $\theta = 0.225$. At that moment two-dimensional condensation sets in and the pressure remains constant until so much substance is adsorbed that θ has reached the value 0.47, whereupon the pressure will increase again when further molecules are adsorbed. At higher pressures saturation values for the amount of substance adsorbed will be reached.

The pressure p at which the surface concentration reaches the two-dimensional saturated gas pressure depends on the strength of the adsorption forces. If the adsorption is very weak, so that k_2 has the value 12·5, the jump occurs just when the three-dimensional pressure is saturated. If the adsorption forces were still weaker the jump would be at relative pressures p/p_0, greater than 1, and so would not occur under normal circumstances. When the adsorption is moderately strong, for instance such that $k_2 = 0·1$, the two-dimensional condensation sets in when the relative pressure p/p_0 is as low as 0·008.

117. Co-operation of adsorption forces and inter-molecular forces

When, with strong adsorption forces, the isotherms show a saturation character, it will be very difficult to find out whether this is caused by very strong adsorption forces or whether less strong adsorption forces, combined with inter-molecular forces, are playing a part. In Fig. 29 the fully drawn curve represents strong adsorption forces, $k_2 = 10^{-3}$, whilst it has been assumed that inter-molecular forces are not present, $k_1 = 0$. The dotted curve is drawn for $k_2 = 10^{-1}$, that is far weaker adsorption forces, whilst we have assumed $k_1 = 6$, which implies moderately strong inter-molecular forces. For all practical purposes the curves have the same character in the higher pressure region. They will only show a different character in the region of very low pressures. The two curves of Fig. 29 both refer to the two-dimensional gaseous state only; there is no two-dimensional condensation.

The same holds, however, when two-dimensional condensation has already set in at low pressure. If, for instance, $k_2 = 0·1$ and $k_1 = 7$, the two-dimensional condensation sets in at a relative pressure $p/p_0 = 0·008$. With higher values of p/p_0 the curve shows complete saturation character (the curve is shown in Fig. 27). The adsorption isotherm for the case $k_2 = 5 \times 10^{-4}$ but $k_1 = 0$ gives practically the same curve over the whole range of p/p_0 from 0·05 onward. It also shows a saturation value of $\theta = 0·85$.

Very strong adsorption forces, therefore, give the same character of curve as strong adsorption forces combined with moderately strong or strong inter-molecular forces. In the regions of very low pressures, however, the curves are bound to show a different character.

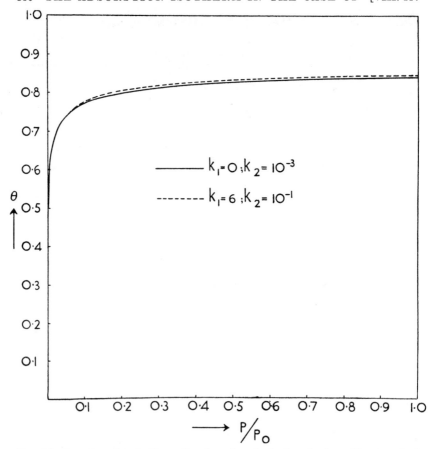

FIG. 29. An adsorption isotherm for strongly adsorbed molecules without mutual interaction and for weakly adsorbed molecules with relatively strong interaction.

118. Critical phenomena

The lowest and highest points of the jumps shown in Fig. 26, and hence the coordinates of coexisting surface phases have been connected by a dotted line. The highest p/p_0 value of that line gives the point where with decreasing value of k_1 a critical curve would just show an inflexion point instead of a maximum and a minimum. It is the critical point in this figure. We want to know at which value of k_1 this occurs and where the point exactly is. The same procedure as that discussed in § 96 may be followed. At the critical point we have the two conditions

$$\left(\frac{\partial p}{\partial \sigma}\right)_T = 0 \quad \text{and} \quad \left(\frac{\partial^2 p}{\partial \sigma^2}\right)_T = 0.$$

Starting with equation (55 b) the first condition gives us

$$2a_2\sigma_c = \frac{RT_{c2}}{(1-\sigma_c/\sigma_0)^2},$$

whilst we obtain with the second condition

$$\frac{RT_{c2}}{(1-\sigma_c/\sigma_0)^3}\left(\frac{3}{\sigma_0}-\frac{1}{\sigma_c}\right) = 0.$$

σ_c and T_{c2} stand for the number of molecules and the temperature, respectively, at the critical point. The last equation gives us immediately

$$\frac{3}{\sigma_0}-\frac{1}{\sigma_c} = 0;$$

hence

$$\frac{\sigma_c}{\sigma_0} = \theta_c = \tfrac{1}{3}. \tag{60 a}$$

At the critical point the degree of occupation is $\tfrac{1}{3}$. This is essentially the same result as already gained in § 96, where we learned that (equation (40))

$$A_c = 3b_2.$$

As $A_c = 1/\sigma_c$ and $b_2 = 1/\sigma_0$, this is the same relation as is given by equation (60 a).

Substituting this in the first condition, we obtain

$$RT_{c2} = \frac{8}{27}a_2\sigma_0 = \frac{8}{27}\frac{a_2}{b_2}, \tag{60 b}$$

which is the same as the result recorded in equation (40).

According to its definition the constant k_1 in equation (59) is

$$k_1 = \frac{2a_2\sigma_0}{RT}.$$

At the critical point, therefore, introducing (60 b), we obtain

$$(k_1)_c = \tfrac{27}{4} = 6\tfrac{3}{4}. \tag{60 c}$$

Substances which, at the temperature of investigation, have a k_1 value greater than $6\tfrac{3}{4}$ will give two-dimensional condensation at the appropriate pressure, substances with a k_1 value smaller than $6\tfrac{3}{4}$ are above their critical temperature and do not condense two-dimensionally.

This rule holds as long as the two-dimensional van der Waals equation holds. The curves of Figs. 25, 26, or 27 are not only independent of the strength of the adsorption forces (k_2 value); provided we choose the appropriate scale for the pressure axis they are also independent of temperature as long as we calculate first the appropriate value of k_1 at the temperature of investigation.

Substituting (60 c) and (60 a) in equation (59) we obtain for the critical value of p/p_0

$$\left(\frac{p}{p_0}\right)_c = k_2 \tfrac{1}{2} e^{\frac{1}{2}} e^{-\frac{3}{2}} = \tfrac{1}{2} k_2 e^{-\frac{3}{2}} = 0 \cdot 087 k_2. \tag{60 d}$$

Similarly, when substituted in equation (55), we obtain

$$p_c = 0 \cdot 087 k_b. \tag{60 e}$$

As we have seen above (§ 114) the value for k_2 is in practical cases of adsorption of the order of magnitude of 10^{-1} or lower, unless the adsorption forces are weak. Equation (60 d) shows that for moderately strongly or strongly adsorbed substances the critical relative pressure is found at values of $0 \cdot 01$ or much lower.

If at the temperature of investigation the substance which we examine has a k_1 value higher than $6\frac{3}{4}$ and if at that temperature the substance is adsorbed moderately strongly or strongly, we shall find two-dimensional condensation phenomena at very low relative pressures.

119. A few examples of two-dimensional condensation of adsorbed substances

We will make a rough estimation of the pressure at which two-dimensional condensation may be expected in practical cases.

In order to apply equation (55) of § 111 we have to know the significance of the constant k_b. As at very low values of θ equation (55) reduces to

$$p = k_b \theta$$

a comparison with equations (14 a), (6 b), and (1) shows us that

$$k_b = \frac{\sigma_0 \sqrt{(MT)}}{3 \cdot 52 \times 10^{22} \tau}.$$

The pressure, p, in equation (55) has then to be expressed in mm. of mercury.

We will now assume a substance of a molecular weight $M = 100$ which is relatively well adsorbed at room temperature ($T = 300$), the time of adsorption, τ, being 3×10^{-6} sec., representing a heat of adsorption of about 10 k.cal./mole (Chapter III, § 29). We will also assume that when closely packed into a unimolecular layer the molecules will take up 40 A² each. The value of σ_0, consequently, will be

$\sigma_0 = 2.5 \times 10^{14}$ molecules per cm.^{2} These data enable us to calculate k_b. We obtain
$$k_b = 0.415.$$

When the value of k_1 of the substance is greater than $6\frac{3}{4}$, the adsorbed molecules will condense to a two-dimensional gas at a pressure lower than $0.087k_b$, hence at a pressure smaller than 0.036 mm.

If at the temperature which we assumed ($300°$ K. $= 27°$ C.) the substance were just at its critical temperature (i.e. $k_1 = 6\frac{3}{4}$), we could calculate the value for a_2 from the data given above. We obtain
$$a_2 = 56,000 \times 10^{-32} \text{ ergs.cm.}^2$$

At a temperature $10°$ lower ($290°$ K. $= 17°$ C.) the value of k_1 would be $k_1 = 7$ and two-dimensional condensation would set in at a pressure
$$0.080k_b.$$

As k_b is also somewhat smaller at this slightly lower temperature the pressure at the example which we have assumed would be about 0.032 mm.

In the elegant experiments of the Chicago workers under W. D. Harkins† it was found that n-heptane when adsorbed on ferric oxide has a two-dimensional critical point at $26°$ C. and that the corresponding three-dimensional pressure, p, was about 0.017 mm. If our above values for σ_0 ($= 1/b_2$) and for a_2 are valid for this case (and we may expect them to be about right), this pressure indicates that the time of adsorption is twice the figure we assumed; hence the heat of adsorption is just over 10 k.cal./mole.

Discussing a second example we will assume a substance with a molecular weight $M = 30$, the molecules of which occupy $12\frac{1}{2}$ A^2; hence $\sigma_0 = 8 \times 10^{14}$ molecules/cm.^{2}, and we suppose this substance to be adsorbed at $-183°$ C. ($90°$ K.) and the time of adsorption to be $\tau = 10^{-3}$ sec., assuming the heat of adsorption to be about 4 k.cal./mole. The value for k_b at this temperature is then calculated to be 11.8×10^{-3}. If the substance is at its boiling-point at $90°$ K., the pressure $p_0 = 760$ mm.; hence the constant
$$k_2 = \frac{k_b}{p_0} = 1.55 \times 10^{-5}.$$

If we also assume a_2 to be
$$a_2 = 5,400 \times 10^{-32} \text{ ergs.cm.}^2,$$

† See reference in § 98.

the k_1 constant at 90° K. is

$$k_1 = 7\cdot0.$$

These results mean that two-dimensional condensation may be expected at a relative pressure of

$$\frac{p}{p_0} = 0\cdot080 \times 1\cdot55 \times 10^{-6} = 1\cdot24 \times 10^{-7},$$

or at a pressure of

$$p = 0\cdot080 \times 11\cdot8 \times 10^{-4} = 9\cdot5 \times 10^{-5} \text{ mm.}$$

Shereshefsky and Weir[†] found two-dimensional condensation of nitrogen on glass spheres at 92° K. at pressures of about 10^{-5} cm., that is at the same pressure as calculated in our example, where we assumed data which fitted nitrogen very well when the molecules were orientated into positions with their long axis perpendicular to the surface.

These examples make it clear that two-dimensional condensation phenomena are to be expected at low values for the pressure. The stronger the adsorption the lower this pressure will be. Comparing p values for one substance, adsorbed on various adsorbents (k_1 the same, k_2 different) the pressure at which two-dimensional condensation may be expected to occur will be inversely proportional to the time of adsorption, τ.

120. Composite surfaces

Up till now we have assumed the surface to be homogeneous. This means we have assumed the heat of adsorption to be the same over the whole range of adsorption and to be independent of the number of molecules adsorbed. The heat of adsorption meant here is the energy due directly to the interaction between surface and adsorbed molecule; it does not include contributions from the mutual forces between the adsorbed molecules as those contributions are represented by the term with a_2. A constant heat of adsorption means, in the language of equations (55) and (59), a constant value for k_2.

We will now consider two-dimensional condensation phenomena on surfaces which are not homogeneous. Suppose we have a mechanical mixture of two adsorbents, the surface of each being homogeneous. The resulting adsorption isotherm would be a superposition

† J. L. Shereshefsky and C. E. Weir, *Jour. Am. Chem. Soc.* **58** (1936), 2022.

of two adsorption isotherms on the two constituent parts, the addition being made in the right proportion.

Let us, to consider an arbitrary example, imagine that we adsorb a given substance at a composite surface. We will assume that 20

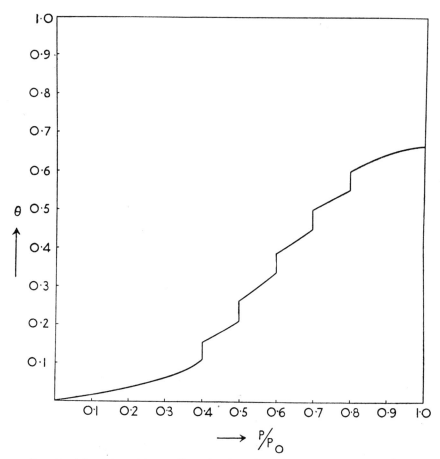

FIG. 30. Adsorption with two-dimensional condensation at a composite surface.

per cent. of the surface gives in its interaction with the adsorbed molecule a value of $k_2 = 5$; another 20 per cent. we will imagine to give $k_2 = 6\frac{1}{4}$, a third 20 per cent. $k_2 = 7\frac{1}{2}$, a fourth 20 per cent. to have $k_2 = 8\frac{3}{4}$, whilst the remaining 20 per cent. may be supposed to show $k_2 = 10$. We can easily calculate the isotherms on the five different parts from equation (59). If we assume for the substance a value $k_1 = 7$ and we add the isotherms, a curve as shown in Fig. 30

results. Instead of one jump at a certain pressure, we obtain five jumps.

If we assume a less regular distribution of the constituent parts of the surface, the resulting curve will be a less regular stepwise

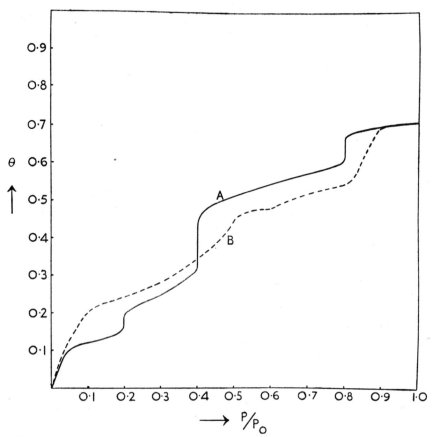

FIG. 31. As Fig. 30, but for a surface with a less regular distribution of activities.

curve. In Fig. 31 curve A is constructed, suggesting a substance with $k_1 = 7$ to be adsorbed at a composite surface, $12\frac{1}{2}$ per cent. of which has $k_2 = 0.1$, another $12\frac{1}{2}$ per cent. has $k_2 = 2.5$, 50 per cent. with a $k_2 = 5$, and the remaining 25 per cent. with $k_2 = 10$.

If we cannot speak of definite parts of the surface, showing different but constant k_2 values, but if there is some variation of k_2 in the different parts, smoother curves are obtained. Curve B in Fig. 31 is constructed for the adsorption of the same substance with $k_1 = 7$ on a composite surface of the following composition: 10 per cent. has $k_2 = 0\cdot1$, 20 per cent. has k_2 about 1, 30 per cent. has k_2 about 5, and for the remaining 40 per cent. a k_2 of about 10 holds.

Stepwise adsorption curves were found experimentally by Allmand and collaborators† in 1932 and have in later years also been examined

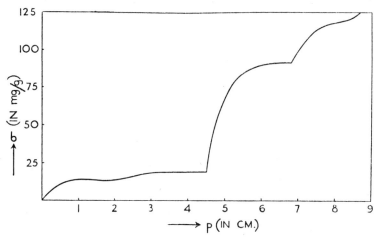

FIG. 32. Stepwise adsorption (Chambers and King).

and published by other investigators. Some of the curves published by Allmand, Burrage, and Chaplin and also those found by Benton and White‡ resemble the curve of Fig. 30 closely. In Fig. 32 we reproduce some results which Chambers and King§ found for the adsorption of chloroform on chromic oxide. This curve shows a similar character to those of Fig. 31.

Adsorbents exhibiting surfaces of such composite character are mostly not in a stable state. Since the surface has a highly developed surface area it possesses a high amount of surface energy. The adsorption of various gases at such surfaces causes changes in these surfaces, many of which are of irreversible character. The result of this in successive runs with the same adsorbate is that there is a decrease of the total amount which is adsorbed whilst also the number of steps decreases.

† A. J. Allmand, L. J. Burrage, and R. Chaplin, *Trans. Faraday Soc.* **28** (1932), 218.
‡ A. F. Benton and T. A. White, *Jour. Am. Chem. Soc.* **53** (1931), 3301.
§ H. H. Chambers and A. King, *Jour. Chem. Soc.* (1940), 157.

121. Comparison with experimental data

If we try to identify the vertical jumps in a stepwise adsorption isotherm found experimentally with two-dimensional condensation phenomena on various parts of the surface, we must make sure that the pressures at which these irregularities occur fit in with our considerations.

Allmand and collaborators found these vertical jumps with carbon tetrachloride on charcoal at room temperature in the region of pressures of 0·2–0·5 mm. They also found a great number of steps with CO_2 on charcoal at pressures between 1 and 80 mm. Benton and White found these jumps for hydrogen on nickel, iron, and copper catalysts at $-183°$ C. at pressures ranging from 5 to 50 cm., whilst, as we can see from Fig. 32, Chambers and King found them for chloroform on chromic oxide in the neighbourhood of 5 cm.

We can estimate the value of k_b (equation (55) and § 119) in all these cases from the heat of adsorption and the dimensions of the molecules. In Table 11 we have assembled the data used for our estimations. The values for the isosteric heats of adsorption are only average figures. Their variations at the various parts of the surface are held responsible for the various steps in the adsorption isotherms.

TABLE 11

Gas	Adsorbent	Temp. ° K.	Q heat of ads. k.cal./mole	τ sec.	σ_0	k_b
CCl_4	charcoal	290	9	5×10^{-7}	5×10^{14}	6
CO_2	charcoal	290	$6\frac{1}{2}$	10^{-8}	5×10^{14}	160
H_2	metals	90	$1\frac{1}{2}$	5×10^{-10}	2×10^{15}	1,500
$CHCl_3$	chromic oxide	290	$6\frac{1}{2}$	10^{-8}	5×10^{14}	265

τ is calculated from Q with the aid of equation (13). From the figures found for k_b we can estimate the pressures at which the jumps will occur if we know the value of k_1. Assuming k_1 to be 7 for all four cases we must multiply k_b by 0·080. We obtain the result that, with the assumed data, jumps may be expected for CCl_4 in the neighbourhood of 0·5 mm., for CO_2 in the neighbourhood of 15 mm., for H_2 at pressures round 120 mm. (12 cm.), and for $CHCl_3$ in the region of 20 mm. (2 cm.). If, of course, k_1 is not 7 but, for instance, 10 we have to multiply k_b by 0·03 instead of by 0·08.

The result of our rough calculations is, however, that we may draw the conclusion that at the pressures which are found experimentally two-dimensional condensation phenomena may be expected. There is, therefore, a definite possibility that the stepwise curves have to be explained in this way.

The stepwise curves for H_2 are found at 90° K., hence at a temperature which is even higher than the three-dimensional critical temperature. We have learned in §§ 105 and 106 that mutual orientation of the molecules may bring about a considerable increase in a_2 and a decrease of b_2, both factors which increase the two-dimensional critical temperature. Hydrogen has the peculiarity that its polarizability is highest in a direction perpendicular to its long axis. A mutual orientation of the molecules with their long axis perpendicular to the surface may well result in a value for b_2 of 5 A^2 and a value for a_2 of $2,150 \times 10^{-32}$ ergs.cm.^{2} which are necessary to give a value for $k_1 = 7$ at $T = 90°$ K. The two-dimensional critical temperature would then be 92·5° K. for such an orientation.

122. Gradual variation of adsorption forces

Let us assume that the number of steps increase to such a degree that in drawing a curve through experimental points we can no longer find distinct steps. A gradually sloping curve will result. Fig. 33 shows a number of such curves. Curve A is drawn for the case when the molecules are adsorbed relatively strongly at any part of the surface. It is assumed that $k_2 = 0·1$ for the whole surface. If, however, only 50 per cent. of the surface adsorbs the molecules with this strength, but the other 50 per cent. shows values for k_2 between $k_2 = 5$ and $k_2 = 10$, and so only weak adsorption forces, and we assume the value for k_2 to vary gradually from 5 to 10, we get curve B. If only 25 per cent. of the surface has a value of $k_2 = 0·1$, another 25 per cent. shows a linear variation of k_2 between 5 and 10, whilst the rest of the surface shows a linear variation of k_2 from 10 to 12·5, we get curve C. If the surface has no parts which adsorb the molecules strongly, but shows a linear variation of k_2 between 5 and 10, curve D results. If the adsorption forces emanating from the surface are still weaker, and k_2 varies linearly from 10 to 12·5, curve E results.

All these five curves are therefore drawn for one and the same sort of molecules with the same k_1 value (we assumed a value $k_1 = 7$)

but for different adsorbing surfaces. Each of the five curves shown
is a representative of the five types of adsorption isotherms introduced by Brunauer in his book.† Types *B*, *C*, *D*, and *E*, when they

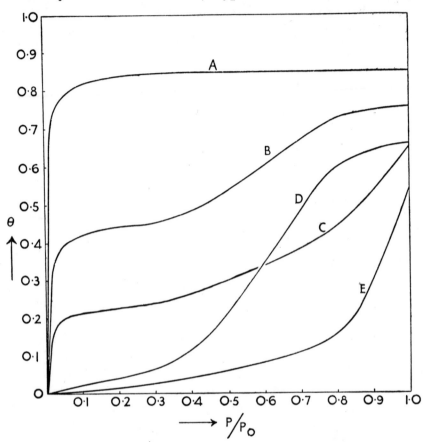

Fig. 33. Various types of adsorption isotherms resulting from gradual variation in
adsorption forces.

occur in practice, are mostly considered to be proof that multimolecular adsorption has taken place. We emphasize the point that
in the considerations which lead to Fig. 33 only unimolecular adsorption has been considered. It does not mean that multimolecular
adsorption could not take place or could not give rise to curves of
the types shown; we only want to point out that the occurrence of

† S. Brunauer, *The Adsorption of Gases and Vapours*, Oxford Univ. Press, London,
1943.

adsorption isotherms of these types is not proof in itself of multi-molecular adsorption.†

123. Variation of the heat of adsorption and the two-dimensional critical temperature

A gradual rise in k_2 means a gradual fall in the heat of adsorption, Q. If the heat of adsorption, Q, is a function of σ, its derivatives with respect to σ enter into the equations of §118. To examine this we look again at the constant k_b of equation (55 c). We have already seen that we can write

$$k_b = \frac{\sigma_0 \sqrt{(MT)}}{3\cdot52 \times 10^{22}\tau}.$$

Introducing $\qquad\qquad \tau = \tau_0 e^{Q/RT}$

from equation (13), we obtain

$$k_b = \frac{\sigma_0 \sqrt{(MT)}}{3\cdot52 \times 10^{22}\tau_0} e^{-Q/RT},$$

which we will write (at constant temperature)

$$k_b = k_0 e^{-Q/RT}.$$

Introducing this into equation (55) we obtain

$$p = k_0 \frac{\theta}{1-\theta} e^{\theta/(1-\theta)} e^{-(Q+2a_2\sigma)/RT}. \tag{61}$$

The last e power contains the heat of adsorption caused by the forces between surface and adsorbed molecules as well as the energy resulting from the lateral forces between the adsorbed molecules. If Q decreases linearly, that is if it is a linear function of σ, the order of the equation is still the same and we may again expect a distinct critical point and distinct pressures where condensation occurs. The first derivative of Q with respect to σ is then negative, but constant; the second derivative is zero.

Establishing the conditions for the critical point, the first condition

$$\left(\frac{\partial p}{\partial \sigma}\right)_T = 0$$

gives us $\qquad\qquad \sigma_c\left\{\left(\frac{\partial Q}{\partial \sigma}\right)_T + 2a_2\right\} = \frac{RT_{c2}}{(1-\sigma_c/\sigma_0)^2}.$

The second condition $\qquad \left(\frac{\partial^2 p}{\partial \sigma^2}\right)_T = 0$

† J. H. de Boer, *Rec. trav. chim. des Pays-Bas*, **65** (1946), 576.

would give us
$$\sigma_c\left(\frac{\partial^2 Q}{\partial \sigma^2}\right)_T = \frac{RT_{c2}}{(1-\sigma_c/\sigma_0)^3}\left(\frac{3}{\sigma_0} - \frac{1}{\sigma_c}\right).$$

We have, however,
$$\left(\frac{\partial^2 Q}{\partial \sigma^2}\right)_T = 0.$$

The second condition, therefore, teaches us that
$$\theta_c = \tfrac{1}{3}$$

still holds. Therefore equation (60a) still holds. Introducing this into the equation of the first condition, however, gives us
$$\tfrac{1}{3}\sigma_0\left\{\left(\frac{\partial Q}{\partial \sigma}\right)_T + 2a_2\right\} = \tfrac{9}{4}RT_{c2},$$

i.e.
$$RT_{c2} = \tfrac{8}{27}a_2\sigma_0 + \tfrac{4}{27}\sigma_0\left(\frac{\partial Q}{\partial \sigma}\right)_T.$$

As the last term is negative, we get in this case
$$RT_{c2} < \frac{8}{27}\frac{a_2}{b_2};$$

hence
$$RT_{c2} < \tfrac{1}{2}RT_c.$$

Consequently
$$(k_1)_c > 6\tfrac{3}{4}, \qquad \left(\frac{p}{p_0}\right)_c < 0\cdot087k_2,$$

and
$$p_c < 0\cdot087k_b.$$

If the decrease of Q is not a linear one, we cannot analyse the equation in the above way. There will not be a definite point where, at a given k_1 value, two-dimensional condensation sets in. There will be a gradual slope instead of a jump. This is shown in Fig. 33 for the case of a linear increase of k_2, which means a logarithmic decrease of Q.

In the next chapter we shall find cases where Q increases with σ.

If the molecules are reorientated during the two-dimensional condensation process we encounter a far more complicated relationship. As discussed in §§ 108 and 109 erection of the molecules means that b_2, and so σ_0, is not a constant any more, but a function of σ. Usually a_2 will also not be constant and will be a function of σ. We may, nevertheless, expect two-dimensional condensation to occur at definite pressures and we may expect the two-dimensional critical temperature to have a definite value. Both Figs. 21 and 22 show this behaviour; the critical temperature in both these cases is lower than

156° C., which would have been T_{c2} if the molecules had shown a b_2 value of 25 A² right from the beginning. In both cases we also find the critical surface concentration at lower values; hence here we have

$$\theta_c < \tfrac{1}{3},$$

which is clearly seen from Fig. 21.

An increase in a_2 during the erection process will increase T_{c2}.

MULTIMOLECULAR ADSORPTION AND CONDENSATION

124. Forces emanating from a first unimolecular layer

Two-DIMENSIONAL condensation of an adsorbed unimolecular layer creates a new surface, offering a new possibility of adsorption: a second layer can be started. As long as there are only singly adsorbed molecules, far apart from each other, there is hardly a possibility of adsorption in a second layer. The forces between a singly adsorbed molecule and a molecule of the gas striking on top of it are small compared with the forces emanating from a condensed layer where all the molecules assist each other in attracting the one on top. The heat of adsorption of a molecule on top of a single one is so small that the corresponding time of adsorption, τ_1, is too small to contribute materially to adsorption in a second layer (§ 57). As soon as the molecules of the first layer are more or less close together, a molecule striking on top of that layer may come simultaneously into contact with three or four of them. This results in a heat of adsorption which is at least three to four times as great and this may be great enough to warrant a time of adsorption, τ_1, of a sufficient order of magnitude to form a second layer.

Even if the first layer is more or less closely packed, the heat of adsorption of molecules of a second layer on top of this first one will generally be smaller than the heat of adsorption of the molecules of the first layer itself. There are various reasons for this: we will mention three of them.

(1) In most practical cases of the adsorption of gases we are dealing with the adsorption of gas molecules of relatively volatile substances on the surface of solid adsorbents. The mutual forces of the gas molecules are smaller than the forces between them and the constituent atoms of the molecules of the surface. The newly formed adsorbent layer consisting of the first unimolecular layer of adsorbed molecules exerts, therefore, far weaker forces than the adsorbent itself.

(2) The orientation of the molecules in the first layer is often such that those parts which have the weakest attraction forces are

exposed to the outside. It is those parts that compose the new surface for newly coming molecules. Polar molecules, having a polar group on one end only, are often adsorbed with that polar end in contact with the surface, the non-polar part then forms the new surface, offered for forming a second layer. The forces emanating from this first unimolecular layer are, in the case of adsorbed fatty acids and similar substances, hardly strong enough for any odd molecule to be bound in the second layer. The adsorption is typically unimolecular in character.

(3) Immediately after two-dimensional condensation has set in, the molecules of the condensed layer, though close together, are not as close together as they can be. A glance at Fig. 25 shows that θ still increases with pressure after condensation has occurred. The density of the unimolecular layer, therefore, increases with pressure. The heat of adsorption of a molecule of the second layer is therefore not as great as it might be. This heat of adsorption may be considered to increase approximately linearly with the density of the layer underneath.

The same arguments hold with adsorption from solutions. The free energy of a solute molecule is, generally speaking, certainly lower when it is surrounded by solvent molecules than when it is partly in contact with a molecule of its own kind. It is the heat of adsorption of the first layer, resulting from the strong attraction between solute molecules and the surface, which causes adsorption to take place. A unimolecular layer of adsorbed solute molecules does not give such a strong attraction. Also, several of the above arguments, especially the second one, hold strongly in this case. Generally, however, the first unimolecular layer will be an excellent surface for adsorption of solvent molecules. When, for instance, palmitic acid is adsorbed from a hexane solution on a solid surface of an inorganic compound, the adsorption is unimolecular, as far as palmitic acid is concerned. On top of this layer there is certainly 'adsorption' of hexane molecules.

125. Adsorbing a second, third, etc., layer

Using the results of the previous chapter we will formally discuss the various possibilities of forming a second, a third, and higher layers.

Let us assume a substance with relatively strong van der Waals forces, the constant a_2 being about $50,000 \times 10^{-32}$ ergs.cm.^{2} and b_2 being 25×10^{-16} cm.^{2} ($\sigma_0 = 4 \times 10^{14}$ molecules/cm.^{2}), then the constant k_1 of equation (59), being

$$k_1 = \frac{2a_2\sigma_0}{RT},$$

would at room temperature, where RT (per molecule) $= 400 \times 10^{-16}$ ergs, amount to $k_1 = 10$. Let us assume this substance to be strongly adsorbed at the homogeneous surface of an adsorbent and let us assume $k_2 = 0.1$. We assume, therefore, that the heat of adsorption (apart from the contribution due to mutual lateral forces) is constant. The corresponding adsorption isotherm of the first unimolecular layer is the curve already shown as curve $k_1 = 10$ in Fig. 27. From small values of the relative pressure onwards, a new surface is already offered for further adsorption. As the surface density does not alter materially, owing to the strong saturation character of this adsorption, we may also assume a constant heat of adsorption for the second layer. This heat of adsorption, however, is far smaller, as we saw in the previous section. The result is that the value of k_2 for the formation of the second layer is far higher. We will assume $k_2 = 25$ (i.e. 250 times greater). This results in a very *weak* adsorption on top of the first layer and it is not until the relative pressure p/p_0 reaches values higher than 0.5 that we notice an increase in the amount of adsorbed molecules. At $p/p_0 = 0.75$, however, the amount of adsorbed molecules in the second layer has risen to $\theta_2 = 0.05$. (We denote by θ_n the θ in the nth layer.) At this surface concentration two-dimensional condensation sets in. The surface density of the second layer rises rapidly to $\theta_2 = 0.75$.

On this second layer a third one may now start. As, however, the density of the second layer is smaller than that of the first one, where $\theta_1 = 0.9$ holds, the value of k_2 for forming a third layer will again be greater, which means a somewhat smaller heat of adsorption of the third layer. The difference, however, will be much less than between the first and second layers. We assume for the third layer $k_2 = 30$. This means that at $p/p_0 = 0.9$ two-dimensional condensation sets in in the third layer, θ_3 rising to 0.75 again.

For the fourth layer we again assume a slight increase of k_2, namely, $k_2 = 32$. The fourth layer will show two-dimensional condensation at $p/p_0 = 0.96$, and so it may go on. The resulting adsorp-

tion isotherm is shown in Fig. 34, where the dotted lines show the
completion of the successive layers. The amount of adsorption is

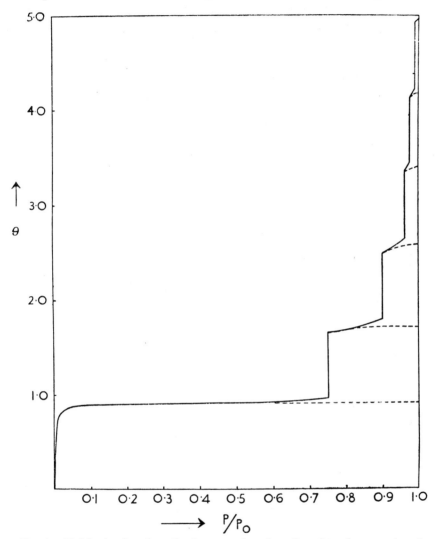

FIG. 34. Multimolecular adsorption by successive adsorption of new layers on top of
condensed adsorbed layers.

indicated as a total θ value, but just as in Chapter V it rises here
far above 1 and can reach high values. A typical multimolecular
adsorption has occurred.

It looks as if the adsorption isotherm in Fig. 34 will approach asymptotically the vertical at $p/p_0 = 1$; however, this is not so. There is a definite point where the adsorption isotherm cuts this axis.

126. Multimolecular adsorption on a super-critical layer

Two-dimensional condensation is not an essential condition for the formation of the second layer. In the case of a two-dimensional gas above its critical point as soon as such a surface density is reached that over half of the surface is occupied ($\theta > 0.50$) the mutual distance of the molecules is only 1·4 times that which would be observed if they were closely packed together. If we place a molecule on top of such a layer it will also make direct contact with three or four molecules of the first layer. The attraction may be great enough to give adsorption in a second layer, though it will be smaller than in the case where the packing is closer. When the pressure increases the packing in the first layer also increases. This in turn increases the heat of adsorption for the second layer.

In Fig. 35 we have constructed an adsorption isotherm on these lines. The molecules are assumed to have a value of $k_1 < 6\frac{3}{4}$ (see § 118 and also Figs. 25 and 26). We choose $k_1 = 6$. We have assumed a moderately weak adsorption on the surface, $k_2 = 1$. The adsorption isotherm of the first layer only is shown as a dotted curve in the figure. In order to account for the increase of heat of adsorption of the second layer, due to the increasing density of the first layer underneath, we have assumed that the values for k_2 for the second layer *decrease* gradually from 15 at $\theta_1 = 0.20$ to 10 at $\theta_1 = 0.9$ and $\theta_1 = 1.0$. These k_2 values may be somewhat on the low side for a substance having an a_2 value corresponding to $k_1 = 6$. On the other hand, the entropy of the molecules in this type of mobile film is rather high, giving lower k_2 values.

There are in this example just a few molecules adsorbed in the third layer, at high values of the relative pressure. Nevertheless, the total amount is hardly greater than that of a unimolecular layer when fully packed. θ, therefore, hardly exceeds unity. Such a result depends, of course, on the assumption which we make, especially on the values which we assign to the various constants.

Adsorption on metal surfaces may, owing to the polarization of the adsorbed molecules which we encountered in § 110, result in very low values of a_2. The possibility of finding super-critical adsorption curves on metal surfaces is therefore even greater than on the surfaces of other substances. Nevertheless, multimolecular adsorption may be expected. In § 60 the adsorption of acetone on mercury was discussed and the adsorption isotherm as it may be derived from

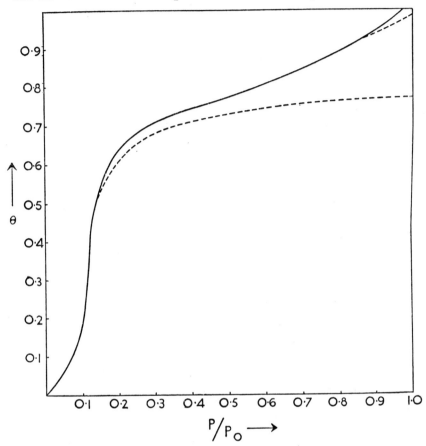

FIG. 35. Multimolecular adsorption on a super-critical layer.

Kemball's work was shown in Fig. 11. We stated there that the curve was drawn through the points as smoothly as possible. If we follow the course of the points more closely we obtain a curve as shown in Fig. 36, indicating multimolecular adsorption on a first layer which has not condensed two-dimensionally.

127. Influence of orientation

We learned in §§ 104, 105, and 106 that a special orientation of the molecules in the first layer may lead to an increase in a_2 and a decrease in b_2, the result being that the two-dimensional critical temperature increases and two-dimensional condensation is facilitated. The constant k_1 of equation (59) is increased.

We need not assume this to happen for a second layer adsorbed

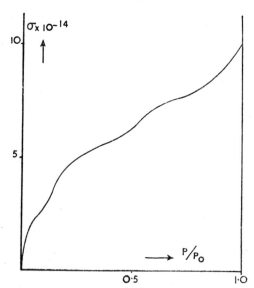

Fig. 36.   Adsorption isotherm of acetone on mercury,
as derived from Kemball's work.

on top of the first orientated one. If the first layer consists, for instance, of diatomic molecules adsorbed in perpendicular positions, the second layer may be built up by molecules lying flat on this first layer. This would lead to a mutual orientation of the molecules, often found in their crystals. If this happens the second layer has a lower value for k_1 than the first one.

In Fig. 37 we have assumed a substance to be relatively strongly adsorbed $(k_2 = 0.1)$ and to show strong inter-molecular forces $(k_1 = 10)$. A first layer of saturation character is already found at low values of the relative pressure. If we now assume the same sort of molecules to be adsorbed on top of this layer with a value of $k_2 = 5$, whilst at the same time because of their different orientation, $k_1 = 7$, curve A results. We have assumed that for the molecules of the third, fourth, etc., layers slightly higher values of k_2 hold (as in § 125).

If we assume a still lower value for k_1 in the second layer, namely,

$k_1 = 6$, the substance is above its critical point. This would mean that whilst the first layer shows strong condensation phenomena, the second, third, and higher layers, because of their different orientation, do not. If we start to build up the second layer again with

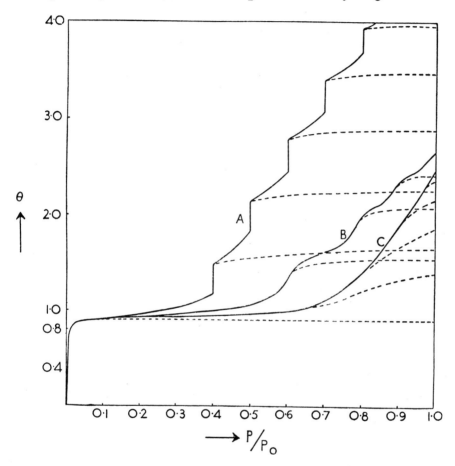

FIG. 37. Multimolecular adsorption with a different orientation of the molecules in the second and higher layers.

$k_2 = 5$, and assume still higher values for k_2 in the higher layers, we obtain curve B.

The wavy character of curve B depends strongly on the degree of increase of k_2 which we assume for successive layers. A certain increase has to be assumed because the density of the layers underneath is smaller the higher we go. A smaller increase in k_2 than assumed in curve B, but starting at $k_2 = 7 \cdot 5$, gives curve C, which is smooth for all practical purposes.

128. Combined steps

In all the examples discussed so far in this chapter the original surface is assumed to be a homogeneous one. No variation of the heat of adsorption of the first layer has been assumed. If, however, the surface is a composite one we obtain a superposition of various curves as already discussed in § 120. The various parts of the surface give condensation jumps at various pressures, this jump being higher the higher the corresponding k_2 value.

In addition, multimolecular adsorption may set in on the various parts but at various pressures. The second layers on the various parts have higher k_2 values than the first layers on the same part of the surface. All the third layers have higher k_2 values than their second layers, etc. We get a superposition of various curves of the type of Fig. 37 and of Fig. 30.

Fig. 38 gives an example. We have assumed a substance only weakly adsorbed ($k_2 = 5$) on one fifth part of the surface, on the following fifth parts the k_2 values may be $6\frac{1}{4}$, $7\frac{1}{2}$, $8\frac{3}{4}$, and 10, respectively, as in the example of § 120. We have assumed the k_1 value not to vary, so we do not assume differences in orientation; $k_1 = 7$ throughout. All the k_2 values for the second layers are chosen to be slightly higher than those for the first layer, etc. The resulting curve is curve A, showing many steps. The steps may have different heights depending on the parts of the surface where they occur, whilst also some condensation phenomena may occur at the same pressure on various parts of the surface. The first step shown in curve A is the two-dimensional condensation in the first layer on that part of the surface which shows the strongest adsorption. The second and third steps are condensation phenomena in the second and third layers on that part. The fourth step is the two-dimensional condensation in the first layer on that part of the surface which has the next strong adsorption forces, etc. The high jump at $p/p_0 = 0 \cdot 75$, for example, is caused by two-dimensional condensation in the seventh layer adsorbed on the first fifth of the surface together with two-dimensional condensation in the sixth layer on the second fifth part and in the second layers on the fourth and fifth parts of the surface.

If the parts of the surface are not so sharply distinct from each other, but show gradually changing k_2 values, a smooth curve results.

We assumed the first layer to be weakly adsorbed, its heat of

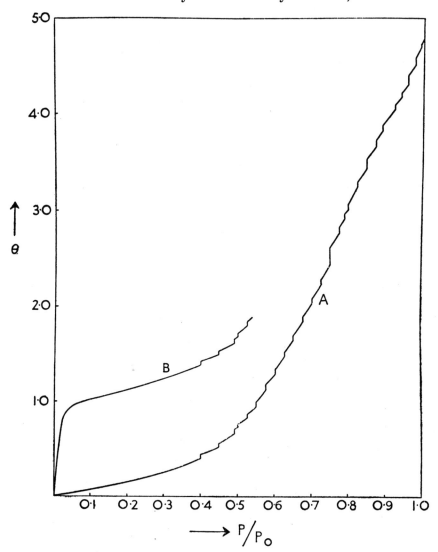

FIG. 38. Multimolecular adsorption on heterogeneous surfaces.

adsorption not exceeding the heat of condensation. If the adsorption of the first layer is strong, curve B may result, of which only the beginning is shown in the figure. In the first steep part the five original jumps in the first layers on the various parts occur. We cannot distinguish them on the scale of our drawing.

129. Influence of capillaries

Adsorbents of a highly developed porous character or of a lamellar structure not only possess a large surface area per gram of material, but their surfaces may be rather unhomogeneous. Many capillaries of microscopic as well as of macroscopic dimensions will exist, including a great number of capillaries of molecular dimensions. When adsorbed in such pockets the adsorbed molecules are surrounded by far more surface atoms than on a flat surface. This means that owing to the additivity of the van der Waals forces the heat of adsorption is far greater in those holes than on a plane surface. It has been pointed out† that adsorption in such pockets, holes, and cavities accounts for the experimentally known values of the heat of adsorption. If all adsorption took place on a plain surface the heat of adsorption would be far smaller than that actually found.

In the light of our considerations we may therefore expect the k_2 values for the adsorption of the first layer to be low in such capillaries. The lower it is the narrower the cavity, or rather the more surface atoms are in direct contact with the atoms of the adsorbed molecule. We may also expect the k_2 value to increase gradually from its lowest value to higher values during the completion of the first layer throughout the whole of the capillaries. As there may be capillaries of various dimensions, we may expect a whole range of k_2 values, all increasing slightly with increasing degree of occupation. If this is the picture, nothing will be left of the stepwise adsorption; only smooth curves will result.

In building up the second and higher layers we may note that the available space for each higher layer will be smaller in such holes and cavities but that it will be increasingly larger for hills and extruding parts of the surface. There is, therefore, less room for higher layers in the region of smaller k_2 values and more room in the region of weaker adsorption. The direct result of this peculiarity will be that the adsorption isotherm will rise less in the region of lower p/p_0 values than it would do on a plain surface with the same k_2 values. The rise will be steeper at higher p/p_0 values. A curve as indicated in Fig. 39 (curve A) results. The slope of this curve may

† J. H. de Boer and J. F. H. Custers, *Z. Physikal. Chem.* B **25** (1934), 225.

be compared with that of curve *A* in Fig. 38. It is possible that
many capillaries may be filled up when three or four layers are

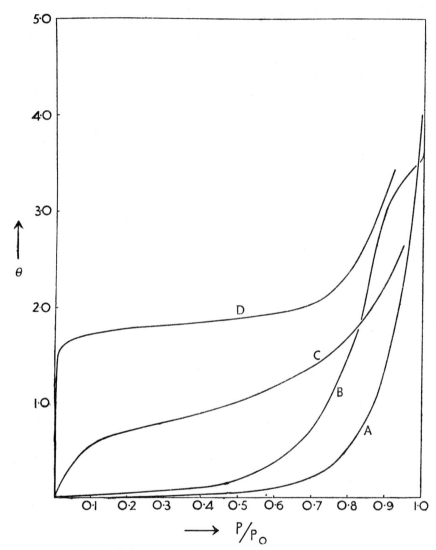

FIG. 39. Influence of capillaries in multimolecular adsorption.

adsorbed, thus decreasing the total surface area of the adsorbent.
At the highest p/p_0 values a less steep slope such as that indicated
by curve *B* in Fig. 39 will then result.

In both curves *A* and *B* we have assumed that the heat of

adsorption of the initial layer has the same order of magnitude as the heat of adsorption of higher layers. This is generally not so. In the case where there is a moderately strong adsorption of the first layer on most parts of the surface we may obtain a curve of the character of curve C.

Adsorption in capillaries may cause the heat of adsorption of molecules even in the second or higher layers to be far higher than

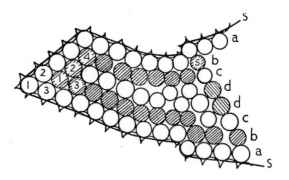

FIG. 40. Molecular picture of adsorption in a capillary of molecular dimensions.

the heat of condensation. Let us assume a capillary of the size and structure of that sketched in Fig. 40. The line S indicates the surface of the adsorbent. The actual surface atoms are indicated. The row of molecules, aa, is the first layer, bb (shaded) may be considered to be the second layer, cc the third, and the molecules d play the role of a fourth layer. Molecules 1, 2, and 3 of the first layer are very strongly adsorbed, so are 1, 2, 3, 4, and 5 of the second layer; they have more neighbours than usual. All the molecules of the third layer, as indicated, are adsorbed with a heat of adsorption higher than the usual one. The same holds for the molecules d. Let us now assume that half of the surface consists of capillaries of this kind; half of the surface therefore has low values of k_2. If adsorption were only unimolecular an adsorption isotherm would result with a steep first part, a more or less sharp bend at approximately $\theta_1 = 0.50$, followed by a flatter, moderately rising part. If, however, part of the second, third, and higher layers are also adsorbed strongly, these molecules will also contribute to the steep first rise. A curve of the character of curve D of Fig. 39 may result with a more or less sharp bend when θ is substantially higher than unity.

130. An attempt to derive a mathematical formulation

In previous sections (§§ 61, 111, and 112) we have already mentioned Terrell L. Hill's excellent studies on multimolecular adsorption and the Brunauer, Emmett, and Teller theory in particular. Whilst still adhering as closely as possible to the original picture of Brunauer, Emmett, and Teller he studied the influence of mutual attraction forces and of two-dimensional condensation in the first layer. This first layer may either have the character of a mobile layer or it may be 'localized' (see § 82). In the original theory of Brunauer, Emmett, and Teller the first layer is assumed to be localized completely; the molecules of the second and higher layers are added to molecules which are adsorbed in a lower layer, whilst mutual interactions in each layer are neglected. Dropping this last condition Hill,[†] also starting from a localized first layer, assumes higher layers also to be built up by vertical addition in a simple cubic lattice, each molecule being above a molecule in the layer below. If the 'horizontal' interaction in the first and in the higher layers is great enough, two-dimensional condensation may occur, often simultaneously in successive layers. If this picture of multimolecular adsorption is assumed to occur between parallel walls, the 'last' layer—just filling up the space—would in itself condense at a lower three-dimensional pressure, which, of course, cannot happen. The result is that the simultaneous two-dimensional condensation of all layers is shifted to a lower pressure; the lower this is the smaller is the size of the capillary; this being in qualitative agreement with the experimental facts.

Starting from the picture of a mobile first layer, applying the two-dimensional van der Waals equation to it, and adding by vertical addition molecules in the second and higher layers, Hill[‡] derived an expression which rewritten to fit the form of our equations is

$$\frac{p}{p_0} = x = k_2 \frac{\theta(1-x)^2}{1-\theta+\theta x} e^{\theta(1-x)/(1-\theta+\theta x)} e^{-k_1\theta}, \tag{62}$$

where $x = p/p_0$ and k_2 and k_1 have the same meaning as in our equation (59) of § 114. At low values of x equation (62) reduces to equation (59). If the e powers of equation (62) are neglected it reduces to equation (19) of § 48 with $k = 1/k_2$. Equation (62) has the same relation to the normal Brunauer, Emmett, and Teller

† Terrell L. Hill, *Jour. Chem. Physics*, **15** (1947), 767.   ‡ Ibid. **14** (1946), 441.

equations as our equation (59) has to the normal Langmuir equation (compare § 113).

Hill has shown that if k_1 is so large that two-dimensional condensation takes place in the first layer, the resulting isotherm according to equation (62) closely follows the normal Brunauer, Emmett, and Teller curve for values of p/p_0 in the region which is recommended, namely, between $p/p_0 = 0.05$ and $p/p_0 = 0.35$. At lower values of p/p_0 there is a strong deviation between the equations.

Though equation (62) is a valuable attempt to describe the multimolecular adsorption by mathematical formulation, it must be said that the picture which is used in its derivation cannot be considered as a satisfactory description of the physical phenomenon. We will discuss this problem in the next two sections.

131. The structure of the multimolecular layer

It may be difficult to distinguish between the successive layers on adsorbents of a highly developed surface structure, but even on flat and smooth surfaces or on flat and smooth parts of surfaces, such a distinction may become rather arbitrary. If the packing is not as close as it would be at higher pressures, we may expect molecules of one layer to penetrate half or wholly into another layer. There will be material exchange between the layers. Moreover, reorientation due to the adsorption of a layer on top of an existing one may occur in the existing layer. If such a mobility exists it will be difficult to continue speaking of separate two-dimensional layers, each of which shows the coexistence of two separate two-dimensional phases. Instead of this picture it would be better to treat the whole assembly of adsorbed molecules as one surface phase of a thickness greater than one molecule.†

Our formal treatment as sketched in the preceding sections can therefore only give a rough description of the actual happenings. The same holds of course for the description of multimolecular adsorption as given in Chapter V. The approach made there and the approach in the present chapter are not opposed to each other; on the contrary they are supplementary.

In Brunauer, Emmett, and Teller's original theory the heat of

---

† R. M. Barrer and A. B. Robins, *Trans. Faraday Soc.* **47** (1951), 773, have now published a first attempt of this kind. They describe multilayer adsorption in terms of the van der Waals equation of state.

adsorption in the second and higher layers is considered to be equal to the heat of liquefaction of the substance which is adsorbed. We will examine how this fits in with our considerations of the present chapter. In equation (61) (see also § 123)

$$p = k_0 \frac{\theta}{1-\theta} e^{\theta/(1-\theta)} e^{-(Q+2a_2\sigma)/RT} \tag{61}$$

$(Q+2a_2\sigma)$ is the total heat of adsorption arising from the interaction with the surface as well as from the forces between the molecules.

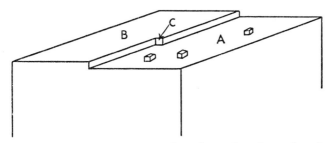

FIG. 41. A layer in process of condensation on top of a condensed layer.

If the layer which we are considering were fully occupied (i.e. $\theta = 1$), the degree of occupation would be $\sigma = \sigma_0$. The heat of adsorption would then become $(Q+2a_2\sigma_0)$. Let us assume that the layer which we are considering is in process of condensation and that the layer underneath is in its condensed state. Let us also assume that the inter-molecular distances in both condensed parts are the same as they would be in the liquid or solid state. The situation may be that sketched in Fig. 41, where A represents the layers underneath, B the layer under consideration and in process of condensation. At point C we find the last molecule of the row of molecules which is in process of growing along the sheet which is already formed. Any new molecule adsorbed on A contributes to the two-dimensional gas phase in equilibrium with B. As this gas phase is saturated, one new molecule must be added to B for every new molecule arriving on top of A. This addition will take place at point C, lengthening the row in process of growing. Adding a molecule on top of A involves the heat of adsorption Q. Adding the molecule to the sheet at point C involves the amount of energy, $2a_2\sigma_0$. The total heat of adsorption is therefore gained in two steps.

If the layers are closely packed, according to a hexagonal pattern, the molecule is in direct contact with three of its own kind when it is adsorbed as a gas molecule on top of A. It gets into direct contact with three more of its own kind when it is added to the sheet at point C. Both contributing parts of the heat of adsorption will then be approximately equal to each other. If the layers are closely packed according to a cubic pattern, the molecule is in direct contact with four others when adsorbed on A and gets into direct contact with two more when added to the sheet at point C. Q will then be roughly twice $2a_2\sigma_0$.

According to the molecular picture we should not take $2a_2\sigma_0$ but $a_2\sigma_0$ for the contribution of the van der Waals forces, the molecule being only in contact with half of the amount which it will have when surrounded completely. According to this picture it would be better if the factor 2 in equation (61) were not there. This is connected with the original derivation where b_2 is twice the molecular area. As, however, we have defined $\sigma_0 = 1/b_2$ we have retained the factor 2. At point C, nevertheless, the total heat of liquefaction is involved. Addition of molecules, one after another at point C, means increasing the volume without altering the size of the surface. C is very often called a repeatable place. Addition at this point gives just the right heat of condensation of the structure which is involved.

We have assumed a_2 and b_2 to be constant. In reality they are dependent not only on temperature but also on the distance of the molecules. Deviations will become serious when the molecules come close together. We therefore can only expect that the heat of adsorption in the second and higher layers, and hence the heat of liquefaction, will be roughly between two and three times the value of the product $a_2\sigma_0$.

This is indeed true. If we take for instance the values for a_2 and σ_0 ($= 1/b_2$) for argon from Table 8 we see that $a_2\sigma_0 = 0\cdot35 \times 10^{-13}$ ergs/molecule. The heat of evaporation (liquefaction, condensation) for argon at its boiling-point is $1\cdot5$ k.cal./mole, which means $1\cdot05 \times 10^{-13}$ ergs/molecule, a value three times the value of $a_2\sigma_0$. For nitrogen we find $a_2\sigma_0$ is equal to $0\cdot29 \times 10^{-13}$ ergs/molecule, the heat of evaporation is $0\cdot93 \times 10^{-13}$ ergs/molecule. The same relation holds for the other gases mentioned in Table 8.

Our picture, therefore, is quite in accordance with the view that the heat of adsorption of the second and higher layers is in the neighbourhood of the heat of liquefaction of the substance which is adsorbed, provided two-dimensional condensation takes place. We have already seen that two-dimensional condensation is one of the factors facilitating multimolecular adsorption.

As stated above (§ 124) the mutual distance between the molecules in the various layers will always be somewhat higher than it would be in the case of close packing. The heat of adsorption will therefore usually be somewhat smaller than the heat of liquefaction. In the sense of Chapter V, § 55, this means that Q_1 will be somewhat smaller than Q_0, hence q somewhat greater than p_0. It is for this reason that we introduced q in Chapter V.

In all the discussions of this and the previous chapter we have excluded the influence of the surface itself on the mutual distances of the adsorbed molecules. The periodical fluctuations of the adsorption energy over the surface tend to force the adsorbed molecules to be fixed in certain positions (sites), the mutual distance of which may deviate more or less strongly from the mutual distance which they would occupy if they were allowed to be free. This factor only plays an important role when the molecules come very close together. It then influences the magnitude of q with respect to p_0. In most practical cases $q > p_0$. There are, however, some examples of $q < p_0$, as we have already discussed in Chapter V (§ 55).

132. A physical picture of multimolecular adsorption

In the original theory of Brunauer, Emmett, and Teller the molecules of the second and higher adsorbed layers are assumed to have the same evaporation-condensation properties as the liquid state. It is particularly the heat of adsorption in the second or higher layers which is assumed to be equal to the heat of evaporation of the liquid (see § 50). As we have stated already in § 58 and also in the preceding sections of this chapter we may only assume this to be roughly true if and when the layer underneath is closely packed. Even if the heat of adsorption were equal to the heat of evaporation of the liquid, however, adsorption would not take place at pressures lower than the saturation pressure if the entropy of the adsorbed state were not higher than that of the liquid state. In the physical picture of the Brunauer, Emmett, and Teller theory molecules are added vertically to existing ones including therefore molecules which are in contact with one other molecule only. This same picture is used by many other authors who have tried to improve on the original theory; it is also used, though sometimes altered slightly, in the excellent series of studies by Terrell L. Hill (see § 130), and it is, of course, also used in our Chapter V. The entropy of such an imaginary system, a sketch of a cross-section of which is shown in Fig. 42, may be rather high; the heat of adsorption for atoms such as A in Fig. 42, however, is so small that adsorption will not take place. We

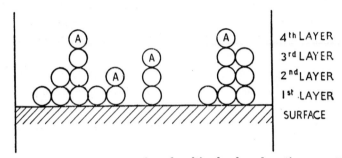

FIG. 42. Sketch of a cross-section of multimolecular adsorption according to the theory of Brunauer, Emmett, and Teller.

might just as well suggest the forming of clusters of two or more molecules in the gas at pressures lower than the saturation pressure.

The formation of a first layer of sufficiently high surface density is, therefore, an essential first condition. The heat of adsorption will then be in the neighbourhood of the heat of evaporation of the liquid, as shown in the previous section, or it may even be greater if the structure of the surface is essentially a porous one (Fig. 40 in § 129). The heat of adsorption may also be somewhat increased if the molecules of the layer underneath are polarized in such a way that induced polarization takes place in the next layer. This polarization principle was the base of the oldest conception of a picture for multimolecular adsorption.† This principle has been criticized by Brunauer in his well-known book,‡ where he states that such a polarization cannot account for the magnitude of the heat of adsorption. It need not do so since the polarization is only giving a small additional amount of binding energy over and above the normal heat of adsorption, thus rendering it higher than the heat of evaporation and enabling adsorption to take place at pressures lower than

† J. H. de Boer, *Proc. Roy. Acad. Sci.* (Amsterdam), **31** (1928), 906; J. H. de Boer and C. Zwikker, *Z. Physikal. Chem.* B **3** (1929), 407.

‡ S. Brunauer, *The Adsorption of Gases and Vapours*, Oxford Univ. Press, London, 1943.

the saturation pressure, if necessary without the aid of entropy. In the Brunauer, Emmett, and Teller theory there is no such extra amount of energy.

As we have seen, adsorbed molecules, even those of the rare gases on surfaces of metals and graphite (§ 110), are practically always polarized; this effect may, therefore, after all, play a more important part than was imagined when the original theory was advanced in 1928. The physical picture of the polarization theory is probably more in keeping with reality than the picture on which the Brunauer, Emmett, and Teller theory is based.

It is not the place here to discuss multimolecular adsorption theories more fully, nor to discuss the various methods in use for estimating surface areas. It may, however, be stated that though multimolecular adsorption usually leads to a sigmoid shape of the adsorption isotherm, the occurrence of this shape does not necessarily mean that multimolecular adsorption has caused it† (see also § 122). If in an experimental case (e.g. nitrogen at low temperatures) multi-molecular adsorption takes place and if it is accompanied by two-dimensional condensation in the first layer the Brunauer, Emmett, and Teller equation, as an interpolation equation valid for inter-mediate values of p/p_0, may describe the shape of the isotherm reasonably well and may lead to reasonably usable values for the surface area (see also § 143).

133. Crystal growth‡

The picture which we gave in Fig. 41 also holds for the condensa-tion of molecules on their own crystals. In crystal growth we also have the phenomenon that molecules hit the surface either from the vapour phase or from the melt or solution at any possible place. These molecules migrate along the surface until they either evaporate (dissolve) again or are fixed at places where the attraction is higher. The heat of condensation occurs in two steps in the same way as sketched in the previous section. The steps are exactly the same as those mentioned there.

In crystal growth there is moreover the possibility that the mole-cules move across the boundary to another face of the growing

---

† See also J. H. de Boer, *Rec. trav. chim. des Pays-Bas*, **65** (1946), 576; S. J. Gregg and F. A. P. Maggs, *Trans. Faraday Soc.* **44** (1948), 123.

‡ See 'Crystal Growth', *Discussions of the Faraday Society*, No. 5 (1949).

crystal where they are bound more strongly. Molecules will be bound more strongly on face B of the growing crystal sketched in Fig. 43 than on face A. An adsorbed molecule, a, will roll over face A and fall into position 1. The next one may take up position 2, a third one position 3, etc. The result is that addition to face B enlarges

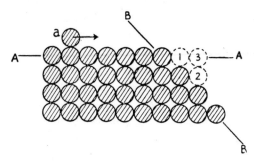

FIG. 43. Migration in crystal growth.

face A. Thus faces of the crystal which show the strongest adsorption attract more material than other faces and by growing perpendicularly they disappear. The boundary faces of well developed crystals are those faces which show the weakest adsorption forces.

As early as 1921 Volmer and Estermann, in a more or less classical experiment,† grew mercury crystals at $-63°$ C. from vapour at a temperature of $-10°$ C. As the vapour pressure was known exactly, they also knew exactly how many molecules were hitting the various surfaces of the tiny crystals which they exposed to the vapour (equation (6)). Their experiments showed that the amount of mercury atoms collected on the small prism faces was about 1,000 times the amount of molecules which would have hit those faces from the gas phase. No material adhered to the hexagonal base of the crystals. Apparently all the molecules hitting those base faces migrate over them to contribute to the perpendicular growth of the prism faces. The result was that very flat hexagonal plates were obtained.

Similar phenomena have been found by later observers. Sometimes the structure of the crystals is such that the adsorption on some of their faces is very weak with respect to the adsorption on other faces. Substances crystallizing in so-called layer lattices show far less adsorption on their cleavage faces than on any other face. They tend to

† M. Volmer and I. Estermann, *Z. Physik*, **7** (1921), 13.

grow out into plates; well-known examples are boric acid, palmitic acid, cadmium iodide, graphite, etc. In some cases there is even more distinction in preference and one of the faces more or less perpendicular to the cleavage face has a greater preference for adsorption than the other face perpendicular to the cleavage face. In such instances there is a strong tendency for the crystals to grow out into needles or bundles of needles (dendrites). All these phenomena are made possible by the migration of molecules along the surfaces. They move until they are fixed or condensed in more favourable positions.

When a nucleus of a crystal is grown whilst other foreign molecules which adhere strongly to the more strongly adsorbing faces are present, the result may be that these faces just cannot collect more material because of the foreign molecules adhering strongly to them. The relative growth of the various crystal faces is then changed and other forms showing other boundary faces result. One of the best-known examples is sodium chloride which crystallizes into octahedrons if urea is present in the solution. The normal form is the cubic form. Urea is strongly adsorbed on the octahedral faces. We will not discuss these phenomena but only mention that many dyestuffs, polar molecules, or also hydroxyl ions may influence crystal growth in this way.

134. The formation of nuclei

In order that a crystal may be formed there must be a nucleus. It is very likely that in the phenomenon of the formation of crystals from either the vapour phase or from solution on to a solid wall, the formation of the nucleus has to start with the formation of a two-dimensional nucleus. It is highly probable, therefore, that two-dimensional condensation (or generally the formation of a two-dimensional layer of such close packing that adsorption can take place on top of it) is an essential condition for the formation of a nucleus which then can grow out to become a crystal. This two-dimensional condensation or the formation of the above-mentioned layer is, in its turn, the result of adsorption of the molecules on the solid wall.

If the adsorption of the molecules on the wall is rather small there may be some trouble in getting the first two-dimensional condensed layer formed. It has been known for more than 30 years that when a stream of molecules of, for instance, iodine, cadmium, zinc, or similar metals is directed against a cool glass wall, condensation will only take place if the temperature is below a certain value, T_w. This temperature was originally thought to be a sort of critical temperature. Later it was found that T_w depends on the density of the gas stream: the higher the density of the stream of molecules or the higher the corresponding pressure, p, the higher is the temperature above which no condensation takes place. The relationship between p and T_w can be expressed as

$$p = ge^{-h/T_w},$$

where g and h are constants. Semenoff[†] explained these phenomena in 1930 on much the same lines as have been developed in our discussions. He also based his considerations on the theory of van der Waals and he also expected two-dimensional condensation to be the introductory act for the formation of a three-dimensional nucleus. Using the same figure as Semenoff did we can discuss his theory more completely with the aid of our equations (55), (59), or (61).

When the heat of condensation is greater than the heat of adsorption, as it is in these cases, k_2 has high values. This means (§ 118) that the two-dimensional critical pressure p_c and also $(p/p_0)_c$ (equations (60 d) and (60 e)) have high values, whilst also the pressure at which condensation occurs will be high. If, for instance, the constant $k_1 = 10$, the relative pressure at which two-dimensional condensation sets in is given by the expression

$$\frac{p}{p_0} = 0{\cdot}03k_2.$$

If k_2 is greater than 34, therefore, this relative pressure is higher than unity. A situation occurs like that expressed in Fig. 44, where we assume $k_2 = 100$.

If no 'spontaneous' three-dimensional condensation takes place we can enter into the field of supersaturated pressures. Past the line $p/p_0 = 1$ a value of $p/p_0 = 3$ may be reached. At this point two-dimensional condensation sets in. Following this, three-dimensional condensation takes place on top of the two-dimensional nucleus and the pressure falls back to $p/p_0 = 1$.

135. Two-dimensional supersaturation

We may ask whether supersaturation will also be possible in the two-dimensional phase relationship. Shereshefsky and Weir[‡] in 1936

† N. Semenoff, Z. Physikal. Chem. B 7 (1930), 471.   ‡ Loc. cit., § 119.

found definite indications of such phenomena in the adsorption of nitrogen on glass spheres at low temperatures. We have seen already

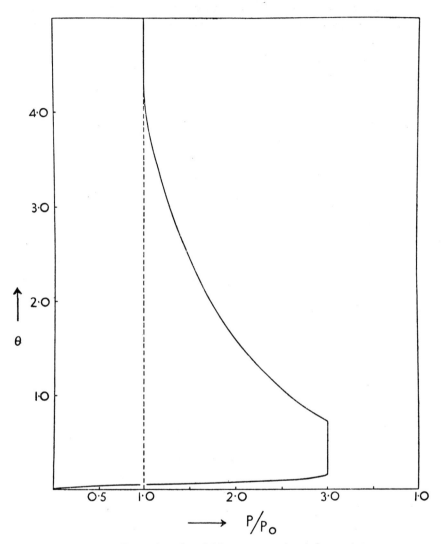

Fig. 44. Formation of nuclei from super-saturated vapours.

in § 119 that two-dimensional condensation occurs at very low pressures, namely, of the order of magnitude of 10^{-4} mm., in their experiments. They could, however, raise the pressure sometimes to 3×10^{-4} mm., the adsorption being only very small, and practically linear with pressure. Suddenly a large adsorption sets in and the pressure drops to, for instance, 0.5×10^{-4} mm. The number of adsorbed molecules increases in some cases to 10 or 20 times its previous value. It looks as if the k_1 value was very high under these circumstances. A glance at Fig. 25 shows us that the higher k_1 the greater the degree of supersaturation may be if conditions are favourable. It just means that we move along the dotted line.

136. Hysteresis phenomena in adsorption

It may be that in some cases where hysteresis is found in adsorption measurements, phenomena such as described in the previous section may be responsible. Very often the adsorption isotherm is lower when it is measured with increasing pressure than when it is measured with decreasing pressure.

The adsorption branch lies lower than the desorption branch. Supersaturation of the two-dimensional condensation gives a most natural explanation for this behaviour, as has been pointed out by Cassel.[†]

In most cases, however, hysteresis phenomena observed in adsorption-desorption experiments can be ascribed to the filling and emptying of capillaries of suitable shapes and sizes. These frequently observed hysteresis phenomena are only found with microporous adsorbents. Hysteresis phenomena based on two-dimensional supersaturation should not be restricted to microporous adsorbents.

For further details the reader is referred to 'The shape of capillaries', by the author as published in D. H. Everett and F. S. Stone, *The Structure and Properties of Porous Materials* (Butterworth, London, 1958).

[†] H. Cassel, *J. phys. Chem.* **48** (1944), 195.

X

SOME EFFECTS OF CAPILLARIES

137. The rate of diffusion into capillaries

CAPILLARIES play an important role in adsorption phenomena as we have seen in previous chapters. The magnitude of the heat of adsorption is given by the presence of capillaries and the whole shape of the isotherm depends very often on the distribution, size, and structure of capillaries. As we have already described in §§ 24 and 30 the passage of molecules through capillaries may involve a great length of time. While physical adsorption itself is a phenomenon taking place with an enormous speed, the penetration of the molecules into the deepest depth of the capillaries of the adsorbent may last a long time. There have been observations that in some cases adsorption equilibria are only reached after many hours or even days.

The penetration of molecules into these capillaries may be treated as a diffusion problem. We will not enter into the various attempts which have been made to express this diffusion in terms of adequate equations and we will also not discuss the various models which have been proposed. Whatever mechanism is suggested we shall always get an equation between the increase of σ, the number of molecules which are adsorbed per cm.^{2} at a given pressure and at a given temperature, and the time t, the equation being of the form

$$\sigma_t = \sigma_\infty(1 - e^{-k_d t}), \tag{63}$$

where σ_t is the value of σ at the time t and σ_∞ is the equilibrium value of σ which is theoretically only reached after an indefinitely long time. k_d in equation (63) is a constant which, amongst other things, is inversely proportional to the square of the distance which the molecules have to travel (this may be the length of the capillaries) and which is proportional to the diffusion constant D. This latter diffusion constant may be written as

$$D = D_0 e^{-Q_d/RT}, \tag{64}$$

where D_0 is a constant and Q_d is an energy of activation.

The temperature dependence of this diffusion constant, hence the temperature dependence of the constant k_d in equation (63) and of the whole phenomenon of the rate of reaching adsorption equilibria, depends on this energy of activation Q_d.

If the time of adsorption, τ, is very small, the phenomenon is governed by the first term of equation (12) of § 24. For a given adsorbent then, but with various gases, it is the mean velocity $\bar{u}$ of the molecules which plays a dominant role. Barrer and Rideal[†] found in 1935 that the rate of adsorption of oxygen, nitrogen, and hydrogen on sugar charcoal was practically independent of temperature. They found the rates of the three gases to be in the proportion

$$O_2:N_2:H_2 = 1{\cdot}0:1{\cdot}1:3{\cdot}2,$$

whereas the proportion of the mean velocities (§ 6) is

$$O_2:N_2:H_2 = 1{\cdot}0:1{\cdot}07:4{\cdot}0.$$

The charcoal in their experiments apparently had wide capillaries and the influence of τ on the rate of diffusion was negligible.

If τ plays a more important part a strong temperature dependence may be found. The study of the energy of activation may materially help us to distinguish between the mechanisms of diffusion through the capillaries. The molecules may proceed according to three mechanisms. They may collide with the wall of the capillary, evaporate immediately, according to the cosine law, collide again, etc. There will not be an energy of activation in this case. Secondly, the molecules may collide with the wall of the capillary, rest there for a time τ, re-evaporate, collide again, rest again, etc. The energy of activation will then be equal to the heat of adsorption. Thirdly, the molecules may migrate along the wall of the capillary, during a sufficiently long time τ. This migration is governed by the mechanism of moving along the surface as discussed in §§ 66 and 67. If they make the hopping movements of § 67, they will have much shorter resting times τ' (equation (27)) during their movement. The energy of activation is then given by the fluctuations in the heat of adsorption, ΔQ_a. The dependence of the rate of adsorption of ethane and propane on charcoal gives an energy of activation of about 3 k.cal./mole, and this is roughly half the value of the heat of adsorption.

138. Diffusion through surface migration

Equation (12) of § 24 may be corrected for the possible migration along the surface. Clausing[‡] considered a two-dimensional diffusion caused by such a migration; he assumes a picture resembling that

† R. M. Barrer and E. K. Rideal, *Proc. Roy. Soc.* A **149** (1935), 231.

‡ P. Clausing, *Ann. d. Physik*, **7** (1930), 521.

of § 66, where the free path of the two-dimensional movement along the surface is governed by the interaction with surface atoms. The diffusion constant for this surface migration is then

$$D_m = \tfrac{1}{2}\bar{L}_m\,\bar{u},$$

where $\bar{L}_m$ is the mean free path on the surface and $\bar{u}$ the mean velocity of the molecules. If this occurs equation (12) has to be corrected to

$$\bar{t} = \frac{\dfrac{l^2}{2d\bar{u}}+\dfrac{l^2\tau}{2d^2}}{1+\dfrac{3\tau\bar{L}_m\,\bar{u}}{2d^2}}; \tag{12 a}$$

if, however, the mechanism of the hopping molecules (§ 67) governs the migration, the hopping distance a and the lingering time τ' (equation (27)) instead of the free path L_m govern the phenomenon. The diffusion constant for the surface migration in this case is calculated by Kruyer[†] to be

$$D_m = \frac{1}{4}\frac{a^2}{\tau'}.$$

If there are two mechanisms of diffusion, working simultaneously, namely,

   (1) diffusion through the gas by colliding with the wall, evaporating immediately according to the cosine law, colliding again, etc., without there being any collisions between the molecules (hence the free path is large with respect to the diameter of the capillary: Knudsen diffusion),

   (2) diffusion along the surface according to the mechanism of the hopping molecules,

and if there is a definite time of adsorption τ, during which diffusion (2) occurs, whilst diffusion (1) occurs between two successive times of adsorption τ, the total diffusion constant is

$$D = \frac{1}{3}\frac{d^2\left(1+\dfrac{3}{4}\dfrac{\tau}{\tau'}\dfrac{a^2}{d^2}\right)}{\dfrac{d}{\bar{u}}+\tau}.$$

The average time $\bar{t}$ which a molecule needs to pass a capillary with a length l is given by

$$\bar{t} = \frac{l^2}{6D};$$

† S. Kruyer, *Proc. K. ned. Akad. Wet.* B **56** (1953), 274.

hence
$$\bar{t} = \frac{l^2\left(\dfrac{d}{\bar{u}}+\tau\right)}{2d^2\left(1+\dfrac{3}{4}\dfrac{\tau}{\tau'}\dfrac{a^2}{d^2}\right)}$$

or
$$\bar{t} = \frac{\dfrac{l^2}{2d\bar{u}}+\dfrac{l^2\tau}{2d^2}}{1+\dfrac{3}{4}\dfrac{\tau}{\tau'}\dfrac{a^2}{d^2}}. \qquad (12\,b)$$

Both in equation (12 a) and (12 b) the numerator is exactly the same as that in equation (12), with the same physical meaning as described in § 24, whilst the denominator gives the correction for surface migration.

We will, as an example, show how great this correction may be in a few of the cases mentioned in Table 3 in § 30. If we take case 9 of that table, referring to a capillary of $l = 10^{-2}$ cm., $d = 10^{-6}$ cm., whilst, for the molecules, $\tau = 10^{-4}$ sec. and $\bar{u} = 10^4$ cm./sec., and we assume the molecules to behave as a two-dimensional gas with a relatively free movement of the molecules along the surface, we must apply equation (12 a). We assume $\bar{L}_m$ to be 50 A, an arbitrarily chosen figure, denoting the effect of the interference of the surface atoms with the free movement of the adsorbed molecules. Instead of $\bar{t} = 5,000$ sec., a figure which we calculated in § 30, we now obtain $\bar{t} = \frac{1}{150}$ sec. Case 12 of Table 3 in § 30 gives a still more dramatic effect: instead of $\bar{t} = 5,000$ sec., we obtain $\bar{t} = \frac{1}{15000}$ sec.; and even in case 6 the influence of the assumed surface migration is very strong, $\bar{t} = 50$ sec. being reduced to $\bar{t} = \frac{2}{3}$ sec. In all these cases the effect of surface migration is dominating the diffusion and the results are practically governed by a simplified equation

$$\bar{t} = \frac{l^2}{3\bar{L}\bar{u}}, \qquad (12\,c)$$

indicating that the diffusion due to surface migration is independent of the diameter of the pores.

If the molecules are not moving freely over the surface, but instead are making the hopping movements described in § 67, we must apply equation (12 b). Starting again from case 9 of Table 3 in § 30 we may assume the activation energy for the two-dimensional movement to be half the heat of adsorption. The time τ' is then 3×10^{-8} sec.

We may take a to be equal to atomic distances in the surface structure of the adsorbent and, therefore, we may take a to be about 3×10^{-8} cm. Applying equation (12 b) to case 9 of Table 3 and inserting these figures we obtain $\bar{t} = 1,540$ sec. instead of $\bar{t} = 5,000$ sec. as found in § 30. Applying this mechanism and the above figures to case 6 of Table 3 reveals that the migration will not have any effect in that case; case 12, however, gives $\bar{t} = 22$ sec. instead of $\bar{t} = 5,000$ sec. In this latter case it is the surface migration which governs the whole diffusion, and a simplified equation

$$\bar{t} = \frac{2l^2\tau'}{3a^2} \tag{12 d}$$

describes this case adequately.

Whatever the mechanism of surface migration is, its influence with respect to the other mechanisms of diffusion is only of importance in narrow capillaries. This may be seen from equations (12 a) and (12 b); the denominator deviates from unity for small values of d only.

In § 31 we tried to visualize the passage of molecules through a capillary by referring to the 'gas of super bees', introduced in § 12. Applying again this magnified picture to case 9 and molecules migrating over the surface with a mean free path of 50 A we come to the following picture. Our bees move into a tube which is 2 miles long and 1 foot wide, their flying speed being 100 metres/sec. After each collision they stay at the wall for somewhat less than an hour, during which stay they walk in an arbitrary direction over the surface of the tube with a speed of 100 metres/sec.; after having walked for about 16 cm. every bee changes direction and continues its walk in another arbitrary direction, etc. They therefore change their direction 600 times per second, or 2 million times during one period of stay at the surface. It would take a bee an average of $2\frac{1}{2}$ days to pass through the tube in this way. Without this walking it would take the bees 5,000 years to pass through the tube, as we saw in § 31; they could fly the distance in $\frac{1}{2}$ minute.

Applying the magnified picture to case 9 but with the restriction that the bees during the time which they stay at the surface—somewhat less than an hour—make an average of 3,330 jumps of 1 cm. distance in arbitrary directions, resting an average time of 1 sec. between jumps, we derive the conclusion that it will still take them 1,428 years to cover the distance.

If the time of adsorption, τ, is practically infinitely long, surface migration is the only possible way of moving through capillaries and pores.

139. Swelling and the two-dimensional pressure

We saw in § 79 that the two-dimensional pressure F may assume high values which, when compared with the three-dimensional case, correspond to enormously high pressures. We may therefore expect the molecules to exert an enormous pressure on the walls of the adsorbent. This may lead to structural changes, especially when we are dealing with capillaries in which adsorption takes place. The capillaries may be widened, more room is created for adsorption, still more pressure is exerted, leading to more widening and filling of those widened capillaries: the substance swells. Especially when two-dimensional condensation sets in, the pressure F may reach high values and swelling may be such that the volume of the system increases many times.

Numerous substances swell when water is adsorbed on and in them. The well-known swelling phenomena of gelatine, wool, silica gel, starch, etc., with water may be mentioned here. The expansion of charcoal by water, carbon dioxide, ammonia, and many other gases was used by Bangham and collaborators† to study the two-dimensional pressure F exercised by these gases. The linear expansion was directly proportional to the two-dimensional pressure.

The adsorption of caesium by inorganic salts also leads to dominant swelling phenomena,‡ so does the adsorption of caesium and potassium by graphite. Many other examples are known where the adsorption of molecules in between the layers of a layer lattice gives rise to an enormous swelling of the system.

The swelling of rubber in hydrocarbons also belongs to this class of phenomena. It is very difficult to distinguish here between adsorption and absorption. It is in these cases that the term sorption is sometimes used, after McBain's use of this word.

---

† D. H. Bangham and N. Fakhoury, *Proc. Roy. Soc.* A **130** (1930), 81; D. H. Bangham, N. Fakhoury, and A. F. Mohamed, ibid. A **138** (1932), 162; A **147** (1934), 152; D. H. Bangham and R. I. Razouk, *Trans. Faraday Soc.* **33** (1937), 1459, 1463; *Proc. Roy. Soc.* A **166** (1938), 572.

‡ See in J. H. de Boer, *Electron Emission and Adsorption Phenomena*, mentioned in § 66; C. J. Dippel and J. H. de Boer, *Rec. trav. chim.* **57** (1938), 277, 1087.

140. Penetration into the material

When such a phenomenon occurs and capillaries and new adsorption spaces are widened or created by the action of the molecules themselves, work must be done against the forces which combine the constituents of the adsorbents. Such adsorbents consist mostly of small crystallites or micelles of a more or less crystalline or at least ordered nature. These micelles or crystallites are held together by van der Waals forces. By the action of the adsorbing molecules the binding by those van der Waals forces is overcome. The crystallites or micelles are pushed apart and room is created for adsorption. As the work which is done by the molecules has to be derived from the thermal kinetic energy, this diffusion process is accompanied by an energy of activation. Generally speaking this energy of activation will be higher than the heat of adsorption on a plane surface or on the wall of an open capillary, and so higher than the energy of activation of diffusion processes in open capillary structures as discussed in § 135. Here we enter the field where molecules penetrate inside the materials and high energies of activation hold for inter-micellar or inter-crystallite absorption. The diffusion of hydrogen through cellulose and cellulose derivatives, which is a process where the hydrogen molecules have to create their own room whilst they advance, is associated with an energy of activation of the order of magnitude of several k.cal./mole. It is clear that such an energy of activation is far higher than the heat of adsorption that would ever be possessed by hydrogen. The same holds for the diffusion of gases through rubber and other materials of high polymer structure.†

141. Hysteresis caused by swelling phenomena

Structural changes caused by adsorption may be reversible or they may not be. We have mentioned already in § 120 that adsorption on highly active adsorbents, which showed many steps in the adsorption isotherm, resulted in severe material changes of the structure of the surface. It is a well-known fact that gel-forming substances undergo structural changes of a lasting character when they take up water and lose it later by dehydration.

The existence of an activation energy may also lead to hysteresis phenomena. The opening of newly created capillaries may take place at higher pressures than their closing in a desorption process. It

† R. M. Barrer, *Diffusion in and through Solids*, Cambridge, 1941.

will be difficult to decide in practical cases whether supersaturation of two-dimensional condensation phenomena, as discussed in § 136, will be the cause of hysteresis or whether hysteresis is caused by reversible or irreversible structural changes in the adsorbent as just described. The majority of hysteresis phenomena, however, as already mentioned in § 136, are caused by capillaries of suitable shapes and sizes in rigid structures of microporous adsorbents.

142. 'Activated adsorption'

When the molecules enter into a chemical reaction with the surface of the adsorbent, in other words in cases of chemisorption, high energies of activation may also be found. Because of this chemisorption has often been called 'activated adsorption', after H. S. Taylor's† use of this name. Work has to be done in this case against chemical forces holding the molecule together or against chemical forces working in the adsorbent. A discussion of these phenomena would be beyond the scope of our considerations.

143. Final remarks

Starting from a few simple conceptions we have tried to develop a picture of adsorption and related phenomena. We have discussed which phenomena could be expected on the basis of our assumptions and we have compared these expectations with known experimental facts. Despite the many stringent simplifications which we introduced in the course of our discussions, it is surprising to note how far the conclusions to which we came are supported by the facts. By means of our simplified picture it was possible to describe the phenomena in a semi-quantitative way. The data which we derived were of the right order of magnitude despite the rather simple conceptions. The use of τ_0 of equation (13) as a constant (10^{-13} sec.) throughout our discussions is a very rough approximation only. So is the use of the two-dimensional van der Waals equation, particularly so because we actually employ both a_2 and b_2 as constants independent of temperature and of the distance of the molecules. The conception $\sigma_0 = 1/b_2$ is a rough approximation again, and so we have made more rough approximations in the course of our derivations. A complete picture which may be visualized by those who preferably think in pictures has been developed.

† H. S. Taylor, *Jour. Am. Chem. Soc.* **53** (1931), 578.

Before concluding these final remarks we may stress the point that this picture is anything but the final word. Many problems of general and of special interest will have to be examined and their solutions may modify the picture to a great extent. For instance, a problem of a general nature, the magnitude of τ_0, for which we used the constant value of 10^{-13} sec., may be solved with the aid of statistical mechanics. It turns out that the original conception of τ_0 as the time of oscillation of the adsorbed molecule perpendicular to the surface, the conception which Frenkel originally had in mind, is strictly valid only in the case of supermobile adsorption. In other cases the interpretation of τ_0 is somewhat different. A condensed version of the statistical mechanical derivation follows; for fuller details the reader is referred to the original publications of Kruyer and de Boer.[†] In the case of equilibrium between the gaseous phase and the adsorbed phase, the thermodynamical potentials of the gaseous phase and the adsorbed phase, both consisting of just one single component, have to be equal. Denoting the number of molecules in the gaseous phase and the adsorbed phase respectively by N_g and N_a, and the corresponding partition functions by $_gf$ and $_af$, then the condition of equilibrium may be written as

$$\frac{_gf}{N_g} = \frac{_af}{N_a} e^{Q/RT},   (65)$$

where Q is the heat of adsorption. Each partition function is made up of translational, rotational, and vibrational contributions; consequently (65) may be written as

$$\frac{_gf_{\text{tr}} \times _gf_{\text{rot}} \times _gf_{\text{vibr}}}{N_g} = \frac{_af_{\text{tr}} \times _af_{\text{rot}} \times _af_{\text{vibr}}}{N_a} e^{Q/RT}.   (66)$$

For an ideal gas, $_gf_{\text{tr}}$ is equal to

$$\left(\frac{2\pi mkT}{h^2}\right)^{\frac{3}{2}} \frac{N_g kT}{P};$$

while for an ideal two-dimensional gas, $_af_{\text{free tr}}$ is equal to $(2\pi mkT/h^2)O$. If the two-dimensional gas is non-ideal, viz. if the molecules are hindered in their movements along the surface we may of course write for $_af_{\text{tr}}$

$$_af_{\text{tr}} = _af_{\text{free tr}} \times \frac{_af_{\text{tr}}}{_af_{\text{free tr}}}.$$

† S. Kruyer, *Proc. K. ned. Akad. Wet.* B **58** (1955), 73. See also J. H. de Boer, *Adv. Catalysis* **8** (1956), 85.

If the internal vibrations of the molecules in the gaseous phase are preserved, but one degree of freedom of translation is upon adsorption converted into a vibration perpendicular to the surface, the total partition function of vibration for the adsorbed molecule may be written as
$$_af_{\text{vibr}} = {_gf_{\text{vibr}}}\,f_z,$$
where f_z is the partition function of vibration of the molecule perpendicular to the surface. Making use of the preceding equations and realizing that $\sigma = N_a/O$, σ may be clearly written as
$$\sigma = \frac{P}{(2\pi mkT)^{\frac{1}{2}}}\left[\frac{h}{kT}\times f_z\times\frac{_af_{\text{tr}}}{_gf_{\text{free tr}}}\times\frac{_af_{\text{rot}}}{_gf_{\text{rot}}}\right]e^{Q/RT}. \tag{67}$$
On comparing this equation with the equation preceding equation (14) of § 35, it is immediately clear that τ_0 may be identified with
$$\tau_0 = \frac{h}{kT}\times f_z\times\frac{_af_{\text{tr}}}{_af_{\text{free tr}}}\times\frac{_af_{\text{rot}}}{_gf_{\text{rot}}}. \tag{68}$$
If the rotations of the molecule are unrestricted upon adsorption and if the translations of the two-dimensional gas are unhindered, equation (68) simply reduces to
$$\tau_0 = \frac{h}{kT}\times f_z.$$

In the case of Kemball's supermobile adsorption, f_z is larger than unity, as the vibration of the molecule perpendicular to the surface is excited, and τ_0 is larger than h/kT. If the frequency of this vibration ν_z is low, f_z equals $kT/h\nu_z$ and τ_0 becomes equal to $1/\nu_z$, in concordance with the ideas Frenkel had in mind. In all other cases, τ_0 is smaller than ν_z. In the case of a strong binding to the surface, ν_z may be far larger and the vibration perpendicular to the surface will be unexcited, leading to $f_z = 1$, and consequently to a value for τ_0 of
$$\tau_0 = h/kT. \tag{69}$$
If the molecule upon adsorption is hindered in its translation or rotation, τ_0 is even lower, as is apparent from (68). In the extreme case of localized adsorption, the derivation has to be modified, taking into account the entropy associated with the distribution of N_a molecules over N_s adsorption sites totally available. The following equation for τ_0 may be derived for the case where even the vibrations of the molecules when localized at the adsorption sites may be neglected:
$$\tau_0 = \frac{h}{kT}\times\frac{h^2 N_s/O}{2\pi mkT}\times\frac{_af_{\text{rot}}}{_gf_{\text{rot}}}. \tag{70}$$

As an example, one may consider the adsorption of water on charcoal, which may be considered to be localized adsorbed, the number of adsorption sites roughly amounting to $10^{15}/cm.^2$ In this case, at $300°$ K, if the water molecule retains its rotation, τ_0 equals 10^{-15} sec. If, however, the rotation is restricted, τ_0 may be taken to be of the order of 10^{-16} sec. This is considerably shorter than the value calculated for mobile adsorption. In the case of ethyl chloride on carbon at $331°$ K., which may be taken as an example of an ideal two-dimensional gas, equation (69) predicts a value of τ_0 of $1·45 \times 10^{-13}$ sec. Although the heat of adsorption of water on carbon is higher than that of ethyl chloride, $10·8$ kcal. in comparison with $9·1$ kcal., and although the temperature of the water adsorption is lower, the net time of adsorption, τ, is lower for water at $300°$ K., viz. $1·8 \times 10^{-8}$ sec., than for ethyl chloride at $331°$ K., viz. $1·45 \times 10^{-7}$ sec. This demonstrates clearly the influence of the mode of adsorption on the value of τ_0 and consequently on the value of τ and on the degree of occupation of the surface at a given pressure. It also demonstrates that one has to be careful in adopting a value of 10^{-13} sec. for τ_0 in all cases without further investigation.

In § 41 the reflection coefficient of water near its freezing point is reported to be very high. If the reflection coefficient for water molecules on ice were high the numerical figures given in § 17 would have to be corrected severely. An investigation by Kramers and Stemerding[†] has shown that there is practically no reflection of water molecules at the surface of ice between -40 and $-60°$ C., which is the region important for the operation of freeze drying.

In § 42 it is stated that water molecules are relatively weakly bound to a graphite surface. A closer examination shows this not to be correct in every respect: it looks more as if only a two-dimensional condensed water layer is formed with difficulty; isolated water molecules are bound with a rather large heat of adsorption.

The statement in § 70 that the process of adsorption of gases is essentially exothermic is, as a general statement, true only for adsorption by van der Waals forces. In cases of chemisorption endothermic adsorption of molecules may play an important role as a metastable transition state in catalysis.[‡]

[†] H. Kramers and S. Stemerding, *Appl. scient. Res.* A **3** (1951), 73.

[‡] J. H. de Boer, 'Endothermic chemisorption and catalysis' in *Adv. Catalysis*, **9** (1957), 472.

Section 132 concludes with the remark that an application of the Brunauer, Emmett, and Teller (BET) equation may lead to reasonably usable values for the surface area. This is true, but a warning must be given that there are many cases of taking up water by gel-forming substances where the 'sorption'-curves (§ 139) are well described by the BET equation (see, for example, Figs. 7 and 9 in § 55) although this equation cannot be used for the estimation of the surface area. If one tries to evaluate a surface area from these isotherms, one usually obtains a figure many times higher (e.g. 100 times higher) than the surface area available for gases that do not give rise to gel-formation and consequent swelling.

A theory, to be useful, must be able to describe phenomena adequately. The fact, however, that a certain theory does describe the phenomena more or less quantitatively is not, in itself, a proof that the underlying picture is correct. The author believes that his original picture (1928) of multimolecular adsorption (see § 132) is more in keeping with the reality than the picture that is used to derive the BET equation. This latter picture, however, has proved to be a fertile ground for further investigations.

The author hopes that the picture which is developed in the present book may also lead to many new experiments, discovering new facts. This is the main purpose of any picture and of any theory.

INDEX

REPRINTED LITHOGRAPHICALLY IN GREAT BRITAIN
AT THE UNIVERSITY PRESS, OXFORD
BY VIVIAN RIDLER
PRINTER TO THE UNIVERSITY

264693

1-MONTH